301.4778
N42f

91940

| DATE DUE | | | |
|---|---|---|---|
| Aug 12 '75 | Feb 2 78 | | |
| Nov 11 75 | Oct 7 78 | | |
| Nov 26 75 | Nov 19 78 | | |
| Jul 1 '76 | Dec 7 '81 | | |
| Jul 8 '76 | Nov 24 '82 | | |
| Oct 4 '76 | Jul 6 '83 | | |
| Oct 18 '76 | | | |
| Nov 11 '76 | | | |
| May 5 7 7 | | | |
| May 16 '77 P | | | |
| P Jul 6 '77 | | | |
| Nov 28 '77 | | | |

# Family and
# Mental Health Problems
# in a Deaf Population

*(Second Edition)*

# Family and Mental Health Problems in a Deaf Population

*Edited by* John D. Rainer, M.D.

Kenneth Z. Altshuler, M.D. *and* Franz J. Kallmann, M.D.

*with the assistance of*

W. Edwards Deming, Ph.D.

**CHARLES C THOMAS • PUBLISHER**
*Springfield • Illinois • U.S.A.*

*Published and Distributed Throughout the World by*
CHARLES C THOMAS • PUBLISHER
BANNERSTONE HOUSE
301–327 East Lawrence Avenue, Springfield, Illinois, U.S.A.
NATCHEZ PLANTATION HOUSE
735 North Atlantic Boulevard, Fort Lauderdale, Florida, U.S.A.

*With* THOMAS BOOKS *careful attention is given to all details of manufacturing and design. It is the Publisher's desire to present books that are satisfactory as to their physical qualities and artistic possibilities and appropriate for their particular use.* THOMAS BOOKS *will be true to those laws of quality that assure a good name and good will.*

First Edition, 1963
Department of Medical Genetics
New York State Psychiatric Institute
722 West 168th Street, New York 32

Second Edition, 1969

*Printed in the United States of America*
BB-14

## CONTRIBUTORS

Kenneth Z. Altshuler, M.D.

George S. Baroff, Ph.D.

W. Edwards Deming, Ph.D.

Arthur Falek, Ph.D

Lissy Feingold Jarvik, Ph.D., M.D.

Franz J. Kallmann, M.D.

M. Michael Klaber, Ph.D.

Edna Simon Levine, Ph.D.

John D. Rainer, M.D.

Rose M. Salzberger, M.A.

Diane Sank, Ph.D.

M. Bruce Sarlin, M.D.

The programs represented in this volume have been supported by the Social and Rehabilitation Service of the U.S. Department of Health, Education, and Welfare, and by the New York State Department of Mental Hygiene.

# CONTENTS

# PREFACE TO SECOND EDITION

In the six years since the first edition of this book was published, concern with the psychiatric needs of the deaf has grown throughout the world. The data in this volume, accumulated over the seven years of the first New York State pilot study, and the recommendations emanating therefrom have served as the basis for further work, both by ourselves and by others.

Because of the continuing demand for the present volume, this second edition is now issued. Added to the original material are two papers, *Personality Traits and Depressive Symptoms in the Deaf* (KZA) and *Interpretation, Communication, and Understanding* (JDR). While these chapters repeat some of the data in the earlier portions of the book, they are reprinted as written (with the permission of Plenum Press and the Deaf American respectively) because of their further exploration of the psychodynamic implications of deafness. The only other changes in this edition involve correction of certain typographical errors.

Further developments in mental health care for the deaf can be found in our books *Comprehensive Mental Health Services for the Deaf* published in 1966 by the New York State Psychiatric Institute, and *Psychiatry and the Deaf* published in 1968 by the U.S. Government Printing Office.

The death of Dr. Franz J. Kallmann in 1965 meant a serious loss to us who worked with him since the beginning, carrying out his dream of responsible and dedicated professional attention in a totally neglected field. We hope that subsequent events have justified and will continue to justify his devotion.

JOHN D. RAINER, M.D.
KENNETH Z. ALTSHULER, M.D.

# PREFACE

This monograph represents the final report of the Mental Health Project for the Deaf conducted by the Department of Medical Genetics of the New York State Psychiatric Institute. It was brought to fruition by the dedicated teamwork of an interdisciplinary staff of workers in the fields of clinical, social and genetic psychiatry, audiometry, cytogenetics and psychology, population statistics and twin research, with the cooperation of many federal, state, and local agencies concerned with deafness and vocational rehabilitation.

The editors wish to express their appreciation to all the collaborators in this volume, those who are still with us and have individually contributed to the final report, as well as those who had to leave our project at a certain date and are now working with the deaf in other parts of the country. Also, the editors wish to acknowledge their indebtedness to the esteemed members of the Advisory Council, especially to Dr. Paul Hoch, New York State Commissioner of Mental Hygiene, Dr. Henry Brill, Deputy Commissioner of Mental Hygiene, and Dr. Lawrence C. Kolb, Director of the New York State Psychiatric Institute. Without the guidance of these experienced leaders in mental health work the project would not have reached its authoritative status.

Among the other persons whose consistent advice and aid deserve grateful recognition are Miss Mary E. Switzer, Commissioner, Mr. Gilbert R. Barnhart, Chief, Division of Research Grants and Demonstrations, and Mr. Boyce R. Williams, Consultant, Deaf and the Hard of Hearing, Office of Vocational Rehabilitation,* U.S. Department of Health, Education, and Welfare; and Mr. Adrian Levy, Assistant Commissioner for Vocational Rehabilitation, N.Y. State Department of Education.

With deep sorrow we note the passing of three persons whose counsel propelled the work of the project beyond measure. Two of them were members of the Advisory Council: Professor Carney Landis, renowned psychologist, and Dr. Daniel T. Cloud, respected educator of the deaf. Mr. Donald H. Dabelstein of the Office of Vocational Rehabilitation, a true pioneer in his field, was likewise one of the early guiding spirits of our program.

Finally, the editors gratefully acknowledge that the entire project was supported since April 1955 by a research and demonstration grant from the Office of Vocational Rehabilitation, U.S. Department of Health, Education, and Welfare.

FRANZ J. KALLMANN, M.D.
*Project Director*

* Now Vocational Rehabilitation Administration

# INTRODUCTION

Before the organization of the Mental Health Project for the Deaf on April 1, 1955, it had long been known to rehabilitation specialists, family counselors and genetic guidance workers that early deafness created unique adjustment problems and posed a special challenge with respect to psychiatric help. Because of formidable road blocks in communicating with the deaf and a general lack of knowledge about the type and severity of their problems, few if any psychiatric diagnostic and treatment facilities existed for this large group. In fact, the very size of the group, its geographic and socio-economic distribution among the population, and its family structure were inadequately documented.

The members of the Department of Medical Genetics at the New York State Psychiatric Institute had devoted many years to the investigation of the genetic and demographic aspects of mental health and the application of this knowledge to guide people when confronted with marriage or parenthood concerns or with mental illness. Among the many families seen for guidance were a number with early total deafness. In 1955, this group applied for and received one of the first Research and Demonstration Grants established by the Office of Vocational Rehabilitation to make possible a comprehensive approach to the problems of the deaf.

The Psychiatric Institute, where the project was organized in the Washington Heights section of New York City, is one of the oldest teaching, research and training institutions in psychiatry in this country. Founded and maintained by the New York State Department of Mental Hygiene, it forms an integrated unit of Columbia-Presbyterian Medical Center.

The departmental staff assigned to the project at the outset consisted of research workers in psychiatric and psychological genetics familiar with the methods of psychiatric diagnosis, psychotherapy, counseling psychology, and population studies. In addition, we were fortunate in receiving the expert help of a special Advisory Council composed of six prominent members of the medical faculty of Columbia University and six distinguished educators from the field of the deaf.

The plans formulated for this venture with the aid of the Council were made possible by the support, moral as well as financial, of the Office of Vocational Rehabilitation of the Department of Health, Education, and Welfare. Without this generous assistance, there would have been neither the courage nor the means to launch such an ambitious undertaking.

The proposed program of activities was designed to cover three general areas: research, psychiatric guidance, and training of specialized guidance workers. These three phases were scheduled to proceed simultaneously so that the work could be coordinated as it progressed (112).

Obviously, the goal of psychiatric guidance for any group of people requires an intimate knowledge of their potential and actual life performance levels. Yet the information available on the adjustive norms of the deaf population was incomplete. Unless one knows how the best adjusted members of a deaf group deal with such important personal matters as mate selection, marriage and parenthood, one cannot be constructive in attempting to help those who appear poorly adjusted. For this reason, what was needed as the basis for developing effective procedures in guidance work and training was knowledge derived from research data on the personal and intra-family patterns of adjustment specific to the deaf. Following is a brief description of the research design as planned for this project:

### Research Activities

In order to obtain all essential information about the range of adjustive variations in deaf populations, a study of two statistically representative and entirely independent samples was planned. The main sample consisted of the total New York State population of literate deaf persons over 12 years of age. Adjustment data on these persons were particularly important for an understanding of behavior patterns that may lead to poor, fair, or adequate levels of life performance.

All available agencies were called on for help in locating the research subjects for this sample—schools, hospitals, statistical bureaus, and various cultural, social and vocational organizations. Lists were prepared of the names, ages, addresses, club or school affiliations and family interrelationships of ascertainable deaf persons in New York State. The task of collecting verified information about the total deaf New York State population, rather than about any selected group, required extensive field trips into all districts of the State to construct a suitable list ("frame," in the statistician's terminology) of deaf people in the State of New York.

Personal interviews were conducted in a random sample of names drawn from the list (Chapter 1). The results were differentiated according to age, education, and the socio-economic status of the family. On the adolescent level, the emphasis of the study was on sexual maturation patterns, and the variable attitudes developed in preparation for marriage and parenthood. Illegitimate birth rates, homosexual tendencies, and the motives for celibacy and a preference for hearing or non-hearing mates were also studied.

On the adult level, the inquiries were focused on problems of marital adjustment or maladjustment, the planning and corollaries of family size, and those specific intra-family relationships encountered in homes where only some of the members were deaf. Under certain conditions, especially those of gross parental immaturity or social inadequacy, it may be as frustrating for hearing children as for non-hearing ones to be the offspring of deaf parents.

From time immemorial, social need and charitable concern had always outdistanced the strides toward actual knowledge in these areas. A basic goal of this project was to render intuitive attitudes articulate by securing statistically verified data through research.

In appraising the adjustment of deaf subjects in various social roles, special attention was allotted to current attitudes of the hearing world toward the deaf. Fortunately, the deaf are no longer thought of as unteachable, thanks to the magnificent efforts of our fellow workers in the educational field. Yet it is all too apparent that the deaf may continue to be the victims of more subtle misconceptions fostered by ignorance or the increasing pressure generated by modern societies. Social isolation may be enforced as much from without as from within. Emotional deprivation may be due in large measure to the erroneous notion that handicapped people, such as the deaf, live in a sheltered world and therefore need less rather than more adequate provision for psychiatric help.

As to the diagnostic criteria to be used in classifying the literate deaf in our main sample, deafness was defined as a *stress-producing hearing loss, from birth or early childhood, rendering a person incapable of effecting meaningful and substantial auditory contact with the environment.*

Literacy in a deaf person had to be measured by his ability to enter into meaningful communication with the investigator, either verbally (spoken, written, or fingerspelled language) or by means of the sign language. A prerequisite for each member of our research staff was the ability to conduct an interview by manual communication. The histories of research subjects who were unable to use any means of communication were recorded for statistical purposes only.

Our second research sample consisted of deaf twins of all ages living in the eastern half of the United States. Fortunately, the twin study method provides us with a rather unique human laboratory experiment for comparative investigations into the interaction of genetic and environmental factors in personality development. Of the two kinds of twins, fraternal and identical, the so-called identical or one-egg twins are a very special class of human beings. A single egg, fertilized by one sperm cell, will falter in its growth long enough to split into two halves and lay the basis for two equal embryos. Each of them then continues to grow normally. So it happens that two embryos may have an absolute likeness of genes, those elements transmitting hereditary characteristics. By contrast, fraternal or two-egg twins, aside from being born at the same time, are no more alike than any two brothers and sisters.

In connection with deafness, it is important to know how a child's personality development is affected by an early hearing loss. Patently, the adjustment of such a child will depend on the nature and degree of his hearing impairment, as well as on the age when it occurred. Other variable factors to be considered are the learning capacity of the child, the emotional atmosphere of the home in which he lives, and the educational opportunities available to him.

Since the number of variables is reduced in one-egg twins, the situation encountered here is more easily controlled. Of the two members of a twin pair, perhaps only one or both may be deaf since birth. In the former instance, differences in personality development can be ascribed almost entirely to the impact of deafness. In the latter, different methods of training or treatment may be revealing. Equally instructive can be the study of pairs with a complete hearing loss in one twin and only a partial loss in the other, or twins whose deafness occurred at different ages.

In addition to these samples of the general population drawn for intensive study, a more extensive survey was planned to determine general demographic patterns including marriage and fertility rates.

Finally, some special groups were earmarked for study. At the lower end of the distribution of deafness-specific adjustment patterns, special attention was paid to the frequency and causation of such severe forms of maladjustment as mental retardation, psychoses, delinquency, sexual deviations, alcoholism, and drug addiction. An attempt was made to secure reliable rates for suicide and death by accident. As for marriages in this group, information was needed on the frequency of broken homes due to desertion, divorce, or hospitalization of a parent.

By contrast, a special study of deaf persons who achieved outstanding vocational status according to criteria established by an expert committee was aimed at determining some of the correlates of such achievement.

## Guidance Activities

Regarding the clinical aspects of the project, the goal from the outset was to make it possible for the deaf to benefit from all the effective methods of diagnosis, therapy and prevention afforded by modern psychiatry and related disciplines to the same extent as do hearing persons in distress.

Operating on a two day per week schedule, the pilot clinic was soon flooded with applications for the diagnosis and treatment of deaf individuals. The patients came from schools, clubs, religious organizations and family counseling agencies, as well as offices of the Division of Vocational Rehabilitation in the State of New York.

It had to be realized that there are at least as many different types of emotional disturbance and mental disorder in non-hearing persons as there are in hearing ones. Moreover, the prospects of effective therapy for deaf as well as hearing patients generally depend on an adequate and early diagnosis. Once a pattern of disturbed behavior has become chronic the chances of readjustment are considerably diminished.

For obvious reasons, the usual diagnostic dilemmas are compounded in the deaf. Incompleteness of background information and obstacles in communication make every psychiatric diagnosis in the deaf an extremely complex affair. Therefore, it was clear that deaf people with symptoms of maladjustment need to be referred to the most competent diagnosticians available. Educators and counselors may be highly skilled in their own fields, but they cannot be expected to have the specialized knowledge required for an early diagnosis of schizophrenia. For that matter, even epilepsy or a brain tumor is not always easy to diagnose.

The diagnostic facilities developed as part of the project on an ambulatory basis involved so much extensive work with each patient that they had to be reserved in most cases for the deaf population of the New York City metropolitan area, or those who could come to the Psychiatric Institute. All agencies and schools dealing with the deaf in New York State were informed that they could refer suitable cases for diagnostic and consultative purposes.

As to marriage and parenthood counseling facilities for families where there is deafness, it may be stated that a surprising amount of superstition and misinformation is encountered by those specializing in this work. Often tragic situations are found that might have been prevented by a genetically trained counselor. Fortunately, we are able to reassure many severely troubled people that their fears are groundless. Even the most intelligent people in this area have a tendency to exaggerate anxieties over things they do not understand. In regard to questions having to do with family planning, the importance of considering each family on its own merits cannot be overemphasized.

## Training Activities

The pluridisciplinary personnel of the pilot project was able to provide for a succession of trained individuals by gradually adding new professional workers to its staff. In addition every conceivable effort was made to hold special classes and seminars in sign language and problems of the deaf for all departmental workers and other persons interested in the clinical or investigative aspects of the project.

The purpose of this report is to set forth in the chapters that follow the realization of these plans in the various research and treatment areas and to outline a set of recommendations for the future extension of this work. Some of these recommendations have already been achieved. The report is at once a record of pioneering activity in this peculiarly neglected field and a pilot to open the way toward further investigation and permanent mental health planning with preventive and therapeutic programs.

JOHN D. RAINER

# HISTORICAL REVIEW OF SPECIAL EDUCATION AND MENTAL HEALTH SERVICES

Every specialist looks at deafness from the viewpoint of his own particular discipline. The otologist takes the medical perspective; the speech therapist the angle of speech involvement; the audiometrist is mainly concerned with the measurement of hearing acuity; and the psychologist with related mental, emotional, and behavioral adjustment processes. We could go on in this vein through many of the specialties engaged in work with the deaf, and still the sum of their separate findings would not add up to the total scope of impairment that early severe deafness can inflict.

The discipline that comes closest to embracing this scope is special education for the deaf. Underlying its philosophy and practices is the concept that early severe deafness is an audio-communicative disturbance which, by blotting out conversational hearing ability, blocks the learning of verbal language and is thereby capable of severing fundamental relations between an individual and his environment. The efforts of special education are directed toward setting up alternative lines of communication through which a deaf person can learn what the rest of the world is saying and thinking, and by learning, can enter into normal living-relations with society. That these efforts have borne fruit may be seen in the respected positions attained today by many deaf members of society, among them figures noted for outstanding achievement. But it was not always so, neither in regard to the philosophy of education nor the status of the deaf.

In ancient times until well into the Middle Ages attitudes toward the deaf were cloaked in ignorance and superstition. The deaf mute was seen as queer, comical, depraved. His lack of the "instinct of speech" was considered a mark of Divine displeasure that only a Divine miracle could erase. Unless and until it came to pass, the deaf mute would remain a witless thing on a par with the beasts of the field.

Such opinions were held not only by the public at large but also by prominent scholars of the day. Aristotle himself whose word was law in those times failed to recognize the relationship between the ability to hear and the ability to speak. He regarded the sense of hearing as the sense of instruction, and concluded that those who lacked it had no capacity to learn. The deaf were therefore uneducable, a misconception that held sway for many hundreds of years.

It was not until the sixteenth century that the first shadow of doubt was

---

Portions of this review are reproduced, by permission of the author, from *Youth in a Soundless World,* Edna S. Levine, New York University Press, 1956.

cast on the Aristotelian view. Backed by a prestige equal to Aristotle's own, the brilliant physician, Geronimo Cardano of Milan, declared that the deaf were educable, that they could be taught to "hear" by reading and to "speak" by writing. Scholars were alerted to watch for this educational miracle.

They had not long to wait. During this same century, the Benedictine monk, Pedro Ponce de Leon, succeeded not only in teaching several deaf scions of noble Spanish houses to read and write, but what was even more astounding, to speak. This stupendous feat created a great stir of interest in the deaf among contemporary scholars of language and they became engrossed in the game of inventing manual alphabets for the deaf and in conventionalizing the natural language of signs.

Before the close of the seventeenth century, the basic means of communication used with and among the deaf today had already been formulated and were being used by pioneer teachers and their selected pupils. These lines of communication were speech, reading and writing, the manual alphabet, and the language of signs. No sooner had they been set up than a difference of opinion sprang up as to which could best serve the needs of the deaf—spoken language or read language.

Fired with missionary zeal, Pedro Ponce de Leon's desire was to bring his deaf pupils into the fold of Christianity by enabling them "to pray, to assist at the Mass, to know the doctrines of Christianity, and to know how to confess themselves by speech" (202). Toward this end, oral confession and prayer were obligatory in order to remove the veto of Romans X. 17 on the religious development of the deaf (99). To start his pupils off Ponce used signs, but soon thereafter articulation together with some reading and writing. His major aim, however, was speech and his motive to bring religious acceptance and fulfillment to his pupils.

On the other hand, Juan Pablo Bonet, an eminent countryman of Ponce de Leon, held that the greatest need of the deaf was mental development, and that the major means toward this end was written and read language. Bonet also taught speech, but mainly for legal purposes. In those days it was necessary for the wealthy deaf to be able to speak in order to be considered "persons" in the eyes of the law and so entitled to inherit property. But Bonet believed that mental growth would be retarded if the tempo of language learning were slowed down to the pace required by speech learning. To bring language to his pupils as rapidly and fully as possible, he used gestures, pantomime, signs, and the manual alphabet. He is also said to have been the first teacher of the deaf to make deliberate use of lipreading (99).

In the light of present knowledge it appears that Bonet stood on rational ground. Scholars of language today tell us that of the four basic "vocabularies" of literate persons—the speaking, writing, reading, and recognition vocabularies—the one for speaking is the smallest, "usually much the smallest" (126) while the one for reading is the largest. Evidently, Bonet was aware of this fact when he questioned the effects on mental development of limiting a deaf pupil's language skills to man's smallest vocabulary.

The differences between the philosophies of Ponce de Leon and Bonet raised no critical issues at the time. Education of the deaf was still a highly experimental enterprise and conducted on a very limited scale. Only the very wealthy received instruction, and on a private tutorial basis. Both teachers used oral as well as manual methods and both reported successful results, making a comparative evaluation of outcomes impossible. Later, when private schools were established, again for the wealthy few, the systems of instruction were often closely guarded secrets, adding to the difficulties in any attempt at evaluation.

It was not until public education was made available for the deaf at large that serious dissension over methods entered the picture. The great name in public education for the deaf was Charles Michel de l'Epee, a French priest who in the eighteenth century gathered together a group of poor deaf children of Paris for the unprecedented purpose of teaching them in the mass. Eventually, he evolved a system of pantomime and systematic arbitrary signs that provided a complete manual equivalent of verbal language, both spoken and written. Philosophically, he shared Bonet's view that the greatest need of the deaf was language for thinking and reasoning rather than for speech. His work and opinions were to play an important part in fashioning the policies of the public schools to come.

In this country, the first free permanent public school for the deaf was opened in 1817 at Hartford, Connecticut under the spirited leadership of Thomas Hopkins Gallaudet, with others following in fairly rapid succession. Never again shall we see such masses of mute, illiterate creatures as sought admission to these first schools. Here were the uneducated deaf—children, adolescents, adults—described in the literature of the day as "perfect ciphers," "living automatons," "having little in common with mankind but the human form" (22). Psychologically, they were likened to infants "excepting for their greater strength and stronger passions" (166). But at least they were now considered educable, and that in itself marked an epochal advance over the "beasts of the field" stigma.

But educable though they might be, the questions that confronted the early teachers of the deaf were: To what extent educable? With what psychological substance could these "perfect ciphers" be filled? By what techniques? These persons were not wealthy young noblemen who could afford individual attention, nor yet the selected pupils of private schools. They were the deaf at large who would one day hopefully take their places in communities at large. Could these "perfect automatons" actually be converted into human beings on a par with their hearing fellows?

The teachers of the period struggled mightily with these problems, and mostly alone. Those were the early days not only in public education of the deaf but also in the scientific study of human behavior. Psychology could offer no assistance; it was still in its infancy and busy coping with its own evolutionary problems. As for audiology, it was more than a century away. Teachers of the deaf had to use their own judgment in making appraisals and deductions, with the schools their laboratories and the students their experimental subjects.

Unparalleled in the annals of human effort was the task these early educators had before them. Working with the raw material of human substance they had to force the cultivation of human beings. Questions of method and goal loomed large, and, following the pattern laid down centuries before, two main schools of thought emerged. Both agreed that the basic problem of deafness was mental isolation, but one held that this could best be dispelled by teaching the deaf to speak, while the other maintained that the way out of isolation was through acquiring the great body of language necessary for mental development.

Characteristically, the general public supported the speech view, for the feat of teaching the deaf to speak has stirring dramatic appeal. The results were used not only to win over community attitudes on the educability of the deaf, but also the support of state legislatures in establishing more schools for the deaf.

Thus encouraged, the opinions of the speech adherents, or oralists as they came to be called, grew stronger and the communicative methods used in education narrower. Not only was speech development the "first and primary objective" (202) but it also became the major method of instruction. Teach speech by speech was the policy. Lip-reading and writing were also used, but manual reinforcement such as used by Ponce de Leon was outlawed. Before long, deeply outraged voices were raised by the language-through-all-methods adherents, the so-called manualists, demanding "What of the children who could not fit into this philosophy?" The latter group favored a combined approach whereby classic oral instruction would be provided for children who could profit from it, and for those who could not, oral instruction plus a greater or lesser amount of manual techniques according to the needs of the pupil. The reply to this approach was that oral instruction could not be satisfactorily conducted unless the oral pupils were completely segregated from the manually taught.

In reviewing this period, it should be noted that with the sharp increase in the number of schools for the deaf, hard of hearing children were admitted along with those who had lost their hearing before the development of speech and language. For most hard of hearing children there was no other provision. The oralists could no more see subjecting these "partially deaf," "partially hearing," and "deafened" pupils to manual methods than the manualists could see subjecting the congenitally deaf to none but classic oral methods. There was something to be said for both sides.

However, so strong were the feelings of partisanship concerning methods that even such obvious individual differences as time of onset of deafness and amount of hearing loss were given little more than lip service in educational thinking. The method rather than the pupil took the spotlight. The "psychology" of the deaf child was glossed over as being "no different from the hearing." To many educators, the prime testing ground for their theories—the adult deaf population—was a completely unknown community, and so too were its mental health problems.

Toward the end of the nineteenth century the Battle of Methods raged furiously. The oralists were accused of espousing the principle of "education by imitation," of being more concerned with outer appearance than inner enrichment, and of producing for all their pains nothing but watered down versions of the hearing. The manualists, however, fell into the same trap when they modeled curricula in schools for the deaf after the three R's type then currently used in schools for hearing children. By so doing, they gave tacit support to the proposition that the deaf child could be molded into a hearing one by following the same scholastic lines as those used in the "hearing" schools. It was inevitable that a condition of psycho-educational malnutrition should gradually pervade the deaf pupil population, since the hearing child learns as much and more out of school as in, but the severely deaf child, not being able to hear what the world has to say, is singularly dependent upon his school for most of what he learns.

To the educators' concern over the unsatisfactory state of scholastic achievement on the part of the deaf, there was gradually added an awareness that despite the remarkable increase in speech instruction in all schools of whatever persuasion, speech intelligibility lagged far behind expectations. As Caroline Yale put it, the need was not for "more speech but better speech" (202).

Many remedies were suggested to correct both unsatisfactory school achievement as well as poor speech intelligibility. There were proponents of day school placement for deaf pupils to bring them into everyday contact with their families and communities; day class placement to bring them into closer relations with hearing pupils; nursery school placement to give the deaf the earlier educational start they needed to make up for the slower pace of learning imposed by deafness; residential school placement to enable deaf pupils to have fuller social experiences and planned extracurricular activities.

There were those who opposed special schools and classes altogether, maintaining that deaf children could best enter the hearing world by way of hearing schools. Improved methods of aural training, speech development, and language instruction made their appearance. Interestingly enough, almost every view expressed in these and other late nineteenth and early twentieth century proposals is in operation today in one facility for the deaf or another, with the resultant heterogeneity in educational background of our deaf population.

Before long, complex problems of pupil management, appraisal and classification arose on all fronts. The educator, still coping with matters single-handedly, was badly in need of help. It was about this time that psychology came forth with its classic instrument—the objective psychological test. Educators of the deaf eagerly seized upon the idea as a possible solution for some of their more pressing problems.

Psychology entered the field in the early years of the twentieth century, and under the gifted leadership of Rudolf Pintner there followed a period of extensive investigation that continued until his death in 1942. Everything, it seemed, was in need of scrutiny—pupils, methods, outcomes. This was a large order for a new specialty but Pintner, his pupils and coworkers carried on undaunted. Included in studies of the Pintner Period (132, 135) were intelligence, personality, achievement, learning ability, speech and speech reading, memory, social competence and maturity, special aptitudes, motor and mechanical abilities. Comparisons were made between deaf and hearing groups, congenitally and adventitiously deaf groups, groups of children who had lost their hearing at different ages, and groups of children with different amounts of hearing loss.

Large scale surveys were conducted. Orally and manually taught pupils were compared. The mental levels of families of congenitally deaf children were investigated. Non-language and performance mental test scales were designed for and standardized on deaf pupils. In short, the scope of inquiry and activity was phenomenal (13, 173). The findings, however, were not very helpful to the educator, as Pintner's summary of the period would indicate: "The results of these tests seem to indicate a slightly lower general intelligence for the deaf as a group when compared with the hearing. . . . The motor and mechanical ability and the concrete intelligence of the deaf are their great assets. Their abstract verbal intelligence, their academic achievement (which was found to be about four years behind that of the hearing) are their great liabilities" (173, pp. 177, 179).

On the basis of these findings, Pintner recommended that the whole system of education of the deaf be reoriented with the emphasis on the motor, the mechanical, the concrete. "Make the learning of language subsidiary and ancillary to making and building and doing" (173, p. 179). Only a few should be permitted to follow an academic curriculum. "Shopwork, home economics, trade training of all kinds, dramatics, gardening, and the like, these would be the main 'subjects,' and reading and writing and arithmetic would be subsidiary and incidental aspects of the main 'courses' " (173, p. 179).

Some educators, impressed with Pinter's recommendations, proceeded to put them into practice, thereby introducing still more variables into the educational picture (76). Others protested that Pintner's recommendations were tantamount to using points of greatest weakness in educational outcomes among the deaf and making them standards for educational planning and attainment. What the educator was seeking, they claimed, was guidance in eliminating these very weaknesses. In the ensuing agitation, psychologists were accused of not being "fully qualified to deal with the psychology of the deaf . . . they simply do not get hold of the subject of their examinations . . . their lack of familiarity with the deaf is too obvious to inspire a teacher of the deaf with confidence" (15), much of which was probably true.

An unfortunate outcome of this period was the two-year mental devaluation suffered by the deaf. From the belief that "the psychology of the deaf is the same as the hearing," there was a shift to the idea that it was of some lower order. Fusfeld (76) commented in 1955 that there still were some educators who entertained this notion, despite ample psychometric evidence to the contrary.

During the years following the Pintner Period, dissatisfaction among educators with the psychoeducational outcome of their efforts was expressed more and more openly. Concerning language development, Vinson (230, p. 114) declared that, "In spite of the great amount of attention which its seriousness attracted to the problem . . . the majority of deaf pupils still leave school without language adequate for their simplest general needs." Fusfeld often deplored the language disabilities of even top-level pupils from schools for the deaf throughout the country, namely, the candidates for admission to Gallaudet College for the deaf (76).

In regard to speech, a distinguished oralist stated that "As followers of the oral system of educating the deaf, we should . . . be careful not to create the impression . . . that we believe all deaf children can learn to speak fluently and naturally. We know this is not possible . . ." (202, p. 80). Concerning the comparative achievement of oral versus combined-system pupils, Myklebust in a study of approximately 1,000 deaf pupils found "serious language retardation in the deaf child irrespective of whether he has been taught by the oral or combined method" (154, p. 382). And from Goldberg came the plaintive query: ". . . why are teachers of the deaf still so satisfied with so many of their pupils who can talk intelligibly, lip-read successfully and write correctly, but who understand so little and have so little to say about our world?" (81, p. 379).

The subjects of the foregoing comments are the more than 27,000 pupils currently attending 415 schools and classes for the deaf in the United States: 15,826 in 72 public residential schools and classes, 2,050 in 10 day schools, 7,082 in 254 day classes, 1,333 in 16 denominational and private residential schools, 1,107 in 48 denominational and private day classes, and 191 in 15 schools and classes for the multiple-handicapped (56). In addition, there is a scattering of deaf pupils in the regular classes of "hearing" schools, as well as numbers of very young deaf children who receive instruction in speech and hearing centers. The systems of instruction used with these pupils vary with the schools; the combined system is favored by the public residential schools, and the oral system by day schools, day classes, and by private and denominational schools.

Among other variables involved in the education of the deaf pupil population are: age of beginning school, age of leaving school, total length of time under instruction, systems of language instruction used in the schools, method of communication favored by the pupil, quality of instruction and experience of the teacher, nature of extracurricular learning experiences, personal adjustment services provided by the school, vocational adjustment services provided by the school.

To be sure, education of the deaf has come a long way since the days when the first teachers confronted their pupils in the first schools. But, as Elstad remarks, "The fact that an agreement has not been reached in this country since 1817 regarding the education of the deaf is an indication that there is still a real question as to methods and their effectiveness" (64, p. 161).

The more pressing problems requiring investigation, as reported at a recent special research conference in the vocational rehabilitation of the deaf (192), include the following:

1. Effects of language deprivation on the emotional, social, and mental development of deaf persons.

2. Effects of different methods of communication on language development.

3. Relationship between written language and the language of signs.

4. The educative value of extracurricular activities in residential schools for the deaf.

5. The adult educational needs of the deaf.

6. Relationship between educational variables and adult adjustment.

7. The value of integrated programs for deaf pupils in the regular schools.

8. Influence of attitudes on educational motivation and adult adjustment.

9. A study of methods to develop more comprehensible speech among the deaf.

10. Studies in the developmental psychology and emotional adjustment of the deaf from early childhood through adolescence.

It should be noted in passing that none of these basic problems has as yet been subjected to systematic research. Nonetheless, the relationship between educational practices and the psychological welfare of the deaf was recognized as early as 1895, when Clarke (42) urged teachers to observe the psychology of their deaf pupils and gear their instructional approaches to individual needs.

With the spread of psychological thinking in succeeding years, this relationship was exposed to increasing scrutiny. Educators of the deaf were told that the mental health of deaf pupils requires a homelike environment, understanding and interested teachers, and school work that the pupil is capable of doing if he is to feel secure (235); they were alerted to maladjustments among their charges (176); they were warned that the deaf need special help in their adjustments (174); and that the attitudes, reactions, and personality of the teachers play a paramount role in the adjustment and attainments of deaf pupils (242).

Deaf leaders of the deaf expressed their concern with the mental health of deaf pupils by informing the schools that the three R's were not the only responsibility of educators, but that "considering the whole educational situation and the social and economic difficulties of adult life for the deaf, character training might be considered the major responsibility of the schools" (47).

A few schools responded to their mental health responsibilities and opened the door to psychologists and social workers. It would be gratifying to be able to report that they were rapidly followed by others, but that was not the case. For one thing, the accumulated problems of this special educational area were far too complex to attract the uninitiated. For another, the field of the deaf had existed in a state of professional isolation for so long that its intrinsic scientific worth and excitement went unrecognized by "outsiders." And, finally, not all schools could see the advantage of adding mental health specialists to their staff.

The more forward-looking educator sought to fill the gaps in specialized personnel by broadening his scope of mental health services to include parent educational programs and closer working relations with his professional colleagues in audiology, otology, psychiatry, psychology, social work, vocational rehabilitation, and pastoral guidance.

However, workers inexperienced with the deaf operate under a serious handicap regardless of what their specialized competencies may be. As a result, the advantages of broadened team relations have been offset by "poorly informed educators who do not know what is available educationally for the deaf child; by enthusiastically established clinics all too eager to promise sure-fire educational results with normalcy guaranteed; by avid audiologists who exaggerate the possibilities of small remnants of hearing; by all-knowing critics who condemn well-established schools for the deaf that have been in this work for many years; by well-meaning enthusiasts who promise parents that the child can be taught with hearing children after a few years of intensive training; by clinicians who treat the deaf child as a statistic instead of a handicapped child who has a long way to go educationally and cannot get there on figures and percentages" (64, p. 165).

As for the "outcome" of special education—the deaf adult—his problems of adjustment were outside the chronological range of school responsibility; but since there were no mental health facilities geared to his special needs, it was to the school he turned in times of trouble. Here, he felt, were his friends, the people who had reared him and who understood him. Thus, in addition to their other obligations, the schools had to do the best they could for the adult deaf as well.

Such is the climate of opinions and practices we find in education of the deaf today. Having to grow up in a world of public ignorance and indifference, confused professional thinking, and untested professional hypotheses is the major handicap of early severe deafness. The deaf adult shows the cumulative effects of this state of affairs. But the deaf adult is a relatively unknown quantity in educational thinking. The appeal of a child and the easy accessibility of deaf children through the schools have made for a traditional pupil-monopoly on professional attention.

Nevertheless, it is the deaf adult who most likely holds the key to many of the unsolved problems in the education of the deaf. He represents the ultimate testing ground for educational hypotheses and psychological theory. The present project is based on the belief that by serving and exploring the mental health needs of an adult deaf population and by tapping its vast reservoir of information and experiences we may come at last to a clearer understanding of early severe deafness and of the best means for preserving the psychological integrity of the deaf.

EDNA S. LEVINE

# PART ONE

# THE NEW YORK STATE DEAF POPULATION:

# RESEARCH PROGRAM

# Chapter 1

## METHODOLOGICAL ASPECTS: SAMPLING PROCEDURES

### W. Edwards Deming

This chapter describes the sampling procedures used in the investigative areas of the deafness project. One part of this research was to investigate the adjustive norms and family problems of the literate deaf in two specific deaf populations: (1) the literate totally deaf population of the State of New York; (2) all literate deaf twins in the eastern half of the United States. There were also studies of special groups such as deaf twins, deaf patients in mental hospitals, deaf delinquents, and deaf persons of outstanding achievement.

### The Frames

The frames, or the lists of subjects, were acquired with the help of many agencies, including schools for the deaf, hospitals, statistical bureaus of the State, and various cultural, social, religious, vocational, and fraternal organizations of the deaf. Personal visits to all sizable communities, and questioning of local officials, aided by clues furnished by deaf people already on our list, led to the discovery of many additional names that we should otherwise have missed. After almost two years, such efforts had built up a list of nearly 12,000 names and addresses in the general file.

The State of New York was divided into 14 regions, to facilitate field work. Each region contained, as a rule, a central city and a mental hospital. Region 15 was created to take care of people that, as later information showed, had moved beyond the borders of the State of New York. These people were excluded from studies of the literate deaf population of the State of New York.

Four files were made with the 12,000 names, to serve various purposes. A master list, called the DR-file, kept in a book, showed names line by line in chronological order of accession. These were the so-called DR-cases. Serial numbers 1, 2, 3, and onward gave to each name a serial number, called the DR-number; thus, DR-173 designated the 173d name in the book. Other information on the same line showed the last known address; the age at a given date, if ascertained; the source of derivation; and the family number, if this name appeared in the family-book (q.v.).

Cards in duplicate (3 x 5 inches) showed the same information, along with the DR-number. One file of cards was alphabetic for the State as a whole, to permit easy access to any name. The duplicate cards were separated by region and filed in alphabetic order within the region. These cards were helpful in the field work, as by carrying the file for a region in making a field visit, an interviewer could determine whether any deaf person encountered there was already in our file.

In addition to the DR-file and the sets of cards, there was also the family-book, which was a grouping of DR-cases into families, a family being defined, for our purpose, as two or more deaf people, related by marriage or by blood. Each family had a family-number, the numbers running serially 1, 2, 3, and onward, in the order in which searches of the file and other information indicated pretty definitely that a DR-case, at the time of latest information, formed a family with another deaf person in the file. Entries in the family-book showed the names in each family, with their DR-numbers.

The 12,000 DR-numbers formed the frame for the small intensive sample of interviews described further on in this chapter. The family-book provided information, in the sampling, for equalizing the probabilities of selection. The purpose of this study was to elicit information on patterns of courtship, sexual maturation, attitudes regarding marriage and parenthood, problems of marital adjustment and maladjustment, planning of family size, and other intrafamily relationships, as well as to evaluate life performance in school, at work  and in the community. The results are presented in various other chapters of this monograph.

The names acquired by the early part of 1959, excluding hospital cases and clinic cases, and children in school, formed the frame for a study on mating and fertility patterns, and on other demographic and population-genetic characteristics. This part of the study was carried out by mail. The sampling procedure therefor was very simple: it started off with a 100 per cent mailing to a group of 1700 people that had cooperated in a study on twins a year earlier, and a 20 per cent sample of the remainder, followed by further requests to samples of non-respondents (see Chapter 2).

The samples of the special groups, such as deaf twins, deaf patients in mental hospitals, deaf delinquents, and deaf persons of outstanding achievement, were each 100 per cent of the names on the list.

### Description of the Sampling Procedure for the Interviews

*The frame.* The sampling unit was a DR-number in the book of DR-cases described earlier in this chapter. The DR-cases all had distinct serial numbers, 1, 2, 3, etc., in order of accession.

*The method of selection.* As each case had a serial number, it was simple to use random numbers directly to make selections. The first step in the selection was to draw a master sample of one case in eight. The master sample served as a reservoir, out of which to draw smaller samples for any subsequent purpose. The master sample was not one big sample, but was ten smaller and independent samples, each 1/10th of the whole. In other words, the sample was replicated in ten subsamples, to acquire the following advantages (53):

1. Valid but simple estimates of standard errors.
2. Valid but simple estimates of any mathematical bias in an estimate.
3. Facility for detection of some kinds of operational mistakes.

If any name in a family fell into the sample, the interviewers, according to instructions, would interview also all other deaf members of the household. Every name in the family-book was also in the DR-file. As a family must contain at least two members, it follows that everyone in the family-book could come into the sample through the selection of any one of the names that formed a family in the family-book. Any name in the family-book thus had multiple chance of selection.

Some names in the file had multiple chance of selection without being in the family-book. Thus, as a result of incomplete information, some people in the DR-file lived in the same family with other people in the same file, although none of these names showed in the family-book. An example is anyone in the DR-file who married another person in the file subsequent to our accession of the names: there would be no indication in the file nor in the family-book that the two people now form a family, and that they both, by marriage, had doubled their probabilities of selection.

Moreover, the rule that called for the interview of all deaf members of a family automatically gave all members of a family a chance of selection if any one of them was in the file.

It is a well-known principle of sampling that the probabilities of selection should be equal unless there is good reason to introduce disproportionate probabilities (as when the variances or costs are greatly different in the different classes). However, for reasons just enumerated, it was impossible in this problem to equalize in advance all the probabilities of selection. Moreover, even with a complete file, and with full information, it would have been impracticable to equalize all the probabilities of selection. Most entries (80% of them) in the family-book showed two members, and the proportions dropped rapidly with three, four, or more members. There is little gain in forming small strata (53, p. 298). Consequently, it was sufficient and effective to introduce partial equalization of probabilities, whereby the probability of a name in the family-book would be one-half the probability of a name not in the family-book. This system was optimum for families with two members in the card file, and it was considerably better than selection with equal probabilities for households with three or more names in the file.

*Weighting.** The probability of selection, for every person interviewed, was ascertainable from the initial probability of selection, and from the

---

* Professor F. F. Stephan of Princeton kindly assisted us with the problem of weighting.

number of interviews that the case led to. Thus, suppose that a case not in the family-book had a probability P of selection, and that no other member of his family was in the family-book. Then he and every deaf person found in his family would have weight $1/P$. If one other member of the family actually was in the frame, and if we were unaware of the relationship, then all members of this family had probability $2P$ of selection, wherefore the weight of each member would be $1/2P$.

Every family in the family-book had at least two cards in the frame, and as already explained above, the probability of selecting the DR-card for every individual that belonged to a family in the family-book was reduced to $\frac{1}{2} P$. But as every member of a family was to be interviewed, if any member was in the sample, every member of a family in the family-book had probability $\frac{1}{2} P \times 2 = P$ and weight $1/P$ if there were two members in the frame; probability $\frac{1}{2} P \times 3 = 3P/2$ and weight $2/3P$ if there were three members in the frame; probability $4P/2$ or $2P$ and weight $1/2P$ if there were four members in the frame, etc.

Weighting became a bit complex when one of the deaf people in the family, not in the frame, was close kin (father, mother, child, brother, sister) to someone in the frame, but in another family. Such a person had probability $2/P$ or more, depending on how many people were in the other family, as the rule was to enquire in the interview, the name of any close kin who was deaf, and to interview this relative.

A person who upon interview turned out to have two cards in the frame had weight $1/2P$, as his probability of selection was $2P$. An example was a man with initials on one card, but with one christian name spelled out on the other card, different addresses on the cards, age missing from one card. There was no way to be sure in advance whether these two cards represented one person or two: consequently, both cards stayed in the file, and the man had two chances of selection.

*Nonresponse and missing information.* Only the literate deaf in the State of New York qualified for the study. Not all people in the card-file were literate deaf. Some were deaf but illiterate; some were mentally defective. Some were only hard of hearing but belonged to societies for the deaf, and thus found their way into our file. Some, though hearing, were spouses of deaf people and belonged to deaf societies. One man in the sample had become deaf at age 50; hence did not meet our definition of deaf. Two were too young. Others had moved out of the State of New York, and were thus not within the bounds of this study. The sample thus led the interviewers to deaf people who belonged in the study; also to other people, deaf and not deaf, who did not belong in the study.

Some cases drawn into the sample were not interviewed for various reasons. Some people refused: others could not be found; some were out of reach. Some of these people would doubtless have turned out to be eligible for this study; some probably would not. Table 1 shows the number of cases not interviewed, and the reasons, with allocation to one of the two columns, eligible for the study, or not eligible.

**TABLE 1.**

Disposition of DR-cases drawn into the sample but not interviewed

| Reason for no interview | | Eligible for the study | Not eligible for the study |
|---|---|---|---|
| Case found but not interviewed because | | | |
| — Mentally retarded | | 0 | 16 |
| — Hard of hearing | | | 19 |
| — Became deaf at age 50 | | | 1 |
| — Refused | | 11 | |
| — Under age | | | 2 |
| — Deaf but can't communicate | | | 1 |
| — Could not arrange appointment | | 1 | |
| — Wrong person | | | 1 |
| — Senile | | | 1 |
| Case not interviewed, total | | 51 | |
| — Interviewer made no attempt | 14 | | |
| — Case was not at the address on the card: | | | |
| — moved, left address, but the interviewer did not follow him | 2 | | |
| — moved, left no address | 8 | | |
| — no address, or no information at the address on card | 13 | | |
| — Case had moved out of the State of New York | 10 | | |
| — Deceased | 4 | | |
| Total | | 63 | 41 |

Some of the 14 cases in Table 1 labeled "Interviewer made no attempt" were in areas inaccessible within the time-limits available for interviewing. This excuse unfortunately does not diminish the problem of what to do with the nonresponses.

The first step in the procedure of interviewing was to send a letter with a reply-envelope to ask for an appointment. The postal service forwarded the letters to people that had moved and left forwarding addresses. Envelopes returned by the postal service marked "unknown," or "moved, left no address," put the interviewer on his own initiative.

The only correct cure for nonresponse is response. Interviewers were accordingly expected to make great effort to find all the cases assigned to them. The figures in Table 1 only show what the interviewers did not achieve. They do not tell the story about the ingenious enquiries and vagaries of chance that led to discovery of people that had moved and left no trace of address, or that were entirely unremembered at the address shown on the card.

Table 1 classifies a nonresponse as eligible for the study unless he was obviously ineligible. This classification undoubtedly artificially inflates the proportion of nonresponses, and inflates likewise the apparent number of cases eligible for this study.

There are varying degrees of missing information. At one extreme, an interviewer neglects to fill in the day of birth, perhaps also the month, but shows the year. This is a venial sin, of little consequence, as we still know the age of the case within a year. More serious is omission of the answers to a whole block of questions, which can then only be tabulated as unknown. At the extreme is failure to get any answers at all concerning a case when he and his family refuse to talk to the interviewer, or through the interviewer's inability to find the case.

Fortunately, a refusal is not always a total loss for every characteristic that we study. Thus, it may be possible for the interviewer to ascertain whether a man is deaf, even if the man refuses to answer any questions. It may be possible to ascertain from relatives whether he is deaf and literate. We thus sometimes had definite indication that a man was deaf or hearing, even though there may have been no other information. For this reason the count of deaf and nondeaf in the sample exceeded the number of interviews completed.

People that were living in the State of New York, and with cards in our file at the time it was created, were members of the universe designated for study. As Table 1 shows, there were 63 cases of no interview. Some of the cases not interviewed may be deaf, some not. Some cases may have families, and these families may have several deaf people in them that should have been interviewed. Some of the people had moved out of the state before the interviewer arrived; others, not found, could have done the same. Four had died. Some of the cases not found could also have died. For every case that moved out of the state, or died, someone else moved in, or became 12 years old: otherwise, the deaf population of the State of New York would be on the decrease.

A common way to treat nonresponse and other missing information is to ignore it, and to ascribe to each nonresponse the average characteristics of the responses. This was the course adopted here. This course affords only partial correction at best, as the nonresponses might well have other characteristics. It does, however, dispose of the problem of nonresponse with simplicity. Conclusions from the results of any survey should be drawn with due caution for possible uncertainty that nonresponse may introduce (45, p. 292).

There was still another point that required arbitrary decision. The frame was continually receiving new additions during the course of the study, owing to continual efforts to procure names of deaf people. It was necessary, nevertheless, for several reasons, that interviewing should commence without waiting to close the frame. It was possible to draw a sample that covered the frame at a given date, and to draw a sample later on from additions to the frame. This is simple enough in principle, but it is not always simple in the field, because of the cost of travel to isolated spots in the state to interview a small sample of cases that come from new additions to the frame.

Interviewing was therefore delayed outside the metropolitan area until additions to the frame had dropped off to a trickle. Meanwhile, interviewing had commenced in the metropolitan area, to be supplemented later by a sample of the additions thereto, as travel in the metropolitan area was not a major cost. The sample for the areas outside the metropolitan area was drawn when there were 9200 DR-cases in the frame. An exception was Region 7, for which sampling commenced when the frame had reached DR No. 8800. Additions to the frame between DR No. 8800 and DR No. 9200 would have yielded a sample of only two more interviews in Region 7, and the cost of travel to attempt them was deemed excessive. Table 2 shows the regular additions to the frame, year by year.

### TABLE 2
#### Regular additions to the frame, by year

| Year | Number of names received |
|:----:|:----:|
| 1955 | 943 |
| 1956 | 8210 |
| 1957 | 14 |
| 1958 | 31 |
| 1959 | 44 |
| 1960 | 123 |

*Estimate of the number of deaf.* As stated above, each of the ten subsamples gave an independent estimate of the number of deaf people represented in the interviews. The average of the ten estimates is the final estimate, and the variance of the ten estimates gives an estimate of the precision of the sampling procedure. Table 3 shows the ten subsamples, weighted.

To carry forward the estimate of the number of deaf people in the state, to include the remainder of the frame not sampled, I have ascribed to the part not sampled the same average number of deaf people per DR-case as found in the part sampled, exactly in accord with the treatment of nonresponse. The calculations are in Table 4.

A special portion of the frame had its origin in names of people who had reported with impairment of hearing to the Division of Vocational Rehabili-

**TABLE 3**
Estimates of the number of deaf, by subsample

| Subsample | Estimate |
|:---:|:---:|
| 1 | 7530 |
| 2 | 9110 |
| 3 | 7910 |
| 4 | 8880 |
| 5 | 7300 |
| 6 | 7230 |
| 7 | 7740 |
| 8 | 4460 |
| 9 | 6590 |
| 10 | 6270 |
| **Average** | **7302** |

These estimates cover only part of the frame, as the text explains.

Range $=$ 9110 $-$ 4460 $=$ 4650

Range/10 $=$ 465 $=$ estimate of the standard error of the average

465/7302 $=$ 6.5% $=$ estimate of the coefficient of variation of the final
estimate

tation during the past five years. Any of these names not already in the frame were added thereto with the designation DVR. There were 1835 such names. These were sampled as the regular rate for the metropolitan area, namely, 1 in 40. Further search through the records of the names in this sample showed only three to be deaf. Two upon interview each proved to be the only deaf person in his family. The third case was not interviewed, but I shall assume that he was deaf, and either single or that no member of his family was deaf. I have accordingly added 120 to the count of deaf from the DVR cases.

The estimate of the total of literate deaf people of age 12 and over in the state is 10,355, with a standard error of 6½ per cent. Three standard errors are thus 19 per cent, which means that a 100 per cent census of the frame, carried out with the same diligence, omissions, and definitions, would show a count between 8336 and 12,374.

These limits represent possible margins of uncertainty from sampling alone. There is additional uncertainty from arbitrary decisions that it was necessary to make, specifically, the adjustments already discussed for (a) failure to interview some cases drawn into the sample; and for (b) parts of the frame not subjected to the sampling procedure. If these adjustments are

## TABLE 4
### Estimate of the number of literate deaf
### people aged 12 or over in the entire frame

| | |
|---|---:|
| Number of cards in the frame, Zones 001-115, all regions* | 9200 |
| Father Cribbin's list (DR Nos. 11035-11740) | 706 |
| | 9906 |

Cases in Zones 001-115 that were not subjected to sampling

| | | |
|---|---|---:|
| Region 15 (outside the state) | 375 | |
| Region 10 | 115 | |
| Region 7, Zones 110-115 | 85 | |
| Nonexisting numbers | | |
| (3449-3550 and 5449-5500) | 154 | 729 |

| | | |
|---|---|---:|
| Net number of DR cases in the frame through Zone 115, subject to sampling | | 9177 |
| The 179 interviews give the estimate   7302 (Table 3) | | |
| Expansion at the same rate for 63 non-interviews, 7302 × 63/179 | 2570 | |
| Estimate of the number of deaf people in that part of the frame subject to sampling (7302 + 2570) | 9872 | 9872 |
| Average number of deaf people per DR-case in the file subject to sampling, 9872/9177 | | 1.0757 |

| | | |
|---|---|---:|
| Last serial number as of 1 Oct. 1960 | 11,893 | |
| Exclude DVR-cases | 1,835 | |
| Region 15 | 389 | |
| Nonexisting numbers | 154 | |
| Net number of DR-cases in the file not blanks nor DVR | 9,515 | 9515 |
| Estimate of the number of deaf people in the net number of DR-cases not blanks, as of 1 Oct. 1960, 9515 × 1.0757 | | 10235 |
| Estimate of the number of deaf people in the 1835 DVR-cases | | 120 |
| Estimate of the number of deaf people (literate, 12 years and over) | | 10355 |
| Coefficient of variation of this estimate (Table 3) | | 6.5% |

*This number includes Region 15, which contains cases with addresses outside the State of New York, and not in the universe of study. Correction to exclude these cases is automatic in the calculations.

both wrong by 10 per cent in the same direction, then our estimate of the total deaf would increase or decrease by about 290.

Further uncertainty arises from the fact that our list of people deaf or supposedly deaf can never be complete. Conjecture in respect to the number of people deaf but not in our list is hazardous. The relative rates at which names have come in during the past few years as shown in Table 2, with no relaxation in effort to continue the search for deaf people, is perhaps indicative that we have about pumped dry the sources of names. The figures shown in Table 2 do not add up to the total number of DR-cases in the frame because it omits names received from special sources, some of which were known in advance to consist largely of people hard of hearing, and not really deaf (the DVR-cases, for example, *vide supra*).

The apparent increase in 1960 came largely from additional members of the families of deaf people drawn into the studies, carried out by mail and by interview. It is worth noting that such names had an ascertainable probability of selection, and that the estimate of the number of deaf people includes these additional family-members, even though their names were not in the file at the time when we drew the sample.

# Chapter 2

## DEMOGRAPHIC ASPECTS: NUMBER, DISTRIBUTION, MARRIAGE AND FERTILITY STATISTICS

JOHN D. RAINER and W. EDWARDS DEMING

### Population Statistics

Demography has been defined as "the study of the size, territorial distribution, and composition of population, changes therein, and the components of such changes . . ." (95). Out of the many facets of this science, data on marriage and fertility were chosen as being of special value in the study of the deaf. These may be useful both in helping to understand the family patterns and behavior of this group for counseling purposes, and as an aid to further investigation of the genetic and selective patterns of mating of the deaf.

Concern with the marriage and fertility patterns of the deaf goes back to the time of Alexander Graham Bell. The pre-Mendelian but astute American survey of Fay (66), the pedigree data collected at the Clarke School in Massachusetts (101), and more recent studies by Stevenson and Cheeseman (220) in Ireland, by Deraemaker (54) in Belgium, by Pfändler and Schnyder (170) in Switzerland, and by Close (44) in Texas, have dealt with some of the problems of fertility, consanguineous mating, type of inheritance, and gene frequency.

The study described in this chapter made use of the list of literate deaf persons described in Chapter 1. They were sent a mailed questionnaire, which was followed by a second mailing to names that did not reply to the first one. It was possible, in a few cases, to get help with a personal visit or a personal letter. The sampling procedure and a few words about the difficulties involved appear further on.

The age-sex pyramid (Figure 1) represents the estimated composition of the deaf people on the list, including the school children. It appears that there is a deficit of replies from unmarried persons in the lower age groups, especially females who might be less likely to belong to the clubs or organi-

Portions of this chapter originally formed the subject of a lecture at the 2nd International Conference of Human Genetics, Rome, 1961. They are reproduced by permission of the authors and publisher from the Proceedings of the Conference, Rome, Gregor Mendel Institute, 1963.

## FIGURE 1

Marital status of persons 15 years of age and over by 5–year age periods and sex

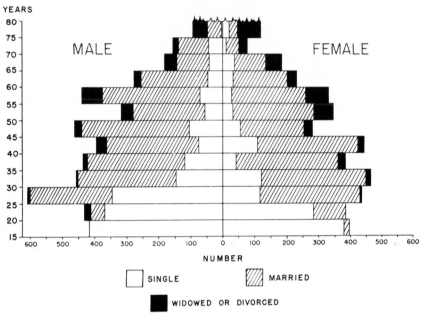

zations that cooperated in our initial search. The sex ratio of the total group is estimated at 113 males : 100 females.

Tabulation of these individuals according to present marital status (Table 1) shows a rate of 60.3 per cent ever married for males, and 68.9 for females. These rates, though below the rates for the general population, are notably higher than they were four decades ago, and markedly higher than those in our group of hospitalized deaf schizophrenics.

Table 2 shows that over 90 per cent of the group of deaf persons are the offspring of two hearing parents. It can be seen, however, that the small proportion that did have one or two deaf parents apparently did not let it deter them from marrying and in turn contributing to the recurrence of deafness in the next generation.

Table 3 presents data which may contribute toward the study of genetic expectancy rates for deafness in deaf families. The complicated task in the genetic analysis of data obtained from a large scale study of a total population is to separate the isolated adventitiously deaf subjects from those whose deafness is on a genetic basis. In this table, the percentage of deaf siblings among all cases of early total deafness varies from 8.4 per cent for no deaf

**TABLE 1**
Percent distribution of deaf according to marital condition

| Population | | Number | Percent Unmarried | | Percent Ever Married | | Percent Married | | Percent Widowed | | Percent Divorced | |
|---|---|---|---|---|---|---|---|---|---|---|---|---|
| | | | Deaf | Gen. Pop.^x | Deaf | Gen. Pop. | Deaf | Gen. Pop. | Deaf | Gen. Pop. | Deaf | Gen. Pop. |
| New York 1960 | Males, Total | 4674 | 39.7 | 27.6 | 60.3 | 72.4 | 53.8 | 66.8 | 3.2 | 4.6 | 3.3 | 1.0 |
| | Males, 25 and over | 3818 | 27.9 | 14.4 | 72.1 | 85.6 | 64.5 | 78.8 | 4.0 | 5.6 | 3.7 | 1.2 |
| | Females, Total | 4079 | 31.1 | 23.2 | 68.9 | 76.8 | 59.1 | 62.9 | 5.9 | 12.4 | 3.9 | 1.6 |
| | Females, 25 and over | 3285 | 18.4 | 12.5 | 81.6 | 87.5 | 69.5 | 70.4 | 7.3 | 15.2 | 4.9 | 1.8 |
| USA 1920 | Males, Total | — | 60.4 | 35.2 | 39.6 | 64.8 | 36.1 | 59.4 | 2.6 | 4.8 | 1.0 | 0.6 |
| | Females, Total | — | 54.4 | 27.4 | 45.6 | 72.6 | 39.4 | 60.7 | 5.2 | 11.2 | 1.0 | 0.8 |
| New York State Hospitals | Schizophrenics, Male | 79 | 82.3 | 61.9 | 17.7 | 38.1 | 10.1 | 26.8 | 2.5 | 1.2 | 5.1 | 9.7 |
| | Schizophrenics, Female | 57 | 61.4 | 34.8 | 38.6 | 65.2 | 24.6 | 44.8 | 3.5 | 5.6 | 10.5 | 14.3 |

^x General population from 1950 census

**TABLE 2**

Marital status of adult deaf according to deafness of their parents

| Adult deaf | Males (4168) | | | Females (3637) | | |
|---|---|---|---|---|---|---|
| | Neither parent deaf | One parent deaf | Both parents deaf | Neither parent deaf | One parent deaf | Both parents deaf |
| Number | 3940 (94.5%) | 78 (1.9%) | 153 (3.7%) | 3332 (91.6%) | 64 (1.8%) | 241 (6.6%) |
| Percent ever married | 67.4 | 83.3 | 64.4 | 77.1 | 100.0 | 73.5 |

### TABLE 3
#### Distribution of siblings of adult deaf by deafness of their parents

| Siblings | Neither parent deaf (7310) | One or both parents deaf (547) |
|---|---|---|
| Total number of siblings | 21,480 | 960 |
| Total number of deaf siblings | 1,804 | 333 |
| Per cent of deaf siblings | 8.4 | 34.7 |

parent to 34.7 per cent for one or both parents deaf. One deaf parent is the condition for a minimal group of hereditarily deaf subjects. Perhaps a more accurate estimate may derive from the fact that for deaf subjects that either state that they were born deaf, or that have deaf relatives, the percentage of deaf siblings is 24 per cent. This is higher than Pfändler and Schnyder's corrected figure (Weinberg method) of 9.5 per cent.

Table 4 shows combined fertility rates for all deaf women in the various age groups, including 1557 women over 45 whose fertility period is considered completed. Again, one may note an apparent higher proportion of deaf women married (68.9%) than there was earlier in the century, when the rate varied from 30.7 per cent in 1900 to 45.0 per cent in 1920. The fertility rate for mothers remains below the level of the general population, the current figures being 229 children born per 100 deaf mothers.

In Table 5, the rates for all deaf women are subdivided into those for the three major religious affiliations, and for New York City, other urban, and rural, as defined in the census. Once again, the lowest marriage and fertility rate is among the schizophrenic deaf females in state hospitals.

The assortative mating patterns found among the deaf are of considerable interest both from a psychiatric and genetic standpoint. In Table 6, using the reported age of onset, and again roughly equating congenital and hereditary deafness, we see that only 5.1 per cent of women born deaf, and 8.7 per cent of those that became deaf at an early age, were married to hearing men. The rest had husbands who had been deaf since birth or early childhood. Almost 30 per cent of the marriages where both partners were born deaf, and from 14 to 21 per cent of those where only one partner was born deaf, resulted in deaf children, usually more than one.

## TABLE 4
### Crude marriage and fertility rates of deaf women by age

| | Age | Number of women | Per cent ever married | | Per cent of married who are mothers | | Children ever born per 100 mothers | |
|---|---|---|---|---|---|---|---|---|
| | | | Deaf | Gen. pop. | Deaf | Gen. pop. | Deaf | Gen. pop. |
| TOTAL DEAF WOMEN 1960 | 15 and over | 4079 | 68.9 | 76.9 | 70.7 | 77.1 | 229 | 235 |
| | 15 - 24 | 784 | 16.3 | 31.1 | 43.2 | 56.0 | 147 | 142 |
| | 25 - 34 | 905 | 74.0 | 82.6 | 74.5 | 79.0 | 229 | 197 |
| | 35 - 44 | 824 | 81.7 | 88.4 | 74.1 | 80.3 | 238 | 241 |
| | 45 and over | 1557 | 86.1 | 89.4 | 69.7 | 79.0 | 228 | 280 |
| 1900 | 15 and over | — | 30.7 | 68.8 | 85.9 | 92.9 | — | — |
| 1910 | 15 and over | — | 41.4 | 79.0 | 79.0 | — | — | — |
| 1920 | 15 and over | — | 45.0 | 72.6 | 78.0 | — | 260 | 330 |

**TABLE 5**

Crude marriage and fertility rates of adult deaf women by
religion, area, mental condition

| Deaf women | Number | Per cent married | Per cent of married who are mothers | Children ever born per 100 mothers |
|---|---|---|---|---|
| All women | 3637[a] | 77.3 | 70.7 | 229 |
| Roman Catholic | 1731 | 72.9 | 65.3 | 239 |
| Jewish | 812 | 87.1 | 73.4 | 220 |
| Protestant | 972 | 76.1 | 76.1 | 220 |
| Others | 122 | 83.3 | 80.0 | 232 |
| New York City | 1804 | 78.3 | 72.9 | 232 |
| Other urban | 1685 | 77.6 | 67.6 | 225 |
| Rural | 148 | 60.8 | 80.6 | 220 |
| Schizophrenics in hospital | 57 | 38.6 | 81.8 | 211 |

As seen in Table 7, almost 10 per cent of all children born to our deaf subjects are themselves deaf, continuing a trend pointed out over 60 years ago. Coupled with today's higher marriage rate, this assortative mating pattern most certainly contributes to the perpetuation of this isolate. In addition, our interviews have suggested that there is a trend toward larger family size in families with a deaf child. This trend may represent an attempt to compensate—a wish on the part of deaf parents to have hearing children.

Further analysis of the data on offspring was based on the type of deafness of the index cases. Table 8 represents the classification of all marriages according to the stated character of the deafness of husband and wife, and suggests a higher fertility when neither admits to being born deaf (1.69 children per marriage in the latter case, 1.29 to 1.41 when one or both was deaf at birth).

The remaining tables furnish material for some speculations regarding the most prevalent mode of inheritance of hereditary deafness. As seen in Table 9, in the marriages where both subjects say they were born deaf, about 22 per cent (or 1/4) of their children are deaf. The hypothesis that a particular single recessive gene is responsible for many cases of hereditary deafness would make it necessary to assume that only half of these congenitally deaf subjects are homozygotes for this gene, the others either having given inaccurate information or being deaf as the result of intrauterine influences, or because of another gene or combination of genes.

Continuing along this line of reasoning (and ignoring the possibility that

## TABLE 6
### Crude marriage and fertility rates of adult deaf women according to type of deafness

| Type of deafness | Per cent ever married | Median age at first marriage | Husbands | Per cent of married who are mothers | | Children per 100 mothers | | Per cent with one or more deaf children | |
|---|---|---|---|---|---|---|---|---|---|
| | | | | 1960 | Fay - 1898 | 1960 | Fay - 1898 | 1960 | Fay - 1898 |
| Born deaf (1514 women) | 71.5 | 24 | Born deaf (30.0%) | 64.3 | 83.6 | 183 | 278 | 29.2ᵃ | 24.8 |
| | | | Became deaf (64.9%) | 67.8 | 84.4 | 235 | 265 | 14.0ᵇ | 8.1 |
| | | | Hearing ( 5.1%) | 68.4 | 89.0 | 192 | 311 | — | 14.7 |
| Became deaf (2123 women) | 81.4 | 23 | Born deaf (19.6%) | 65.0 | 84.4 | 220 | 265 | 21.1ᶜ | 8.1 |
| | | | Became deaf (71.6%) | 72.8 | 85.9 | 240 | 237 | 2.9ᵈ | 3.6 |
| | | | Hearing ( 8.7%) | 90.4 | 86.8 | 230 | 265 | 2.1ᵉ | 3.2 |

ᵃ 11.1% have 2 or more deaf children
ᵇ 6.7% have 2 or more deaf children
ᶜ 6.6% have 2 or more deaf children
ᵈ 1.6% have 2 or more deaf children
ᵉ 2 or more deaf children

### TABLE 7
#### Distribution of children of deaf

| Hearing status of children | Total deaf – 1960 (4518 marriages) | | Fay – 1898 (3078 marriages) | |
|---|---|---|---|---|
| | Number | Per cent | Number | Per cent |
| Deaf children | 646 | 9.3 | 588 | 8.7 |
| Hearing children | 6270 | 90.7 | 5091 | 75.0 |
| Unknown | – | – | 1103 | 16.3 |
| Total | 6916 | 100.0 | 6782 | 100.0 |

### TABLE 8
#### Number of children of married deaf index cases

| Type of deafness of index case and spouse | Number of marriages | | Number of children | Children per marriage |
|---|---|---|---|---|
| | Number | Per cent | | |
| Total deaf index cases | 4418 | 100.0 | 6916 | 1.55 |
| Both born deaf | 314 | 7.1 | 407 | 1.29 |
| Only one born deaf | 1491 | 33.8 | 2098 | 1.41 |
| Neither born deaf | 2613 | 59.1 | 4411 | 1.69 |

there are heterozygotes or homozygotes that develop deafness later in life among spouses not born deaf), we might explain the fact that about one-eighth of the offspring are deaf when only one parent admits to having been born deaf by assuming that the other parent, half of the time, was actually deaf at birth but does not know it or denies it. We have learned from interviews that such is often the case. If, as before, half of these are homozygotes for the assumed gene, the expectancy in the children would be $1/2 \times 1/4$ or $1/8$. Finally, if neither deaf parent admits to congenital deafness, but half really are so, and in turn half of them are homozygotes, the frequency of deafness in the offspring would indeed be about 1/16th.

Table 10 indicates that "born deaf" parents do tend to have either only deaf or only hearing children. However, only the foregoing assumptions regarding the actual status of those who say they were born deaf would explain the high percentage of hearing children born to two such parents (78.3 per cent in this series, 71.9 in that of Stevenson and Cheeseman).

Further light on the nature of hereditary deafness may be sought in con-

**TABLE 9**
Hearing status of children of deaf index cases

| Type of deafness of index case and spouse | Children | | | | | | | |
|---|---|---|---|---|---|---|---|---|
| | Total number | | Deaf | | Hard of hearing | | Hearing | |
| | Number | Per cent | Number | Per cent | Number | Per cent | Number | Per cent |
| Total deaf index cases | 6916 | 100.0 | 577 | 8.3 | 86 | 1.3 | 6253 | 90.4 |
| Both born deaf | 407 | 100.0 | 88 | 21.7× | 0 | 0 | 318 | 78.3 |
| Only one born deaf | 2098 | 100.0 | 268 | 12.7× | 32 | 1.6 | 1799 | 85.7 |
| Neither born deaf | 4411 | 100.0 | 221 | 5.0× | 54 | 1.2 | 4136 | 93.8 |

×These percentages do not depart significantly from 1/4, 1/8, 1/16, respectively.

**TABLE 10**
Composition of families of deaf index cases

| Type of deafness of index case and spouse | Type of children | | | | |
|---|---|---|---|---|---|
| | Total | None | Only deaf | Only hearing | Some deaf and some hearing |
| Total deaf index cases | 4517 | 1405 | 214 | 2727 | 171 |
| Both "born deaf" | 313 | 119 | 55 | 133 | 6 |
| Only one "born deaf" | 1463 | 503 | 87 | 791 | 82 |
| Neither "born deaf" | 2741 | 783 | 72 | 1803 | 83 |

sanguinity data; these have been difficult to obtain in our large population, though for one segment of the whole group of deaf index cases, the cousin-marriage rate among their parents was 8.7 per cent. This high figure, close to that of Deraemaker (6-10%), would certainly be hard to reconcile with the frequency of deafness (.08% total, about one-half of these hereditary) on a single gene hypothesis. Intensive study of deaf twins and their families has been conducted by us in an attempt to explore possible expressivity factors which may have important bearing on these questions (see Chapter 3).

*Sampling Procedure and Problems of Non-Response*

As was stated, the present study on fertility made use of the list of deaf people described in Chapter 1. Excepted were 925 school children, 489 patients in institutions, and 111 deaf people treated in the clinic, as our information concerning all these people was fairly complete. The institutional population was in fact not part of our universe of study, and would have been omitted anyhow. The net number of names available for the present study was 7811.

A questionnaire sent out in February 1958 to enquire of each person if he were a twin, and to enquire after the names of other deaf people to add to our list, had the effect of dividing into 2 groups the 7100 names on the list at that time: Group A, the 1700 people that answered; Group B, the remainder. The study on twins also excepted the three groups mentioned above.

The present study on fertility, which commenced in April 1959, took advantage of this division of the list, to achieve statistical efficiency. The questionnaire went out to every one of the 1700 people in Group A, and to a 20% sample of Group B; also to all 711 names that had come in meanwhile from a church organization (Roman Catholic), called Group C in Table 12.

The next step was a second mailing to the people that did not respond to the first mailing. It was possible, in some cases, to elicit personal solicitation. The degrees of response are shown in Table 11.

## TABLE 11
### Number of questionnaires mailed, and number of responses

| Group | Size of group | Number of names selected for this study | Response | | | Total (after weighting the 20% sample by 5) |
|-------|-----|-----|-----|-----|-----|-----|
| | | | 1st mailing | 2d mailing | 1st and 2d mailings and other assistance | |
| A | 1700 | 1700 | 968 | 191 | 1159 | 1159 |
| B | 5400 | 1080 | xxx | xxx | 303 | 1515 |
| C | 711 | 711 | 183 | xxx | 183 | 183 |
| Total | | | | | | 2857 |

## TABLE 12
### Expansion factors

| Sex | Weighted returns | Number on original list | Factor to reproduce the original list |
|-----|-----|-----|-----|
| Male | 1603 | 4169 | 4169/1603 = 2.60 |
| Female | 1254 | 3635 | 3635/1254 = 2.90 |
| Total | 2857 | 7804 | (2.75) |

For making Tables 1-10, the responses to the 20 per cent samples were given a weight of 5 and added to the returns from Group A (100% mailing); then this sum was expanded separately by sex by the factors shown in Table 12 to fit the total counts of male and female in the list. The school children, having been excluded from the study of fertility, were thereupon added to appear in the age-sex pyramid; also in Tables 1 and 4.

The large amount of nonresponse leaves open the possibility that interpretation based on the responses obtained may differ from the results that would come from persistent personal investigation of every case, were such a thing possible.

One may address two remarks to the problem created by the nonresponse in this study. First, experience gained in attempting to follow by personal contact some of the cases of nonresponse in this study, and experience with the personal interviews in the studies reported in other chapters of this book, point with near certainty to the supposition that a large portion of the gap between the response and the mailing is not failure to respond, but is indication that some cases on the list are not deaf but are hard of hearing; also that some cases on the list have long been dead, while others have moved out of the state. Still others would turn out to be mentally retarded, not eligible for this kind of study. In total, possibly 20 per cent of the names on the list belong to these categories.

Second, some idea of the effect of nonresponse can be gained from comparing Tables 1-10 with tables constructed from only the 990 returns from the first mailing to Group A (179). The first difference that we note is in age-sex pyramid. The difference is undoubtedly attributable mainly to the addition of the 925 school-children, mostly below 18, who were not included in the age-sex pryamid in the first mailing. Some of the difference may of course be attributed to the improvement in response, and some to sampling variation.

Table 13 displays other differences. The difference in crude marital rates in lines 1 and 2, also the crude fertility rates in lines 6 and 7, arises again mainly from the addition of the school-children. The difference in line 3 could arise from sampling variation, as the number of responses in the earlier study in this category was only 11, although improvement in response may also contribute to the difference. The same may be said for lines 4, 5, and 13 to 18. The difference by religion for New York City, in lines 10, 11, 12, is attributable largely to the addition of the deaf church organization (Roman Catholic), mentioned earlier.

## Summary

The total sex ratio of the deaf population of New York State (15 years and older), is estimated at 113 males to 100 females. While there may have been an underascertainment of females, the excess of males may also either reflect a sex-specific increase in the male's vulnerability to deafness-producing agents or possibly point to the operation of a sex-linked genetic factor in some families. Another distinguishing feature of this particular population is a definite increase in the parental cousin-marriage rate. This rate is increased to at least 8.7 per cent in a large segment of the population and may be as high as 12.15 per cent in the group with onset before age four and no suspected exogenous cause.

Tabulation of marriage data reveals a rate of 60.3 per cent ever married for males, and 68.9 per cent for females. These rates are still slightly below those for a comparable general population, particularly for males, but they are much higher than they were reported to be 40 years ago. Apparently, the improved marriage opportunities of the present deaf generation are paralleled by a higher degree of marital instability. The current divorce rate of deaf females exceeds those of hearing females and deaf males.

While the percentage of deaf women ever married increased from 30.7 in 1900 to 68.9 in 1960, the marital fertility rate of deaf mothers decreased, though relatively little compared with that for hearing mothers. Since 1920, the given fertility rates have declined from 260 to 229 children

**TABLE 13**

Display of difference between the initial response of 990 returns from Group A [see (179)], and the results reported in the present study

| Line | Characteristic | Initial returns (Feb. 1958) Per cent or number | Table | Present study (1959) Per cent or number |
|------|----------------|------|-------|------|
| 1 | Males unmarried, total | 33.7% | 1 | 39.7% |
| 2 | Females unmarried, total | 24.2% | 1 | 31.1% |
| 3 | Males ever married, one parent deaf | 54.5% | 2 | 83.3% |
| | Proportion of deaf siblings | | | |
| 4 |    Neither parent deaf | 6.0% | 3 | 8.4% |
| 5 |    One or both parents deaf | 19.4% | 3 | 34.7% |
| 6 | Women ever married, 15 and over | 75.8% | 4 | 68.9% |
| 7 | Women ever married, 15-24 | 27.6% | 4 | 16.3% |
| 8 | Married and mothers, 15 and over | 74.4% | 4 | 70.7% |
| 9 | Children per 100 mothers, 15 and over | 211 | 4 | 229 |
| 10 | Women, Roman Catholic, married | 66.2% | 5 | 72.9% |
| 11 |    Married and mothers | 71.7% | 5 | 65.3% |
| 12 |    Children per 100 mothers | 230 | 5 | 239 |
| | Women born deaf, ever married, mothers | | | |
| 13 |    Husband born deaf | 64.3% | 6 | 64.3% |
| 14 |    Husband became deaf | 74.7% | 6 | 67.8% |
| 15 |    Husband hearing | 80.0% | 6 | 68.4% |
| | Women born deaf, ever married, children per 100 mothers | | | |
| 16 |    Husband born deaf | 178 | 6 | 183 |
| 17 |    Husband became deaf | 222 | 6 | 235 |
| 18 |    Husband hearing | 125 | 6 | 192 |

in deaf mothers, and from 330 to 235 children in hearing ones. The highest observed marital fertility rates for deaf mothers are found in Roman Catholic women (239 per 100 mothers) and in the non-hospitalized New York City population (232 per 100 mothers).

Among the factors perpetuating the size of our deaf population (present population frequency of early total deafness: 0.06%) are the relatively high marriage and fertility rates, a possible compensatory trend toward larger family size in families with at least one deaf child, and the assortative mating pattern that continues to be typical of deaf communities. In our sample, only five per cent of women born deaf and less than ten per cent of those that became deaf at an early age have been found to be married to hearing men. The vast majority have husbands who have been deaf since birth or early childhood. It is not surprising, therefore, that almost 30 per cent of the marriages where both partners were born deaf, and from 14 to 21 per cent of those where only one partner was born deaf, resulted in deaf children, usually more than one.

According to the overall reproductivity data for our deaf population, it may be stated that nearly ten per cent of all children born to deaf subjects are themselves deaf. On the other hand, less than 10 per cent of all deaf members of a large deaf community such as that of New York State may be expected to have one or two deaf parents. However, not even in such a conspicuous family constellation does the possession of two deaf parents tend to keep their deaf children from marrying, and in turn contributing to the recurrence of deafness in the next generation.

# Chapter 3

## GENETIC ASPECTS OF EARLY TOTAL DEAFNESS

DIANE SANK

### Introduction

Early total deafness has been attributed variously to a wide range of genetic factors—dominant, recessive, and sex-linked genes and chromosomal aberrations—as well as to non-genetic influences. The phrase early total deafness as used here is defined as a severe hearing impairment that is present at birth or has its onset during childhood, characterized by lack of speech development in the absence of special training. Once established, the severity of the condition is considered irreversible. The operational definitions used for various aspects of the present study will be given below.

The etiology of early total deafness is particularly complex because exogenous agents, such as infections, trauma, and drugs (49, 70, 73, 79, 253), as well as genetic factors, may be involved. Furthermore, the need to rely on the indirect evidence of family histories, hospital records, and other medical reports compounds the difficulty of pinpointing the cause.

In this chapter, our New York State population data are analyzed with respect to the possible effect of genetic factors that may produce early total deafness. Moreover, comparison is made with the results of a similar study in Northern Ireland by Stevenson and Cheeseman (220). Also, twin-family data are examined to elucidate both the role of expressivity of the gene(s) and variations in the expression of the trait in the dominant, recessive, and exogenous forms of early total deafness, and to offer an interpretation of the mode of operation of the exogenous type. The data presented in an earlier report (194) were based on a preliminary analysis of the same material.

### Historical Survey

There have been a number of estimates regarding the proportion of genetically determined cases in early total deafness. Lindenov (138) arrived at a figure of 46 per cent, while Lamy and Furusho (127, 75) found at least 60 per cent. In the study of Stevenson and Cheeseman in Northern

This chapter is dedicated to Professor L. C. Dunn in commemoration of his noteworthy and important contributions to the science of genetics. Portions of it are reproduced, by permission of the author and the publisher, from *Expanding Goals of Genetics in Psychiatry*, F. J. Kallmann (ed.), New York, Grune & Stratton, 1962.

Ireland, 50 per cent of the cases of early total deafness were considered to be of genetic origin (220). The given cases were divided into those where deafness appeared to have been present at birth (congenital) and those where deafness was acquired following birth.

A good many theories have been advanced to explain the specific mode of transmission of the hereditary form of early total deafness. Genetic mechanisms suggested in earlier reports included single-factor (recessive) inheritance in the studies of Lindenov (138), Albrecht (2) and Hanhart (93), and multiple-factor inheritance in the work of Kraatz (125) and Hammerschlag (92). In the latter type, the presence of a series of genes (from two to four) was said to determine the appearance of total deafness. Many pedigrees in the literature, among them the cases of Waardenburg (232), indicated that this condition may also be caused by dominant genes. Sataloff et al. (198) and Parker (164) published material suggesting that in some families a sex-linked gene may be involved.

The data yielded by the most recent large-scale genetic investigation, that of Stevenson and Cheeseman (220), were analyzed in detail by Slatis (205) and by Chung et al. (37). In this analysis, the latter team of investigators found that most hereditary early total deafness is probably due to homozygosity for one of a set of recessive genes. Another conclusion was that there are many recessive genes, each of which when homozygous can produce total deafness. This theory might explain the numerous matings between presumably hereditary cases of early total deafness observed to produce only hearing children. The data from Northern Ireland also included some cases of early total deafness inherited in a dominant fashion. The proportion of such cases among all the genetic ones observed in that population was 22 per cent, with 68 per cent of them estimated as due to new mutations. An analysis of the pedigrees led Chung and his co-workers (37) to suggest high but not complete penetrance of the dominant gene.

The literature on twins has been limited largely to case reports of clinically interesting twin pairs, one or both of whom presented evidence of early total deafness. Monozygotic twin pairs concordant for this disorder were described by Wildervanck (244), Duis and Eickhoff (61), Post and Hopkins (175) and Gedda et al. (78). Five pairs of dizygotic opposite-sex pairs concordant for deafness were reported by Hopkins and Guilder (101).

Luchsinger and Hanhart (139) described three pairs of monozygotic twins with early total deafness, who showed dissimilarities in audiometric patterns. Matzker (146) reported a six-year-old pair of monozygotic twin brothers with dissimilar hearing loss; one twin being congenitally deaf bilaterally, while the cotwin was deaf in one ear and had a moderate to severe hearing loss in the other. Fowler (72) and Rodin (189) observed monozygotic twins with similar degrees of hearing loss due to otosclerosis, and MacFarlon (142) found identical partial hearing losses in one-egg twins. In these and other older studies, zygosity diagnosis was usually based on Siemens' similarity method.

Audiometric measurements have been employed in some of the genetic studies of early total deafness. Lindenov (138) tested a total of 41 deaf and 56 hearing persons in 32 families with early total deafness. However, a large majority of the nearly 500 deaf individuals included in the report were not tested. In Stevenson and Cheeseman's genetic study of a series of 424 living born-deaf individuals (220), only 68 audiometric tests were made by the investigators, and another 78 audiometric records were secured from schools for the deaf. None of the so-called hearing members of the families were tested for partial hearing loss.

Ciocco et al. (40), who examined sib pairs with early total deafness, found a smaller mean difference and variability in the audiometric tests between them than between unrelated pairs of totally deaf individuals, indicating a familial similarity in audiometric patterns.

Wildervanck (245) studied 13 sets of parents with normal hearing, who had at least one congenitally deaf child. Although seven of the parental couples were cousins, none of them were assumed to be identifiable heterozygotes. In reviewing the given data, one finds that the audiometric tests revealed some hearing loss in 58 per cent of the parents, varying from slight (30 dbs) to total unilateral deafness with 120 + decibels hearing loss.

Wedenberg (238), in a preliminary report, detected some hearing loss among the presumed heterozygotic parents of children with early total deafness—usually only in one parent. It may be borne in mind, however, that the search for heterozygotes through audiometric testing is difficult, considering the degree of hearing loss expected in the normal population.

Several studies have been made of "normal" hearing populations. Testing 1400 school children audiometrically, Ciocco (38, 39) found that about six per cent had a hearing loss of 20-35 decibels and that 9.5 per cent had a hearing loss of 35 decibels or more. Five years later, when about one-third of the original sample was retested, the earlier figures had increased to 13.5 per cent and 19 per cent, respectively.

Johansen (108) studied the hearing of 155 males and 155 females ranging in age from 10 to 90 years. The subjects were noted to have experienced some hearing loss with advancing age, but for all age groups under 60 years the loss was moderate. There was no evidence of a sex difference in the degree of hearing loss—except for one frequency (4000 cps) where males over age 60 showed a greater hearing loss than females of comparable age, a finding consistent with other reports. Similarly, Glorig et al. (79) reported hearing losses no greater than 35 decibels for age groups up to 60 years.

Attempts were made by Fisch (70) as well as by Doyle and McConnell (59) to demonstrate a relationship between audiometric patterns and various causes of deafness, including hereditary ones. Studying congenital deafness, Fisch found three main audiometric patterns: the flat, the sloping, and the residual. In each of these groups, there were individuals with hereditary deafness classified "on the basis of a definite family history."

However, most of the subjects tested were hard of hearing rather than totally deaf, except for the residual group which included most of the cases that we would consider as early total deafness. According to Fisch, there is a statistically significant association between the residual type of graphs and hereditary deafness.

### Population Analysis

In our comprehensive population study of total deafness, various sets of data have been collected which are of considerable help in investigating the role of genetic factors in the causation of early total deafness. Like the classification of Stevenson and Cheeseman, the deaf population in the genetic inquiry was subdivided into two groups: the congenitally deaf, and those deaf individuals who acquired their affliction after birth but early in childhood. These two groups may be combined under the general heading of early total deafness.

We were able to begin our ascertainment of deaf individuals in New York State with the active cooperation of all existing federal, state and local agencies and social, vocational, and religious organizations for the deaf, as well as the special schools for the deaf and their alumni clubs.

At the beginning of this study, a questionnaire (see Appendix 1) was sent to every known deaf resident of New York State over the age of 12 years (8200 in number), requesting information on multiple births among the deaf. Then, in 1958, a second questionnaire (see Appendix 1) was mailed to the 1700 persons who had responded to the first one. This time there were specific questions as to the sex, age, and age of onset of deafness in the respondent, as well as the hearing status of the parents. Because this questionnaire was primarily designed to yield marriage and fertility rates of the deaf, other questions were asked pertaining to the hearing status of the spouse, the age at which the spouse became deaf, the number of children, their age and sex, and whether they were hearing or deaf, dead or alive. The respondent was asked to list all sibs, stating whether they were hearing or deaf, and also any other deaf relatives.

There were 990 replies to this second questionnaire. While 182 letters were returned by the post office as undeliverable, 528 were probably received but not answered. Of the 990 answers, 968 were judged to have been filled out properly by adults of marriageable age, including 20 males and 15 females between the ages of 15 and 19. The information so obtained was coded and placed on punch cards, eventually to be incorporated into detailed marriage and fertility statistics (179 and Chapter 2).

A third questionnaire (see Appendix 1) was sent to the following groups: (a) a new list of 711 deaf obtained from a religious organization, (b) those who received the second questionnaire but did not answer, (c) a 20 per cent sample of those who received the first questionnaire but did not answer. This mailing yielded respectively 183, 191, and 303 responses. Group (c) responses were weighted by five. Marriage and fertility data based on all the responses (the second questionnaire plus weighted replies from the third) did not appear to differ significantly from those obtained from the second questionnaire alone (178 and Chapter 2). For technical reasons, the third questionnaire was not utilized in the following analysis, except where specifically indicated and then unweighted.

In Chapter 2, Table 13, an attempt was made to learn something about the error of non-response by comparing the results from questionnaire No. 2 with those from a weighted average of questionnaires Nos. 2 and 3. For some categories the number of responses was too small for drawing any conclusions. In any event, there was no evidence of bias that would seriously interfere with the genetic analysis.

In the present study, the criteria for hereditary deafness were chosen to make the data comparable to those obtained by Stevenson and Cheeseman (220). In their study a person was considered to suffer from the hereditary form of deafness, if he was said to have been born deaf or if he was recognized as deaf because speech did not develop and there was no other known cause of deafness. Similar criteria were applied to the single-born population reported in this chapter: a person was included as deaf if he stated that he was born as such or that he became deaf before the age of four, without knowing of any specific exogenous cause, such as viral infection, scarlet fever, meningitis, trauma, and so forth.

The criteria for early total deafness were: (a) the assignment of the individual to a deaf group on lists provided by schools or alumni, social, and religious organizations for the deaf, or ascertainment through federal, state, and local agencies for the deaf, and (b) stated age of onset. Some persons were eliminated from the study when they volunteered information that "I am hard of hearing" or "I am not deaf."

To verify that the persons were correctly included, data were obtained by personal interviews of a sample of the deaf population (Chapter 1). Persons were considered here to have early total deafness, if their hearing loss was functionally severe enough to prevent their understanding or recognizing spoken words without seeing the speaker's lips, thus limiting their communication to lip reading, finger spelling, use of sign language, specially learned speech, or written communication. Of 190 persons interviewed, 96 per cent proved to be deaf.

In a young child, failure to talk may be attributed to slowness in starting rather than deafness. Thus the age at which deafness is first recognized varies, depending on the perceptiveness of the parents. The age of four years was chosen as the cutoff point, because most children with congenital deafness would probably be recognized by then. While some of the individuals undoubtedly did become deaf at the time stated, one cannot be sure from a questionnaire alone.

The number of replies accepted for this genetic study was 688. According to their family histories, these index cases were distributed as follows: (a) 92 index cases had deaf relatives in addition to any possible deaf sibs or descendants. In 45 of these cases, one or both parents were deaf, while in 47 cases neither parent was deaf; (b) 95 index cases had deaf sibs but no other known deaf relative; (c) 501 index cases were the only known deaf members of their families. The hearing status of the parents was known in all but a very few instances.

The sibship size, including index cases, and the reported age of onset of the 501 index cases without deaf relatives are tabulated in Table 1. Only 40 per cent of these isolated cases believed they had been born deaf. In another 40 per cent, deafness presumably occurred after the first and before the fifth year of life. The remaining 20 per cent, with a reported age of onset "within the first year," probably included a considerable number of congenitally deaf cases whose hearing impairment was erroneously ascribed to some coincidental event in early life (viral infection, trauma, or the like). Similar reservations would seem justified in some of the 194 index cases with apparently acquired deafness in the second, third or fourth year of life. Without adequate clinical criteria for retrospectively pinpointing the onset of deafness in a child's development, it is not possible to distinguish clearly between congenital and early onset types of deafness in a large population study such as the present one.

The distribution of sibship sizes in Table 1 can be used to shed light on hereditary deafness (probably mainly recessive in this type of family) and sporadic deafness due chiefly to exogenous causes. If the two parents are heterozygous for the same recessive gene, the probability that there will be exactly one affected child in a sibship of size $s$ is

$$(1) \qquad g_s = s(1/4)(3/4)^{s-1}$$

If the probability that a child becomes deaf because of a new dominant mutation or an exogenous cause is $a$, and is independent for different children in the same sibship, the probability that there will be exactly one affected child in a sibship of size $s$ is

$$(2) \qquad m_s = sa(1-a)^{s-1}.$$

Now $a$ will be very small, the number of sporadic cases being appreciable only because all sibships are exposed to risk. Hence, $(1-a)^{s-1}$ will be close to one and can be ignored. Then the ratio

$$(3) \qquad g_s/m_s = (1/4a)(3/4)^{s-1}.$$

The factor $1/4a$ is unknown, but is constant for all sibship sizes, so that the ratio $g_s/m_s$ is simply proportional to $(3/4)^{s-1}$. Table 1 gives the value of this expression.

We can also calculate the observed ratio of the number of sibships of size $s$ with one affected child, where the child was deaf at birth, to the number where the child became deaf during the second to fourth year. However, to make these ratios comparable with the expression $(3/4)^{s-1}$,

## TABLE 1
### Age of onset of deafness and sibship size in 501 index cases without deaf relatives

| Size of sibship (s) | Reported age of onset | | | | Test ratios* (see text) | |
|---|---|---|---|---|---|---|
| | At birth | First year | Second to fourth year | Total | Expected ratio $(3/4)^{s-1}$ | Corrected observed ratio** |
| 1 | 41 | 22 | 18 | 81 | 1.00 | 1.17 |
| 2 | 55 | 26 | 41 | 122 | .75 | .69 |
| 3 | 34 | 15 | 36 | 85 | .56 | .48 |
| 4 | 25 | 11 | 36 | 72 | .42 | .36 |
| 5 | 18 | 12 | 26 | 56 | .32 | .36 |
| 6 | 9 | 7 | 19 | 35 | .24 | .24 |
| 7 | 10 | 5 | 6 | 21 | .18 | .86 |
| 8 | 3 | 3 | 5 | 11 | .13 | .31 |
| 9 | 5 | 3 | 5 | 13 | .10 | .51 |
| 10 | — | — | 1 | 1 | .08 | .00 |
| 11 | — | 3 | 1 | 4 | .06 | .00 |
| Total | 200 | 107 | 194 | 501 | | |

*Ratios used in relating age of onset to type of deafness.
**Number of sibships of sizes with onset at birth: onset second to fourth year (see text for correction factor).

they must be adjusted by multiplying them by a correction factor $c$. We could choose $c$ so that the ratio for $s=1$ is 1, but this would be subject to large fluctuations due to sampling error in the class $s = 1$. A better method is to correct so that the sum of the corrected ratios from $s = 1$ to $s = 6$, for which numbers are adequate, equals the corresponding sum of the $(3/4)^{s-1}$.

These corrected observed ratios, given in Table 1, are in reasonably good agreement with what would be expected if the isolated cases of children deaf at birth were mainly recessive in origin, while those becoming deaf during the second to fourth year were mainly sporadic. By the same method, it can be shown that those becoming deaf during the first year are similar to those deaf at birth. It should be emphasized that this analysis makes no assumption about the distribution of sibship sizes; it merely assumes that two heterozygous carriers who produce a recessive deaf child have the same biological fertility as do two normal parents who produce a sporadic deaf child. This view seems reasonable, for while some recessive genes may have an effect on the fertility of heterozygotes, it will be seen below that many different recessive genes may cause deafness, and heterozygous carriers on the average should have fertility near normal.

Obstacles are encountered in distinguishing between truly hereditary and ostensibly acquired forms of total deafness, especially in cases where it may be hypothesized that a noxious exogenous factor acted before or during birth. For practical purposes, an expedient procedure for the classification of hereditary deafness is based on requiring the presence, besides the index case, of another deaf person in the index families. In the analysis of our population data it will be shown that families with sibships comprising more than one deaf sib and no other deaf relative probably represent instances of *recessive* deafness, while the 92 index families with deaf members other than affected sibs of index cases presumably exemplify the *dominant* mode of inheritance. However, although isolated cases of total deafness preponderate in any given population, they cannot with certainty be categorized as either hereditary or acquired.

The distribution of the 95 index sibships with at least one other deaf sib and unaffected parents is shown in Table 2, according to sibship size and the number of deaf per sibship. Although some families have four or five deaf sibs in one sibship (8 and 4 families, respectively), it may be noted that detailed information about age of onset is available only for the index cases themselves and not for their deaf sibs. Two of the 95 families were ascertained twice, but only one of the deaf children in each was used as an index case.

Of the hearing losses of these index cases, 71.6 per cent were classified as congenital, 9.5 per cent as having developed during the first year, and 18.9 per cent during the second, third or fourth year of life. As described above, the index cases do not include individuals with known exogenous causes of early total deafness.

In attempting to determine whether our data fit the hypothesis of re-

**TABLE 2**
Sibships with more than one deaf member

| Number of sibs | Number of deaf per sibship | | | | |
|---|---|---|---|---|---|
| | 2 | 3 | 4 | 5 | Total |
| 2 | 13 | – | – | – | 13 |
| 3 | 7 | 4 | – | – | 11 |
| 4 | 11 | 4 | – | – | 15 |
| 5 | 13 | 1 | – | 1 | 15 |
| 6 | 8 | 2 | 2 | 1 | 13 |
| 7 | 5 | 2 | 2 | – | 9 |
| 8 | 3 | 7 | 2 | – | 12 |
| 9 | 2 | 1 | 2 | – | 5 |
| 10 | – | – | – | – | – |
| 11 | – | – | – | 1 | 1 |
| 12 | – | – | – | 1 | 1 |
| **Total** | **62** | **21** | **8** | **4** | **95** |

cessive inheritance, certain statistical corrections were necessary because of procedural problems inherent in the extraction of genetic information from human pedigrees. The genetic test for recessive inheritance is predicated on the supposition that when a large group of families is collected, with both parents heterozygous for a gene that in double dose will produce total deafness, the pooling of the sibships of such families would give us a 3:1 ratio of unaffected to affected sibs. Actually, however, the families ascertained could only include those whose sibships contained at least one deaf child. There is obviously no way to identify families where parents, although carriers of the same deafness gene, happen by chance not to have produced a deaf child, and all the children are hearing. Yet only if the latter type of family were included in the test sample, could we expect to obtain the ratio of three normal to one affected.

A further bias may be present in our data due to the fact that our index families were ascertained through a deaf person. Since we did not receive a questionnaire from every deaf individual in the State of New York (i.e., complete ascertainment where all affected individuals are registered independently), we have to assume that our sampling procedure favored families with more than one affected sib. In other words, families with two, three or four deaf sibs are more likely to be represented in our sample than families with only one. Ordinarily, we might expect that the probability of recording a family is proportional to the number of affected individuals in that family, but in this case it is difficult to assign a value to the probability of ascertainment of the deaf individuals in our questionnaire sample. Accordingly, there is an alternative procedure recommended by Haldane (90), i.e., to compute the data twice, once assuming complete ascertainment and once assuming minimum ascertainment. Incomplete ascertainment would increase the proportion of affected children in the sample, and incorrect use of methods based on complete ascertainment would lead to an overestimation of the value of $p$ — the probability that a child with two carrier parents will be deaf.

If the parents of the deaf in our sample were all heterozygotes, then the expected probability ($p$) of deafness in the pooled sibships would be 25 per cent. If some of the deaf children in the sample lost their hearing through an exogenous factor occurring with a frequency of less than 25 per cent, then the $p$ would be reduced, whereas if some parents carried dominant genes which were not expressed the $p$ value would be increased. If, as is likely, both factors were operating, the value of $p$ obtained would depend on the relative frequencies of recessive, exogenous, and dominant cases of deafness. In testing for recessiveness, we used Haldane's method (89), which corrects for the fact that identification of specific heterozygous matings is possible only through an affected child.

In developing the formulae for the method of correction used in the case of complete ascertainment, it will be noted that if $p$ is the probability of an affected child and $q = 1 - p$ that of a normal child, the probability of no affected children in a family of $s$ children will be $q^s$, the last term of the binomial expansion $(p + q)^s$. Hence, the probability of at least one affected child is $1 - q^s$. If one can only investigate sibships with at least one affected child, the probability of a given child being affected is thus increased from $p$ to $p/(1 - q^s)$, and the expected number, $r_s$, of affected children to be found in a sibship of size $s$ is this expression multiplied by $s$ or

$$(4) \qquad r_s = \frac{sp}{1 - q^s}.$$

In the total sample of families, the expected number of affected children is

$$(5) \qquad R = \sum_s \frac{sp}{1 - q^s} n_s,$$

with $n_s$ the number of families of size $s$.

In employing this formula, we may estimate $p$ by specifying trial values of $p$, in order to obtain two values of $R$ (total expected number of affected children in $s$-child families) that bracket our observed number of affected children. Then, by linear interpolation we derive an estimated $p$ value, $\hat{p}$. The standard error of $\hat{p}$ may be obtained from Finney's tabulations (68), or we can calculate values of

$$(6) \qquad W = \frac{1}{V(\hat{p})}.$$

The variance $(V)$ is equal to $1/\hat{W}$ where $\hat{W}$ equals $\sum_s w_s n_s$ interpolated in the same manner as $\hat{p}$. The standard error of $\hat{p}$ is then

$$(7) \qquad\qquad \sigma_{\hat{p}} = \sqrt{\frac{1}{\hat{W}}}.$$

The value $w_s$ for complete ascertainment may be calculated from the formula:

$$(8) \qquad\qquad w_s = \frac{s}{pq} \frac{1 - q^s - spq^{s-1}}{(1 - q^s)^2}.$$

In order to obtain a minimum estimate of $p$, we may consider the case of minimum ascertainment in which each family is ascertained through one and only one affected member. In this case the probability that a given family is represented in the sample is directly proportional to the number of deaf individuals in that family. It has been shown by Haldane (90) that here

$$(9) \qquad\qquad r_s = 1 + (s - 1)p \quad \text{and} \quad w_s = \frac{s - 1}{pq}.$$

In the test of our data for recessiveness (Table 3), the following calculations can be made if the families of the isolated cases of *congenital* deafness (deleting from analysis families of size 1) are combined with the 95 index cases from families with at least two deaf sibs and the parents and other relatives hearing:

In the 254 sibships there are 398 deaf subjects among 1094 persons (36% of all the individuals in these sibships are deaf). If ascertainment were complete a trial value of $p = .25$ would result in a figure of 390.9 for $R$, the expected total number of deaf subjects. Using a trial value of $p = .275$, there would be 408.1 deaf subjects. By linear interpolation the estimate $\hat{p}$ for our sample is .260 with a standard error of $\pm .017$.

In order to minimize the value of $\hat{p}$, we may alternatively calculate $\hat{p}$ on the assumption of incomplete ascertainment. In that case $\hat{p} = .171 \pm .013$.

The maximum value of $\hat{p}$ obtained dovetails with the recessive hypothesis, provided our category of isolated cases of "congenital deafness" is not an artifact. If it is correct that methodologically we cannot distinguish the congenital cases from those with a reported onset of deafness during the first year of life, and if the latter cases are therefore included in the analysis, we find by the same procedure that $\hat{p}$ equals .206 $\pm$ .014 (with a minimum estimate of .129 $\pm$ .010). In this instance we obtain an excess of isolated cases of non-genetic origin. A similar excess ($\hat{p} = .150 \pm .010$, with a minimum estimate of .086 $\pm$ .007) is observed, if the analysis is extended to all the isolated index cases, including those who reportedly lost their hearing after the first and before the fifth year of life.

### TABLE 3
Test for recessive hypothesis (Haldane method)
in deaf sibships with hearing parents*

| Size of sibship | Number of sibships | Number of children | Number of deaf children | Expected number of deaf children | |
|---|---|---|---|---|---|
| | | | | p = .25 | p = .275 |
| 2 | 68 | 136 | 81 | 77.724 | 78.812 |
| 3 | 45 | 135 | 60 | 58.365 | 59.985 |
| 4 | 40 | 160 | 59 | 58.520 | 60.800 |
| 5 | 33 | 165 | 52 | 54.087 | 56.727 |
| 6 | 22 | 132 | 44 | 40.150 | 42.460 |
| 7 | 19 | 133 | 34 | 38.380 | 40.888 |
| 8 | 15 | 120 | 38 | 33.345 | 35.730 |
| 9 | 10 | 90 | 20 | 24.330 | 26.200 |
| 10 | – | – | – | – – | – – |
| 11 | 1 | 11 | 5 | 2.871 | 3.116 |
| 12 | 1 | 12 | 5 | 3.098 | 3.371 |
| Total | 254 | 1094 | 398 | 390.870 | 408.089 |

*Data from index cases having no deaf relatives, and deaf at birth, and from index cases with no deaf relatives except sibs and deaf at birth or before age 4.

The *double case method* of Bruno Schulz (201) may be used to estimate $p$ for those 95 sibships with more than one deaf sib, but no other affected relative. These have been assumed to be *recessive* cases of deafness. Since we are considering only families with two or more deaf sibs, we may delete sibships of size 2 and follow the statistical procedure of Kaelin appropriate for such families (110). For complete ascertainment,

$$(10) \qquad r_s = \frac{sp(1 - q^{s-1})}{1 - q^s - spq^{s-1}},$$

and

$$(11) \qquad w_s = \frac{s}{pq} \left[ \frac{(1 - q^{s-1})^2 - (s-1)^2 p^2 q^{s-2}}{(1 - q^s - spq^{s-1})^2} \right];$$

for minimum ascertainment,

$$(12) \qquad r_s = 1 + \frac{(s-1)p}{1 - q^{s-1}},$$

and

$$(13) \qquad w_s = \frac{s-1}{pq} \left[ \frac{1 - q^{s-1} - (s-1)pq^{s-2}}{(1 - q^{s-1})^2} \right].$$

The $p$ value obtained for complete ascertainment is equal to $.310 \pm .031$. As previously pointed out, this value is probably an overestimate because it assumes complete ascertainment. The minimum value of $\hat{p}$ is $.250 \pm .027$. Hence, our data are in accord with the hypothesis that families with more than one affected sib represent recessive cases of deafness, and that ascertainment is closer to minimal than complete.

Another test for recessiveness was based upon data obtained from the third fertility questionnaire (see Appendix 1) which for purposes of this analysis was not weighted. Among 677 persons who replied to it, 286 whose deafness occurred before the age of four had been asked, "Are your parents cousins?" Of these, 247 answered the question, with 30 of the replies (over 12%) in the affirmative. This figure differs from the 8.7 per cent given in Chapter 2, due to the different criteria used for inclusion in this analysis. Persons with onset of deafness after the age of four years, or with a suspected exogenous cause, were discarded here on the ground that they were less likely to be hereditary. Interestingly, with this omission the incidence of consanguineous matings among the normal parents increased.

The estimated $p$ value for our series of 26 sibships from cousin marriages with two or more children is in accordance with expectation. With complete ascertainment $\hat{p}$ was found to be $.250 \pm .048$, and for a minimum estimate of $p$ we have $\hat{p} = .170 \pm .038$.

The practice of assortative mating, i.e., the tendency of the deaf to marry the deaf, is a striking feature of the social habits of deaf persons. If there were only one or two common recessive genes causing deafness, we should expect that in some deaf by deaf marriages all the children would be deaf. However, if there are many different recessive genes producing early total deafness, it would be rare indeed for two deaf individuals, each homozygous for the same set of recessive genes, to marry and have all deaf children.

Examination of deaf by deaf mating types in our sample, where at least one of the parents was included as an index case, reveals that a total of 176 matings produced offspring.

Table 4(a) shows 147 fertile matings between two deaf partners which produced 294 hearing children. In 57 of these matings, both parents have been included as index cases. Some of these matings may represent unions between deaf individuals who are deaf because of homozygosity for a recessive gene.

Table 4(b) presents 15 matings of the deaf which resulted in families with both hearing and deaf children. Some of these families are likely to be dominant cases of early total deafness, with parents of the index cases also deaf. Of 41 children in this group, 18 are deaf.

Fourteen matings that resulted in all deaf children are shown in Table

## TABLE 4
### Number of deaf dual matings according to
### type of offspring and history of deafness in family

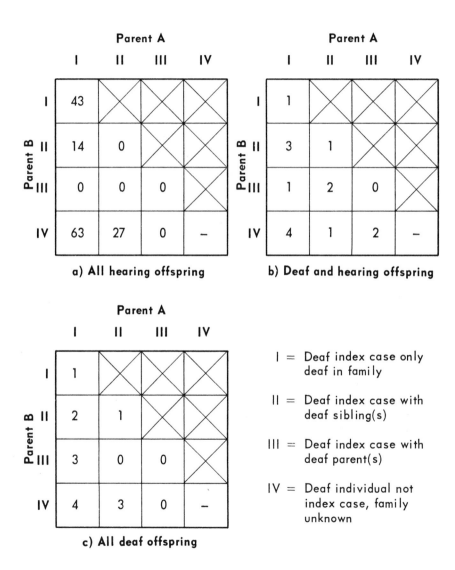

a) All hearing offspring

b) Deaf and hearing offspring

c) All deaf offspring

I = Deaf index case only
      deaf in family

II = Deaf index case with
       deaf sibling(s)

III = Deaf index case with
        deaf parent(s)

IV = Deaf individual not
        index case, family
        unknown

4(c). These represent ten families with two children, three with three children, and one with five children.

The dominant gene or genes causing early total deafness were estimated by Chung et al. (37) from the data of Stevenson and Cheeseman (220) to represent 22 per cent of all deafness rising before age six with no obvious exogenous cause. Of these cases, seven per cent were supposed to have been inherited, with 15 per cent due to newly arisen mutants. The authors suggest that dominant inheritance of early total deafness has high but not complete penetrance. On examining the few segregating families of deaf by deaf and deaf by hearing matings, it was found that the estimate of $p$ was close to .50.

With only six segregating families of deaf by deaf matings in the Northern Ireland data amenable to genetic analysis, we decided to gather all the families in our study that produced both hearing and deaf children from deaf by deaf matings. By including families gathered by questionnaire but not yet analyzed in this genetic inquiry, as well as families where the index case is the child of two deaf parents, we obtained forty families composed of two deaf parents with hearing and deaf children (Table 5). Statistically, the

### TABLE 5
**Deaf dual matings in families with both deaf and hearing offspring**

| Size of family | Number of families | Number of deaf offspring | Number of hearing offspring |
|---|---|---|---|
| 3 | 18 | 25 | 29 |
| 4 | 8 | 13 | 19 |
| 5 | 8 | 10 | 30 |
| 6 | 5 | 8 | 22 |
| 7 | 1 | 1 | 6 |
| **Total** | **40** | **57** | **106** |

majority of these families would be expected to represent dominant inheritance, and the probability $(p)$ of having a deaf child would be expected to be .50. The relatively few cases of recessive inheritance would have both parents homozygous for the same gene $(p = 1)$, one parent homozygous and the other heterozygous for the same gene $(p = .50)$, or both parents heterozygous for the same gene $(p = .25)$. These three situations are listed in order of decreasing frequency.

The genetic test for segregation used here is the *doubly truncated binomial distribution* of Finney (68). Families where parents are deaf and produce no deaf children, but are genetically able to do so, are omitted, as are the deaf by deaf matings that produce all deaf offspring. Assuming complete ascertainment, Finney's tables give $\hat{p}$ for these data equal to .235 $\pm$ .046. This figure suggests strongly that the dominant gene or genes causing early total deafness have low penetrance, something on the order of 50 per cent.

Other evidence tending to support the concept that dominant inheritance is not fully penetrant is the existence of 47 families where the parents of the index case were hearing although other relatives were deaf (Table 6). It

## TABLE 6
### Deaf index cases with hearing parents and at least one deaf relative other than sibs

| Deaf relatives | Number of index cases with no deaf sibs | Number of index cases with at least one deaf sib |
|---|---|---|
| First cousins only | 18 | 5 |
| Sibs of parents only | 4 | 2 |
| Parents of hearing parents | 1 | 2 |
| Combinations | 1 | 1 |
| Others: second cousins, grand aunts, etc. | 8 | 5 |
| Total | 32 | 15 |

will be shown later on that these cases probably represent dominant inheritance with the deafness not expressed in the parent carrying the gene.

It may also be noted that there are several known cases of sex-linked deafness (164, 198). These cases appear to be very rare—eight affected males per million males.

### Twin Analysis

Twins afford a built-in control for genetic investigation through intra-pair comparisons among monozygotic pairs as well as inter-pair comparisons between monozygotic and dizygotic twins. Inclusion of other relatives— parents, sibs and the like—permits extension of the observations obtained from each set of twins. The twin-family method compensates in part for the limitations inherent in a retrospective investigation of human heredity, while allowing a wider scope than is possible in studies limited to twin pairs alone.

In human twin studies it is important that the sample of twins should not be limited to an unrepresentative series of particularly interesting pairs, as such a selection would vitiate the advantages of the twin method. Therefore, an attempt was made in this study to ascertain a statistically representative sample of twins, characterized by the presence of early total deafness in at least one member of each pair. Those personally interviewed were considered to have early total deafness, if they were deaf before age 17 and their hearing loss was functionally severe enough to prevent their understanding or recognizing spoken words without seeing the speaker's lips.

This stipulation limited their communication to lip reading, use of sign language, finger spelling, "specially learned" speech, and/or written communication. When information was obtained from questionnaires, early total deafness was ascertained from information on the above methods of communication or from the information that the person attended a special school for the deaf and/or was a member of a special organization for the deaf.

As previously mentioned, as soon as our project completed its frame of all deaf individuals in New York State, an introductory questionnaire (see Appendix 1) was mailed to every known deaf resident over 12 years of age. Aside from items dealing with name and address, the form contained the question "Are you a twin?". With 8200 letters sent out, approximately 1700 deaf persons replied, while 2000 letters were returned as undeliverable by the post office. In addition, we specifically requested all cooperating agencies, clubs, and organizations as well as schools for the deaf to report the names of twins. It is essential in genetic studies to be able to evaluate the completeness of the registration of the twin pairs, hence the representativeness of the sample. Therefore, to verify the accuracy of our information, nearly 500 names of deaf school children who were native New York State residents of the three upstate schools for the deaf were submitted to the Office of Vital Statistics of the New York State Department of Health, where a search was made of birth records to determine whether any of these pupils were twins. This search yielded nine pairs of twins and one set of triplets, all discordant for early total deafness and all previously reported by the given schools.

Because of the scarcity in New York State of complete twin pairs with deafness (where both twins were living and available for study), it was considered necessary to extend our search to other areas. By means similar to those described above, the deaf populations in Philadelphia and Washington were surveyed, as were the populations of the New Jersey part of the New York-Northeastern New Jersey standard metropolitan area, and Fairfield County in Connecticut.

Twin pairs were classified as completely studied when both members were personally interviewed, received audiometric tests, and, among same-sex pairs, were subjected to tests for zygosity determination. In addition to comparative educational, social and work histories, data were obtained on the time of onset, degree, type, and essential clinical concomitants of any observed hearing loss in the twins, together with comparative histories of developmental abnormalities in their prenatal and postnatal periods, as well as of infections, accidents, medications, and other pertinent facts at or prior to the time when the hearing loss was first noted. Wherever possible, similar fact-finding interviews and audiometric examinations were conducted with parents, sibs, and other relatives, especially those with a reported hearing loss. Nearly all the twins received psychometric examinations.

A total of 110 twin pairs and two sets of triplets were ascertained in the

**TABLE 7**

Geographical distribution of ascertained twin population

|  | New York State* | Philadelphia | Washington | Total |
|---|---|---|---|---|
| Twins | 88 | 18 | 4 | 110 |
| Triplets | 1 | 1 | 0 | 2 |

*Includes the New Jersey part of the New York - Northeastern New Jersey standard metropolitan area, as well as Fairfield County in Connecticut.

areas surveyed (Table 7). Since each of the triplet sets had one deaf member, it was possible to consider each of the two sets of triplets as two pairs, making a total of 114 pairs. Twenty-seven of the twin pairs had at least one member who had died (usually during the perinatal period or early in life) and were therefore unavailable for study. For various other reasons, a number of other sets were either not studied or not included in the analysis.

Family data were obtained on 37 pairs of twins and one set of triplets, plus a twin pair from Florida (Family 5). The Florida pair and two additional pairs were omitted from the statistical analysis for reasons given below, leaving 36 sets, or 37 pairs of twins (including the triplets counted as two pairs).

It is of interest to determine whether the twins that were studied in this investigation differed from those pairs that were not studied. Table 8 shows the distribution of these two groups of twin pairs subdivided into same-sex and opposite-sex and concordant versus discordant for deafness. There is no significant difference between completely studied and incompletely

**TABLE 8**

Distribution of completely and incompletely studied twin pairs

|  | Same-sex pairs | | | | Opposite-sex pairs | | | |
|---|---|---|---|---|---|---|---|---|
|  | Concordant | | Discordant | | Concordant | | Discordant | |
|  | Number | Per cent | Number | Per cent | Number | Per cent | Number | Per cent |
| Completely studied pairs* | 11 pairs | 39 | 17 pairs | 61 | 3 pairs | 30 | 7 pairs | 70 |
| Incompletely studied pairs** | 8 pairs | 30 | 19 pairs | 70 | 2 pairs | 9 | 20 pairs | 91 |

*Classification as to concordance made before analysis of audiograms. Pair number 12 included.

**No audiograms obtained.

studied pairs for same-sex versus opposite-sex ($\chi^2 = 3.18, P = .08$), concordant versus discordant for same-sex pairs ($\chi^2 = .57, P = .48$), or concordant versus discordant for opposite-sex pairs ($\chi^2 = 2.28, P = .13$). These three chi-squares were calculated without Yates' correction, and adding them gives an overall test between the completely and incompletely studied that is not significant ($\chi^2 = 6.01$ with 3 degrees of freedom, $P = .11$).*

In order to obtain a classification of same-sex twin pairs according to zygosity, several factors were considered, including comparison of fingerprints and blood group factors. Blood samples were unobtainable or incomplete in six of the 28 same-sex pairs.

In the zygosity analysis, same-sex twins differing in a blood group factor and all opposite-sex twins were listed as dizygotic. In most of the remaining twins, classification was made by the method described by Smith and Penrose (208). With this method, one calculates the odds of two sibs possessing similar traits by chance. Separate figures were obtained for the quantitative analysis of total finger ridge counts of Nixon (160); the qualitative fingerprint method of Wendt (241); blood group data using the ABO, Rh (five anti-sera), MNS, Kell, Duffy, and sometimes P and Lewis systems; as well as the likelihood that any same-sex twin pair will be dizygotic. From the product of these independent odds one obtains the "likelihood that the twin pair in question is dizygotic," with one minus this figure as the "likelihood that the pair is monozygotic." In using the Smith-Penrose method for blood group frequencies, American white gene frequencies or American Negro frequencies as given by Mourant (152) were used.

There were ten opposite-sex pairs and eight pairs of same-sex twins with differences in one or more blood group factors. Of the remaining twin pairs, two had a dizygotic Smith-Penrose score of at least 99 per cent, while 17 had a monozygotic score over 92 per cent. The remaining pair was Negro (Family 16), and had a dizygotic Nixon score of $+2.77$ and a Wendt score of zero (tending towards monozygosity). The Smith-Penrose method on blood groups gave a probability of .81 of being monozygotic. An attempt to include the fingerprint data in the Smith-Penrose score resulted in a probability of greater than one-half for dizygosity. Accordingly, the diagnosis of zygosity was considered uncertain, and the pair was not included in any statistical analysis or tables based on known zygosity classification.

An estimate of the zygosity distribution of the twin pairs may also be made by Weinberg's differential method (219) which makes it possible to calculate the percentage of monozygotic twins from the percentage of pairs of opposite-sex by doubling the latter and subtracting from 100. By coincidence the estimated and the actual observed zygosity distributions were identical: 17 monozygotic and 20 dizygotic pairs.

From the data of Tables 8 and 9 three tests of concordance versus dis-

---

* A direct overall comparison using a $2 \times 4$ table gives $\chi^2 = 5.78$ with three degrees of freedom, $P = .12$, in close agreement with the foregoing.

**TABLE 9**
Concordance for total deafness in twins*

| Zygosity | Concordant pairs | Discordant pairs | Total |
|---|---|---|---|
| Monozygotic | 10 | 7 | 17 |
| Dizygotic | 4 | 16 | 20 |
| Total | 14 | 23 | 37 |

*Classification as to concordance made before analysis of audiograms.

cordance in various types of twins can be made. A crude test can be based on all the data from Table 8, comparing concordance in same-sex twins (which include both monozygotic and dizygotic) and opposite-sex twins (which are only dizygotic). This procedure gives a chi-square value of 2.74 with a P value of .10. A better test would involve actual diagnosis of zygosity. Using the completely studied sets, a significant difference in concordance is noted between the monozygotic and dizygotic pairs, with a chi-square value of 4.35 and a P value of .04. There is 59 per cent concordance for monozygotic twin pairs, and 19 per cent concordance for dizygotic pairs. Finally, we may use more of the data by noticing that all opposite-sex pairs are dizygotic. Adding the incompletely studied opposite-sex twins to the dizygotic category gives a chi-square value of 10.0, with a P value between .001 and .005. The concordance rates for these data are 59 per cent for monozygotic twin pairs and 14 per cent for dizygotic pairs. These highly significant results confirm that hereditary factors are involved in early total deafness.

Further, an attempt was made to quantify deafness through the use of audiometric testing. By this means, hearing response values were determined for each member of the twin pairs in terms of sound intensities ranging from −10 to +100 decibels (dbs) at various frequencies of sound (cps). For these audiometric tests a portable Belltone audiometer was used with a range of 125 to 8000 cps and calibrated according to the American Standard Association specification for audiometers for general diagnostic purposes (March 1951). Wherever possible, the members of each twin pair were tested by this investigator at the same time under comparable conditions, using both air and bone conduction measurements. No further use was made of the bone conduction, except for the purpose of verifying the conclusions drawn from the air conduction tests. The values for bone conduction are therefore not included in this report. In addition to the twin pairs, 44 parents of twins and 19 sibs were tested audiometrically.

The audiometric analysis was complicated by the fact that many of the deaf twins failed to respond to the highest level of sound intensity presented on the audiometer used (65 dbs for 125 cps; 80 dbs for 250 cps; 100 dbs for 500, 750, 1000, 1500, 2000, 3000, 4000, and 6000 cps; and 80 dbs for 8000 cps). Since the absence of response may indicate a hearing loss above the upper audiometric limit, the true value of intra-pair differences in these cases is difficult to establish. For this reason a statistical method was devised, based on extrapolating from a probability distribution of all observed responses at each frequency, to estimate the actual hearing loss in decibels represented by "no response."

Mean intra-pair differences for monozygotic and dizygotic pairs were computed twice: first, regarding "no response" to the audiometer as representing the decibel loss specified by these extrapolated values; and second, regarding it as representing a decibel loss of five decibels greater than the highest intensity produced by the audiometer at each frequency. The intra-pair differences obtained by these two procedures were found to be equivalent. Therefore, for the sake of simplicity, it was decided to consider "no response" as representing a hearing loss five decibels above the actual upper decibel limits of the audiometer at each frequency. The results of the actual audiometric tests on the twin pairs can be found in Appendix 2.

Investigation of possible errors inherent in measuring hearing thresholds was conducted by means of test-retest trials. For this purpose, the New York School for the Deaf supplied a sample of 22 students (13 boys and 9 girls) whose hearing loss was classified as early total deafness. Each subject was tested twice, one week apart, under similar conditions.

The mean inter-test differences for both sexes at each of the 11 frequencies tested varied from less than one to four decibels, with the males having a higher mean inter-test difference than the females for 10 of the 11 frequencies. The actual inter-test differences generally ranged from 0 to 15 decibels, the latter figures having been recorded in only five of the 484 test-retest pairings. One inter-test difference of 20 decibels was recorded at 125 cycles per second. These data were compatible with the generally accepted variation in inter-test limits.

After audiometric testing, it was found that the cotwins in eight of the 23 pairs listed as discordant for early total deafness in Table 9 actually had a hearing loss. A minimum of 30 decibels hearing loss at three or more frequencies in one or both ears was necessary for this classification. These twin pairs were called partially concordant.

Table 10 indicates the distribution of the twin pairs after audiometric examination. Curiously enough, all of the five one-egg cotwins reclassified as partly concordant are females. Although the group is too small for this finding to be statistically significant, it is noteworthy that in the sample as a whole eight individuals were reclassified and all are females.

From Table 10 it can be seen that the 17 monozygotic pairs were classified as 59 per cent completely concordant, 29 per cent partially concordant and 12 per cent completely discordant. By comparison, the rates for the 20 dizygotic pairs were 20 per cent, 15 per cent and 65 per cent respectively.

**TABLE 10**
Degrees of concordance in twins based on audiometric examination

| Zygosity and sex | | Concordance as to deafness | | | Total |
|---|---|---|---|---|---|
| | | Completely concordant | Partly concordant | Completely discordant | |
| Monozygotic pairs | Male | 6 | – | – | 6 |
| | Female | 4 | 5 | 2 | 11 |
| Dizygotic pairs | Male | – | – | 2 | 2 |
| | Female | 1 | 2 | 5 | 8 |
| | Opposite-sex | 3 | 1 | 6 | 10 |
| Total | | 14 | 8 | 15 | 37 |

These data yield a chi-square value of 10.961 with two degrees of freedom, giving a $P$ value of .005 which is highly significant.

In analyzing the audiometric data, two "difference" values were obtained for each twin pair: a right by right ear pairing, and a left by left ear pairing, according to the method of Ciocco (39, 40). These data were then placed in three categories:

Group I:    250, 500, 750 cps
Group II:   1000, 1500, 2000 cps
Group III:  3000, 4000, 6000 cps

The lowest and highest audiometric frequencies (125 cps, 8000 cps) were omitted from these calculations.

Table 11 presents the mean ($\bar{x}$) and the standard deviation ($s$) as well as the Variance ($s^2$) and the standard error of the mean ($s_{\bar{x}}$) derived from the intra-pair differences (averaged for both ears) of monozygotic as well as same-sex and opposite-sex dizygotic pairs. These statistics are given for each of the three frequency ranges, together with an average value of all three.

The data show that the monozygotic twins have a smaller mean intra-pair difference ($\bar{x}$) than the dizygotic pairs (same-sex and opposite-sex). The smaller mean intra-pair difference in monozygotic twins is another aspect of the fact that the monozygotic twins have the highest proportion of completely and partially concordant pairs (15/17), while the dizygotic same-sex pairs have a concordance rate of only three out of ten, and the opposite-sex pairs have four out of ten.

Student's $t$ test was used to measure the significance of the intra-pair differences (Table 12). Monozygotic pairs show $t$ values that differ significantly at the .05 level or lower from the dizygotic pairs. The $t$ values are

## TABLE 11

### Audiometric data on twins: intra-pair measurements (using both ears)

| Frequency tested | Type of twin pair | No. of measurements (R and L ear for each twin) n | Mean intra-pair difference $\bar{x}$ | Standard deviation of intra-pair differences s | Variance $s^2$ | Standard error of mean intra-pair difference $s_{\bar{x}}$ |
|---|---|---|---|---|---|---|
| I 250-750 cps | Monozygotic | 17 | 31.34 | ±32.92 | 1083.42 | ± 7.98 |
| | Dizygotic | 20 | 58.51 | ±29.36 | 862.03 | ± 6.56 |
| | Dizygotic same-sex | 10 | 59.80 | ±26.49 | 701.96 | ± 8.38 |
| | Dizygotic opposite-sex | 10 | 57.23 | ±33.38 | 1114.21 | ±10.56 |
| II 1000-2000 cps | Monozygotic | 17 | 37.86 | ±40.82 | 1666.06 | ± 9.90 |
| | Dizygotic | 20 | 71.26 | ±35.27 | 1244.22 | ± 7.89 |
| | Dizygotic same-sex | 10 | 74.06 | ±31.02 | 962.58 | ± 9.81 |
| | Dizygotic opposite-sex | 10 | 68.47 | ±40.58 | 1646.75 | ±12.83 |
| III 3000-6000 cps | Monozygotic | 17 | 33.77 | ±40.11 | 1608.95 | ± 9.73 |
| | Dizygotic | 20 | 72.10 | ±39.60 | 1568.43 | ± 8.86 |
| | Dizygotic same-sex | 10 | 72.30 | ±33.61 | 1129.90 | ±10.63 |
| | Dizygotic opposite-sex | 10 | 71.90 | ±46.70 | 2181.13 | ±14.77 |
| Average I - III | Monozygotic | 17 | 34.35 | ±37.42 | 1400.41 | ± 9.08 |
| | Dizygotic | 20 | 67.31 | ±33.70 | 1135.66 | ± 7.54 |
| | Dizygotic same-sex | 10 | 68.75 | ±28.97 | 839.51 | ± 9.17 |
| | Dizygotic opposite-sex | 10 | 65.87 | ±39.41 | 1553.39 | ±12.46 |

**TABLE 12**

**Student's t test for significance of intra-pair twin differences**

| Twin pairs compared* | Frequencies in cycles per second | | | | | | | |
|---|---|---|---|---|---|---|---|---|
| | I | | II | | III | | I - III | |
| | 250 - 750 cps | | 1000 - 2000 cps | | 3000 - 6000 cps | | Averaged cps | |
| | t | P | t | P | t | P | t | P |
| Monozygotic: all dizygotic** | 2.63 | <.01 | 2.64 | <.01 | 2.91 | <.005 | 2.79 | <.005 |
| Monozygotic: dizygotic same - sex** | 2.46 | <.02 | 2.60 | <.01 | 2.67 | <.01 | 2.67 | <.01 |
| Monozygotic: dizygotic opposite - sex** | 1.96 | <.05 | 1.89 | <.05 | 2.16 | <.05 | 2.04 | <.05 |
| Dizygotic same - sex: dizygotic opposite - sex*** | .19 | >.80 | .35 | >.70 | .02 | >.99 | .19 | >.80 |

*Number of measurements for each group of twin pairs same as Table 12.
**P value based on single tail test.
***P value based on two tail test.

not significant when the dizygotic same-sex and opposite-sex pairs are compared (.99>P>.7). Audiometrically, therefore, it is justifiable to conclude that the monozygotic and dizygotic twins are significantly different, while dizygotic same-sex and opposite-sex pairs are not.

Since the distribution of the differences is strikingly nonnormal, a nonparametric test using the Willcoxon sum of ranks method (233) was performed on the data for all frequencies combined. This gave $t = 2.45$, corresponding to a $P$ value of approximately .01, in reasonably good agreement with the Student's $t$ test.

## Twin-Family Study

When the anamneses and family pedigrees are reviewed, it is possible to surmise the factors causing early total deafness for each twin pair, as summarized in Table 13. Three of the monozygotic pairs of twins (all completely concordant) and three of the dizygotic pairs (all completely discordant) probably represent recessive inheritance on the basis of family history or the congenital nature of the deafness, although it is difficult to assign isolated, so-called sporadic cases, with any real assurance.

Although it is unlikely that recessive deafness is always congenital, there is reason to believe that there is an association between deafness being recessive and its being congenital or of very early onset (vide pp. 35, 58, 62). It may be noted that deafness for many of the twin pairs was first observed by parents or diagnosed by physicians when the twins were between one and three years old, usually because, by that time, they had not developed speech. Since deafness is easily overlooked in very young children, particularly when the parents are not very observant, it is possible that some deafness first noted at ages one to three may actually have developed much earlier or may even have been congenital. Thus the number of recessive cases in twins may be underestimated.

Two of the above six pairs of twins (one monozygotic and one dizygotic) were considered recessively deaf, because their parents were first cousins. They were the only deaf persons in their family (their deafness having been noted at the ages of two years and one year, respectively) and they lacked any history of exogenous factors that may have caused the deafness.

The family pedigrees indicate that of the 37 pairs, one monozygotic and four dizygotic probably represent dominant inheritance. In this group there are six deaf and two hard of hearing individuals. Four of the former and all of the latter have a history of possible exogenous factors, suggesting a possible interrelationship between exogenous factors and the dominant genotype (other aspects of the interaction between genetic and exogenous mechanisms are discussed in subsequent sections). In addition, in these five pairs there was no history of exogenous factors in the two twin subjects with normal hearing.

Eight of the 37 pairs of twins studied, or 22 per cent, seem to have a *probable* exogenous factor as at least a contributing factor to the deafness,

**TABLE 13**

Distribution of twin pairs by family history and mode of onset

| Zygosity and concordance | With deaf relatives | | Parents cousins* | Without deaf relatives | | | |
|---|---|---|---|---|---|---|---|
| | Sibs only | Other than sibs (With or without sibs) | | No exogenous factors | | Exogenous factors | |
| | | | | Congenital | Onset after birth** | Possible | Probable |
| **Monozygotic** | | | | | | | |
| Completely concordant | 1 | 1 | 1*** | 1† | 3 | 2 | 1 |
| Partially concordant | — | — | — | — | — | 2 | 3 |
| Completely discordant | — | — | — | — | — | 1 | 1 |
| **Dizygotic** | | | | | | | |
| Completely concordant | — | — | — | — | 3 | — | 1 |
| Partially concordant | — | 2 | — | — | 1 | — | — |
| Completely discordant | 1 | 2 | 2 | — | — | 6 | 2 |
| **Total** | 2 | 5 | 3 | 1 | 7 | 11 | 8 |

*All first cousins except one marriage of second cousins. The twins in this family were dizygotic, completely discordant, with a history of possible exogenous factors.

**One pair of twins (dizygotic, completely concordant) had onset during the first year.

***Paternal grandaunt born deaf.

†Deafness noted at three months; probably congenital.

although gene-determined susceptibility may also be involved. In an additional 11 pairs there was some condition that might *possibly* be involved as an exogenous factor, making a total of 19 out of 37 pairs, or 51 per cent, that may be exogenously determined. This proportion is not excessive compared to estimates for the single-born population (see below). Although it is possible that early total deafness as a result of such environmental influences as the effects of prematurity, e.g. jaundice (62, 71) may occur more often in twins, it would not seem to be reflected in these figures.

In the relatively small group with early total deafness presumably dominantly inherited (5 of the 37 twin pairs), important clues may be discerned for further investigation into the etiology of this condition. For one thing, this type of deafness shows marked variability in penetrance and clinical expression within families, extending from discordance in some one-egg twin pairs (as in Family 5 residing outside the surveyed area and included only in Appendix 2) to unilaterality in individuals. It also tends to associate itself with pigmentary and other non-auditory pathological symptoms, including those comprising the syndromes described by Klein (119) and Waardenburg (232). To be sure, association with other disorders has also been observed in non-dominant forms of deafness. In this

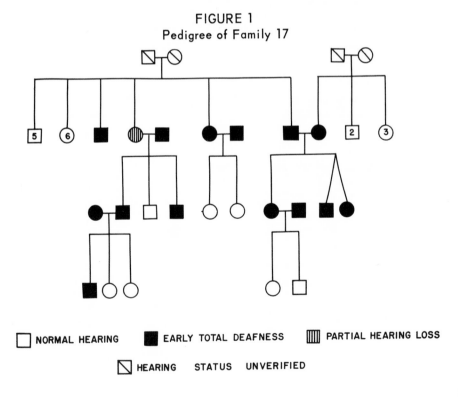

FIGURE 1
Pedigree of Family 17

NORMAL HEARING     ■ EARLY TOTAL DEAFNESS     ▥ PARTIAL HEARING LOSS

◨ HEARING    STATUS    UNVERIFIED

category are Usher's syndrome, combining total deafness with retinitis pigmentosa, as described by Hallgren (91), and the D trisomy syndrome reported by Therman et al. (226), associating deafness with a chromosomal aberration.

Summarized histories of the twin pairs examined in this report are being published separately (195). The following families with apparently dominant forms of early total deafness are of interest as illustrating variable degrees of expression from early total deafness to hearing losses which are of limited extent or expressed only unilaterally or in later life.

Family 17 (Figure 1) was not fully studied, only one twin being examined. Therefore, this family is included only in Tables 7 and 8 and Appendix 2. It includes a pair of opposite-sex twins concordant for dominant deafness, presumably contributed by the father's family. All eight cases of deafness that occurred in consanguineously related members in the paternal line as well as in sibs were fully expressed, with the exception of one case of partial hearing loss in a paternal aunt of the twins. Of the three deaf by deaf matings in this family, one gave rise to deaf offspring only, one to hearing offspring only, and one to a combination of deaf and hearing children. The audiometric patterns of the concordant twins were similar at all frequencies (test conducted by a school audiologist).

One family (Family 5), as stated above, resided outside the three surveyed areas and was included only in Appendix 2. It is discussed here because of its intrinsic interest (Figure 2). There is a pair of monozygotic

## FIGURE 2
### Pedigree of Family 5

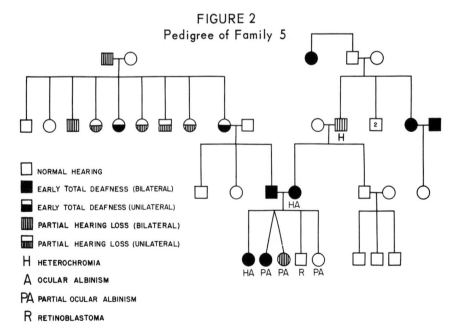

| | |
|---|---|
| □ | NORMAL HEARING |
| ■ | EARLY TOTAL DEAFNESS (BILATERAL) |
| ◧ | EARLY TOTAL DEAFNESS (UNILATERAL) |
| ▥ | PARTIAL HEARING LOSS (BILATERAL) |
| ▤ | PARTIAL HEARING LOSS (UNILATERAL) |
| H | HETEROCHROMIA |
| A | OCULAR ALBINISM |
| PA | PARTIAL OCULAR ALBINISM |
| R | RETINOBLASTOMA |

twins with a Smith-Penrose probability in favor of monozygosity of 99.94 per cent, who are partially concordant for deafness. This family includes members with dominantly inherited bilateral early total deafness, as well as those exhibiting incomplete expression of the gene, indicated by unilateral deafness as well as by bilateral and unilateral partial hearing losses. The monozygotic twin sisters are completely concordant for partial ocular albinism, while the deaf mother and a deaf sister have ocular albinism as well as heterochromia. Two younger sibs have normal hearing, although the girl has partial ocular albinism, and the boy had one eye enucleated because of a histopathologically verified retinoblastoma. Cytological and other laboratory techniques contributed no tangible clue to the etiology of this particular syndrome.

With Family 5 illustrating differences between monozygotic twins with the dominant type of early total deafness, a like phenomenon within a single individual with dominant early total deafness should not be surprising. This variation is observed in Family 31 (Figure 3) where a dizygotic

## FIGURE 3
### Pedigree of Family 31

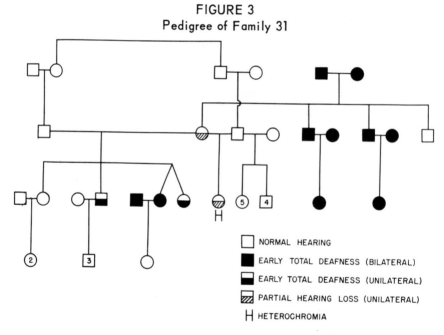

NORMAL HEARING
EARLY TOTAL DEAFNESS (BILATERAL)
EARLY TOTAL DEAFNESS (UNILATERAL)
PARTIAL HEARING LOSS (UNILATERAL)
H HETEROCHROMIA

same-sex pair of twins is partially concordant for dominant early total deafness. The index case has bilateral deafness and her cotwin presents a unilateral severe hearing loss—the right ear having normal hearing and the left a severe hearing loss of probably early onset. The audiometric pattern of the left ear of the cotwin is essentially like that of both deaf ears of the index case. The family pedigree shows a combination of dominant bilateral and unilateral early total deafness in other members, along with pigmentary disorders. In generation III, there is an eleven-year-old girl (III-8) who has a partial hearing loss and heterochromia (one eye blue, the other brown) with both the blue eye and the partial hearing loss appearing on the right side. This association of unilateral hearing loss with heterochromia has been described by Waardenburg (232) and Klein (119) among others, with the blue eye on the same side as the affected ear.

In Family 37 there is a pair of dizygotic, opposite-sex twins with dominant deafness who are partially concordant. In this case, the partial hearing loss in the female cotwin may be of late origin (after the age of 40-50 years). Here, too, is seen the association of complete or partial hearing loss with unusual pigment conditions (white or platinum hair and blue eyes as well as heterochromia). Although a relationship appears to exist between early total deafness and some pigment disorders, the exact mechanism of this interaction has not yet been elucidated.

### Discussion and Conclusions

Early total deafness may be divided into the following categories: (1) deafness due to an autosomal recessive gene; (2) deafness due to an autosomal dominant gene inherited from a parent; (3) deafness due to a sex-linked gene (probably rare); (4) deafness due to multifactorial inheritance; (5) sporadic cases. The sporadic cases may be subdivided into (a) genetic deafness due to a newly arisen mutant gene; and (b) deafness due mainly to environmental causes. Since the phenotype (including deafness as one aspect) is always due to the total genotype interacting with the total environment, this classification is not hard and fast, but it is nevertheless useful in practice.

The family study, based on the mail questionnaire, contains evidence for estimating the relative proportions of the three main classes. The following assumptions are made:

1. Deafness in individuals with a deaf relative who is not a sib is due to a dominant autosomal gene.

2. Deafness in individuals with one or more deaf sibs but no other deaf relatives is due to a recessive autosomal gene.

3. Deafness in individuals with no deaf relatives is due to a recessive gene or to environmental causes. Much deafness arising between the first and fourth years of life and most deafness cases arising after the fourth year are environmentally caused.

4. Sex-linked forms of deafness have been found by other investigators to be rare. In the absence of any specific evidence for sex-linkage in the present study, this cause will be ignored.

The population study presented in this chapter was based on 968 questionnaires accepted for the main deafness survey. Of these, 688 or 71 per cent were accepted for the present study, and 280 or 29 per cent rejected either because there was a known exogenous cause or the deafness arose after the age of four. By the above assumptions, the latter cases would be mainly exogenous ones. Of the remaining 688 persons, 92 have a deaf relative other than a sib and are assumed to be dominant. They represent 13.4 per cent of the subjects in this study, or 9.5 per cent of the total. Thus 596 persons or 86.6 per cent of this series represent either recessive or sporadic cases.

There are two partially independent methods of allocating these cases. The first is based on the 501 isolated cases with no known deaf relative. It was shown previously that the comparison of the distribution of sibship sizes among these isolated cases of deafness arising before the end of the first year of life with that for those arising during the second to fourth years agrees with what is to be expected if the early cases are recessive but by chance had no deaf sibs, and the later cases are due to unique random causes. Since 307 out of the 501 cases are early by this definition and 194 are late (second to fourth years), with an additional 95 cases having at least one deaf sib and no other deaf relative, there are $307 + 95 = 402$ presumably recessive cases, and 194 presumably sporadic ones, or 67 per cent recessive and 33 per cent sporadic among the non-dominant cases.

The second method of estimating the relative proportion of recessive and sporadic cases is based on Haldane's method of segregation analysis applied to all 501 isolated cases, plus the 95 cases with deaf sibs but no other deaf relatives. It was shown previously that on the assumption of complete ascertainment, the segregation frequency $p = .150$, while on the assumption of minimal ascertainment $p = .086$. If we suppose we are dealing with a mixture of recessive cases with $p = .25$ and sporadic cases with $p = 0$, the proportion of recessive cases is .60 for complete ascertainment and .34 for minimal ascertainment.

Thus there are at least three possible estimates for the proportion of recessive cases among the non-dominant cases: 67 per cent, 60 per cent, and 34 per cent. The additional questions of standard error and possible sampling bias have not been considered. Evidently, the percentage of recessive cases cannot be pinpointed, but its order of magnitude is known. For simplicity, an intermediate value of 50 per cent will be taken.

The percentages of dominant, recessive and sporadic cases for the material in the present study are then estimated at 13.4, 43.3, and 43.3, respectively, while for the total New York State population over age 12 (the main study) the corresponding figures are 9.5 per cent, 30.8 per cent, and 59.7 per cent. The total number of deaf in New York State over age 12 was estimated (Chapter 1) as 10,355 in October 1960. The total number of individuals over age 12 in New York State on April 1, 1960 is estimated from published census figures as 13.00 million. This estimate is based on numbers in five-year age groups, and interpolation using numbers of live births for individual years from 1945 to 1950. The ratio between these values gives a prevalence of deafness in persons over age 12 in New York

State of 79.7 per 100,000. Although more individuals become deaf with increasing age, there is evidence that the deaf have a higher than normal mortality rate (22), and it is probable that the prevalence of total deafness will be similar in the lower age groups. The prevalence rates for dominant, recessive, and sporadic deafness are taken to be 7.6, 24.5, and 47.6 per 100,000, respectively, for purposes of further calculations, although this many significant figures are not warranted by the method of derivation.

It was noted previously that for individuals becoming deaf before the age of four, and with no known exogenous cause, the incidence of cousin marriage among the parents is 12.15 per cent, with lower and upper 95 per cent confidence limits of 8.4 per cent and 16.8 per cent. Such high incidence is strong evidence for recessive inheritance, and this interpretation is confirmed by the fact that the incidence of deafness among the sibs of deaf persons whose parents are cousins is in good agreement with simple recessive inheritance.

It is well known that for a single gene there is a simple relationship between $r$, the frequency of homozygotes in the population, $c$, the frequency of first cousin matings in the population, and $k$, the frequency of first cousin matings among the parents of homozygotes (137). In fact, $k$ is large only if $c$ is large or $r$ very small, and the present data give poor agreement with the theory. The usual explanation for such a state of affairs is that there are a number, $g$, of genes, each quite rare, and each capable of causing deafness when homozygous. It then becomes possible to estimate $g$ if the other factors are known.

The smallest estimate of $g$ is obtained if it is assumed that all the genes have equal frequency. Then, if $R$ is the total frequency of homozygotes, $r = R/g$ is the frequency for homozygotes for each individual gene, with $q/g = \sqrt{R/g}$ the frequency of each individual gene, and $q$ the frequency of all genes combined. Then, if $F$ is the inbreeding coefficient ($F = 1/16$ for first cousins), and $b = 1/cF$,

$$(14) \qquad g = R \frac{[b(k-c) + (1-k)]^2}{(1-c)(1-k)}.$$

In the range of values usual for the various constants involved, $g$ increases linearly with the total incidence of recessive deafness, $R$, and approximately according to the squares of $1/F$ and of $k/c$, the ratio of the cousin marriage frequency among parents of the affected individuals to the cousin marriage frequency in the general population.

Now let $p_r$ be the proportion of early total deafness due to recessive genes. Then the proportion, $p_r$, of the parents of the deaf will have cousin marriage rate $k$, and the proportion, $(1 - p_r)$, will have the same rate, $c$, as the general population, so that the observed total rate of cousin marriage among the parents of the deaf will be

$$(15) \qquad k_t = p_r k + (1 - p_r)c.$$

Solving for $k$ gives

(16)
$$k = \frac{k_t - (1 - p_r)c}{p_r}$$

for the unknown frequency of cousin marriage among the parents of the recessive deaf.

The questionnaire, as stated above, asked only, "Are your parents cousins?" There are no figures on general cousin marriage rates in New York State. Other figures are as follows: Chicago Catholics less than .1 per cent (Slatis, 206), Baltimore .05 per cent, Prussia .20 per cent, Netherlands .13 per cent, Vienna .53 per cent, Mormons and relatives .64 per cent—all for first cousins (Stern, 219). Other urban figures for first cousins, first cousins once removed, and second cousins respectively are as follows: England .61 per cent, 0 per cent, .11 per cent (Stern, 219); Japan 4.1 per cent, 1.2 per cent, 1.7 per cent; São Paulo, Brazil .66 per cent, .12 per cent, .16 per cent; Munster, Germany .08 per cent, .09 per cent, .84 per cent (Morton, 150); compared to rural figures of small Utah and Nevada towns .64 per cent, 1.44 per cent, 3.68 per cent (Stern, 219); United States rural 0 per cent, .44 per cent, .88 per cent, and more remote relationships 8.85 per cent (Morton, 150).

While these figures are quite variable, a frequency of first cousin marriage over .5 per cent is most uncommon in American or Western communities, with .1 per cent much more likely for New York State as a whole. In general, second cousin marriages are less frequent than first cousin marriages, except in fairly isolated rural communities where "everyone tends to be related to everyone else." Furthermore, since $F$ is only $1/64$ for second cousin marriages, the ratio of second to first cousin marriages among parents of affected individuals will be about three times smaller than among the population at large.

Finally, because of age difference, marriages between first cousins once removed are always a good deal rarer than between second cousins. In the present study there is a further unknown factor involved in whether the respondents interpreted the question "Are your parents cousins?" as meaning only first cousins. All in all, it seems likely that most of the 30 unions involved were between first cousins. The effect of assuming so is to *underestimate* the number of different genes involved.

The observed value of $k_t$ is $30/247 = .1215$ for all cases of early total deafness not of exogenous origin. It was previously estimated that only about 43 per cent of these cases are recessive ($p_r = .43$), and almost all of the 30 cousin marriages may be assumed to be drawn from the parents of recessive cases. Taking $c = .001$, the value of $k$ among parents of recessive cases may then be estimated by formula 16 as $(.1215 - .0006)/.43 = .28$. Substituting this figure in formula 14 with $F = 1/16$ and $R = .000245$, one obtains $g = 6800$ genes, which is an improbably large number.

What is almost certainly a lower limit for $g$ is obtained by supposing that 80 per cent of all cases of early total deafness, not of exogenous origin, are recessive ($p_r = .80$), by taking an upper limit of $c = .005$, and by taking the lower confidence limit of $k_t = .084$ (see p. 59). This estimate gives $k = (.084 - .001)/.80 = .104$, and $g = 45$, and is probably too low. Thus, while the number of genes is subject to uncertainty, it is almost certainly very large. The lower estimate, $g = 45$ genes, corresponds to a gene frequency for the individual genes of .0023 and a frequency of heterozygotes for individual genes of .0045. The total frequencies of recessive genes and heterozygotes are then .10 and .21 respectively. For the actual (but far too high) estimate of $g = 6800$, the frequencies of individual genes and heterozygotes are .00019 and .00038, giving total frequencies of 1.3 and 2.6 respectively. These latter figures are not to be interpreted as probabilities but as "loads" (that is, the average individual would be heterozygous for 2.6 different recessive genes for deafness). There is a more than tenfold range in the estimated loads, with .5 being a good guess as the most probable value for recessive genes.

The assumptions made above must now be critically reviewed. In what follows, the lower limit of approximately 45 recessive genes will be used. The study of segregating sibships from two deaf parents suggested that if these represented dominant inheritance, the average penetrance of the gene or genes involved was 50 per cent. The conditional probability that a deaf offspring of two deaf parents has received a dominant gene from one of them can then be calculated. This probability is about .95, with most of the remaining probability representing recessive inheritance. Similar calculations show that if one parent, a grandparent, aunt or uncle, niece or nephew, or first cousin is deaf, there is a better than 90 per cent chance that dominant inheritance is involved. Thus assumption 1 is justified.

Even with the margin of error in the various parameters involved, it is safe to suppose that nearly all deaf by deaf matings with deaf children *did* represent dominant inheritance, and that the penetrance estimate of 50 per cent is therefore reliable. An independent estimate of penetrance can now be obtained. Out of 92 index cases with deaf relatives other than sibs and hence presumably dominant, 45 have a deaf parent and 47 have hearing parents, giving a penetrance in the parents of 49 per cent. This is an overestimate of the penetrance, since where the parents have no deaf relative deafness will be considered dominant only if it is expressed in the parent; hence some cases of failure of the gene to be expressed will be missed. While this bias could have been avoided by considering only cases where the parents had deaf relatives, various other questions would still arise which would be hard to answer from the questionnaire data. A more satisfactory treatment can be made where there are complete pedigrees, as in the data of Stevenson and Cheeseman, which will be discussed below.

Further evidence of incomplete penetrance in dominant inheritance is given by twin-family 5 which contains a set of monozygotic twins with one twin deaf, while the cotwin has a partial hearing loss, illustrating incomplete expression of the dominant gene.

To examine the second assumption, one may consider an individual who has inherited a gene for dominant deafness. The probability that it is not expressed in either parent is the penetrance, $1/2$. The probability that it is not expressed in any grandparent is likewise $1/2$. The probability that it is not expressed in a given sib of a parent is $1 - (1/4)(1/2) = 7/8$, while if each parent has two sibs, the probability that the gene is not expressed in any of them is $[1 - (1/2)(1/2)]^2 = 9/16$.

Evidently, if a sizeable number of relatives are available, the probability that the gene is not expressed in any of them is small. Even with small families, it may be expected that in most cases of dominant deafness the probability of some relative, other than a sib, being affected will exceed $3/4$. Thus not too many cases of dominant inheritance will be missed. Nevertheless, it might be well to raise the estimate of the proportion of *all* cases of deafness that are due to dominant inheritance from 9.5 to 10 or 11 per cent. However, this estimate will have little effect on the frequency of the more common recessive and sporadic cases. With dominant and sex-linked inheritance ruled out, most cases with deaf sibs but no other known deaf relatives must be recessive.

Assumption 3 follows by a similar argument and from the earlier discussions. All the data fit well without invoking sex-linked genes, which are shown by all available evidence to be rare. There is but one discrepancy. Deafness in the 30 individuals with parents who are cousins is almost certainly recessive. Then, by our assumptions, one might expect that they would have been deaf by the end of the first year of life. Actually, it was indicated by the data from non-consanguineous matings that most instances of non-dominant deafness with the origin reported to be at birth were recessive, with the proportion of recessive cases to sporadic cases decreasing with increasing reported age of onset. However, many of the cases said to have started after the first year were still recessive. There also was evidence that many cases reported as having onset after the first year were actually congenital. Of the 30 deaf individuals whose parents were cousins, 50 per cent had onset by the end of the first year of life compared to 40 per cent for the isolated cases in Table 1. However, among those with one or more deaf sibs 82 per cent of the offspring of cousins and 72 per cent of those in Table 2 reported onset before the age of one year. The reported earlier incidence of deafness when there were affected sibs may be due to the parents being more alert to signs of deafness after they have had one deaf child. Thus the estimates of percentage of individuals with onset before one year of age may be considered minimal.

With the discussion of the three assumptions concluded, it remains only to consider the order of magnitude of the mutation rates. Fortunately, although it is not possible from data of this kind to obtain any useful estimate of the mutation rate for recessive genes, something can be done with respect to dominant genes. We will let $q$ be the combined frequency of all dominant genes for deafness, $u$ be the combined mutation rate per haploid genome, and $s$ the selection coefficient against heterozygotes, assumed to be the same for all the genes involved since only a combined estimate is possible. (The letters $q$ and $s$ were used with a different meaning in the segregation analysis.) The combined equilibrium frequency is then $\bar{q} = u/s$, giving $u = \bar{q}s$. According to Table 4 of Chapter 2, the number of children ever born per 100 deaf women of ages 45 to 59 is 1.37, while the comparable figure for the general population is 1.74, giving a relative reproductive value of $1.37/1.74 = .79$ for deaf women, and a selection coefficient of $1 - .79 = .21$.

Since a majority of the deaf marry deaf partners, the reproductive rate for deaf married men should be similar to that for married women. Furthermore, as may be seen from Table 1 of Chapter 2, the percentages of married males and females over age 25 are nearly equal, so that the value of $s$ due to differential reproduction between the deaf and hearing can be taken as the value, .21, obtained for females. While the data for the cases presumably of dominant origin, given in this chapter, are scanty, they do suggest that the selection against dominant deafness is no greater than that for deafness in general. However, if the penetrance of the dominant genes is somewhat under 1/2, and if there is no selection when the gene does not cause deafness, then the selection coefficient against the gene is only .10.

Since the prevalence of dominant deafness estimated previously was .000076, the combined gene frequency would be one-half of this figure, or .000038. The formula then gives $u = (.000038) (.10) = 4 \times 10^{-6}$ for the combined mutation rate. This is a not unreasonable value, even though the effect of possible differential mortality of the deaf is not taken into account. Actually, there may be some such disadvantage, but we do not know of any good data substantiating it. In their absence, a reasonable upper limit for $s$ might be 1/4, giving $u = 10 \times 10^{-6}$. Regardless of the penetrance, the frequency of expressed dominant genes that had never been expressed in any ancestor or previously born relative would be $2u (1 - u)$ or about $8 \times 10^{-6}$ and $20 \times 10^{-6}$, using the two estimates of $u$. Since it has been estimated that the incidence of dominant deafness that was expressed in a relative is $7.6 \times 10^{-5}$, the two estimates give about 1/10 or 2/10 as the proportion of newly expressed dominants to all dominants. If we assume 50 per cent penetrance, the proportion of these dominants that are newly arisen is one-half of this value, or 1/20 and 1/10, respectively. In any event, the proportion of deaf individuals, due to a dominant gene, who have a deaf older relative is 9/10 to 8/10.

On the whole, it may be said that there is clear evidence not only for a genetic component in early total deafness, but also for the proportion (about one-half) of cases with a hereditary cause, as well as for their division into about 25 per cent dominant and 75 per cent recessive ones.

Hence, one might wonder why a twin study should be made at all. The fact is that the tables on concordance and the $t$ tests on audiometric measurements give no information beyond the probable existence of a hereditary component, and are thus merely confirmatory. When the present study was planned, it was hoped that the audiograms of twins would reveal common patterns facilitating a distinction of different genetic entities. Actually, there is comparatively little variability among audiograms of individuals who qualify as deaf by the standards of this study. What differences there are may sometimes be found between the two ears of a single individual. On the other hand, the audiograms did reveal that five out of seven of the non-deaf cotwins of deaf monozygotic index cases had a partial hearing loss (30 decibels or more at three or more frequencies in one or both ears), as did three out of 16 of the non-deaf cotwins of deaf dizygotic index cases.

Ciocco (38) estimated that 19 per cent of older non-deaf school children had a partial hearing loss of similar extent. At least for the monozygotic twins, the incidence of partial hearing loss is high enough to suggest that some genotypes may result in either total or partial hearing loss. While possible exogenous causes were present in all of these seven cases of discordant monozygotic twins, the response to such a cause would still be genetically determined.

The hypothesis that genetic and exogenous factors interact in producing early total deafness is further supported by a pair of dizygotic, opposite-sex twins (Family 19) who were completely concordant for early total deafness. The hearing loss in the female twin occurred suddenly (overnight) at the age of three years, after a history of tonsillitis with fever followed by a bilateral earache. Subsequently, the deaf girl lost her speech. The twin brother spoke simple baby words until the age of 18 months when he had a minor ear infection and suddenly failed to respond to his parents. A week or two later, he had a mild case of German measles. Attempts to restore his hearing by removal of his tonsils and adenoids and insertion of radon capsules were unsuccessful. Interestingly, the boy showed symptoms of polyarthritis (Still's disease) in both knees at the age of three, while the girl developed a rheumatic condition in only one knee 30 months later.

The literature (46) abounds with other instances of a close relationship and interaction between genetic and exogenous factors in producing various pathological conditions. Tuberculosis and possibly leprosy have been shown to require both a hereditary predisposition and a specific bacterial agent to precipitate the illness, while the gene for glucose-6-phosphate dehydrogenase deficiency produces anemia only in the presence of specific nutritional factors. On the other hand, a genetically determined condition such as sickle-cell trait either may predispose an individual to infection with certain exogenous agents such as Salmonella or may provide protection against infectious agents such as falciparum malaria.

Although the exact mechanism of the interaction of genetic and exogenous factors in early total deafness has not yet been identified, the family histories of the twins in the present study (195) point to such an interaction (Table 13).

The use of the twin-family approach offers further benefits. Where there is reason to believe that a specific mode of inheritance is involved, monozygotic twins give particularly good data on penetrance. Unfortunately—with the exception of pair No. 5 from Florida, that was partially concordant—only one of the monozygotic twins had deaf relatives other than sibs and they were fully concordant. The three presumably recessive pairs were also concordant.

Finally, an incidental benefit of a complete twin-family investigation such as the present may be seen in the possible discovery of families with interesting syndromes associated with deafness. Such families tend to be of little more than curiosity value as only the rare is apt to be noted. In the present study, complete ascertainment was aimed at. Hence, 112 sets were ascertained, but only 38 yielded adequate family histories. One pair was not included because of incomplete zygosity diagnosis, and another was omitted because only one twin could be seen. The remaining 36 sets include one set of triplets counted twice, giving a total of 37 twin pairs. At any rate, there is no reason to believe that unusual families formed a biased sample. In other words, the families discussed here in detail (other than Family 5 from Florida) may be said to constitute a significant representative fraction of all cases of early total deafness.

Animal studies have also revealed interesting syndromes associated with congenital deafness, particularly in mice, rats, guinea pigs, cats and dogs. Perhaps the earliest such report was Darwin's description of deafness in cats associated with white fur and blue eyes. The combination of deafness with both albinism of the fur and heterochromia of the irises was confirmed by others in cats as well as Dalmatian dogs (163, 228). In addition, the combination of motor anomalies and disturbances in equilibrium with congenital deafness was observed in "dancing" or "waltzing" (including some "shaker") mice. These syndromes appeared to be due to the effect of a single recessive gene. "Dancing" and deafness were also found associated in guinea pigs and *Peromyscus*. Apparently, several independent genes may produce these syndromes in mice, similar to the situation noted in human deafness.

What remains is the task of comparing our conclusions with those drawn by Stevenson and Cheeseman (220) from their Northern Ireland study as well as with those of Slatis (205) and Chung et al. (37) who further analyzed these data.

The investigation in Northern Ireland utilized a generally restricted ethnic population, while the New York State survey comprised a more heterogeneous group. For both studies, virtually all affected individuals were listed. However, the Northern Ireland data were based on personal interviews of nearly all affected individuals or their relatives, whereas in the New York State study answers to a mail questionnaire were obtained for about 10 per cent of the total deaf population. The latter data confirmed a major part of the findings of the Northern Ireland study, thus validating its observations for a more heterogeneous population. However, the prevalence of early total deafness was found to be greater in New York State (80 per 100,000 population) than in Northern Ireland or the Danish population (Lindenov, 138), both estimated at 45 per 100,000. Qualitatively, these populations provided roughly the same genetic information: total deafness arising early enough to require attendance at a school for the deaf consists of approximately one-half sporadic cases, with the remainder being genetic. For the genetic group, the estimate made by Chung et al. on the Northern Ireland population and our New York State data yielded comparable values: 75 per cent recessive and 25 per cent dominant for New York State, with 90 per cent recessive and 10 per cent dominant cases in Northern Ireland, if new dominant mutant genes are included with the sporadic cases. (If penetrance of the dominant gene in Northern Ireland were assumed to be about 50 per cent as in New York, instead of 100 per cent as stated by Chung et al., the figure for inherited dominant deafness in Northern Ireland would approximate 20 per cent).

Consanguinity data in both populations indicated that the recessive form of early total deafness is determined by a number of autosomal recessive genes, minimally estimated by Chung et al. as 36. The New York State study yielded a somewhat higher minimal value of 45, with the probable number being much greater.

Stevenson and Cheeseman (220) did not believe that dominant genes play an important role in the etiology of the born-deaf. Slatis (205) was the first who showed by a re-analysis of their data that dominant genes were present in the population, accounting for about five cases per 100,000 population.

Chung et al. reaffirmed the concept of a dominant factor in early total deafness and suggested (on the basis of a study of eight pedigrees where affected individuals had deaf aunts or uncles) that there was high but not complete penetrance. In fact, in these eight pedigrees (of parents who presumably transmitted the dominant gene expressed by the deaf aunt or uncle), eight persons were normal and two affected, giving a penetrance estimate of .2. This analysis of the Northern Ireland pedigrees may be extended in such a way as to include deafness shown to be dominant, either by the presence of deaf relatives other than sibs or descendants (only relationships closer than second cousins being considered), or by the absence of cousin marriage. Then one obtains nine parents who were "hereditary deaf," one who had "acquired deafness," and 15 with normal hearing, that is, about 40 per cent penetrance.

Chung et al. also considered the six segregating deaf by deaf matings and three segregating deaf by hearing matings in Stevenson and Cheeseman's data, and found $p$ about .50, giving nearly complete penetrance. Our data, utilizing a larger number of segregating families, showed the gene penetrance to be somewhat under 50 per cent. The estimated penetrance in parents, presumed to have transmitted a dominant gene for deafness to their offspring, was also less than 50 per cent, even with a bias that would make this estimate too large.

Of course, neither the estimates of the mutation rate of the dominant form of deafness calculated by Chung et al., nor those derived from the New York State data, can be regarded as very accurate. It should also be noted that Chung et al. used a mutation rate per diploid genome, while we have considered the rate per haploid genome. However, both estimates are in reasonable agreement, as are the values for the proportion of dominant deafness that was previously expressed in an older relative.

## Summary

Early total deafness (deafness present at birth or of early origin) was studied by a population survey and by the twin-family method.

In the population survey, the deaf residents of New York State were sampled by a mail questionnaire. In spite of a high rate of non-response, no evidence of any serious bias was found so that our conclusions may be regarded as reliable. Hence, it was established that about one-half of all deafness is sporadic, which means that these cases are due to exogenous causes, complicated modes of inheritance, or new genetic mutations. Inherited autosomal dominant genes account for about 10 per cent of all deafness, while the remainder is mainly of autosomal recessive origin.

Certain analyses were limited to persons who became deaf before the age of four years with no obvious exogenous cause (about 70% of the total). The frequency of such individuals in the New York State population was .06 per cent, with cousin marriage in their parents showing an incidence of 12 per cent. These large values, when considered together, not only provided strong evidence for an important recessive component, but can only be explained by the presence of many different genes, each producing early total deafness when homozygous. Depending on the assumptions made, the number of genes involved ranges upward from a minimal value of 45.

Data on parents presumably transmitting a dominant gene to their offspring, as well as on segregating progenies of deaf by deaf matings, indicated an average penetrance of 50 per cent for the dominant gene or genes involved. These findings are in good agreement with the conclusions drawn by Chung, Robinson, and Morton from an earlier study of congenital deafness in Northern Ireland (Stevenson and Cheeseman). However, on the basis of much fewer data than are available in the present study, Chung and his co-workers concluded that the dominant form showed nearly complete penetrance.

A fairly complete listing of deaf twins in New York State, Philadelphia, and Washington, yielded over 100 pairs. About one-third of them were available for study. In working up this series, individual and family histories were taken and audiometric examinations were made of the twins and a number of their relatives. After audiometric testing, 12 per cent of the one-egg twins and 65 per cent of the two-egg twins were found to be completely discordant for deafness. In addition a sizable proportion of the concordant pairs in both zygosity groups showed differences in the degree of their hearing loss. These data confirmed the presence of the hereditary component of deafness, as well as the incomplete penetrance (including unilateral expression) of the dominant form. Another interesting observation was the demonstration of a definite hearing loss in one-half of the cotwins of monozygotic index cases believed to be deaf from exogenous causes. This finding suggested an interaction between genotype and environmental agents in the production of some cases of deafness.

A number of twin families showed an association of deafness with pigmentary or other non-auditory pathological conditions. In view of the method of ascertainment used in these twin families, it is probable that special syndromes of this kind occur in a significant fraction of all cases of early total deafness.

*Acknowledgments*

A genetic study of this scope depends upon the combined efforts of many persons and organizations. The United States Department of Health, Education, and Welfare, through the Office of Vocational Rehabilitation, and the New York State Department of Mental Hygiene, through the Department of Medical Genetics of the New York State Psychiatric Institute, provided the funds and facilities for the Mental Health Project for the Deaf, of which this study was one facet. In addition, the following organizations and institutions extended their facilities and cooperation: all the schools for the deaf in New York State, Philadelphia, and Washington; vocational and religious organizations for the deaf; the Office of Vital Statistics of the New York State Department of Health; the Departments of Ophthalmology and Otolaryngology of the Columbia-Presbyterian Medical Center; and the cytogenetic laboratory of Dr. E. Chu in Oak Ridge, Tennessee. Sincere thanks are especially extended to Dr. F. J. Kallmann of the Department of Psychiatry of Columbia University for his continuous support, suggestions and critical evaluations of this study; Dr. H. Levene of the Departments of Mathematical Statistics and Zoology of Columbia University for his exhaustive, thoughtful and highly valuable examination of the data; Dr. I. L. Firschein for professional advice and personal encouragement; Dr. E. P. Fowler, Jr. for placing all the facilities of his Department of Otolaryngology at our disposal; Dr. W. Edwards Deming for his invaluable help in all matters of sampling statistics; the following former and present co-workers in the Department of Medical Genetics: Drs. H. G. Furth, J. D. Rainer and L. J. Ross as well as R. Pecorale, S. Pellman and L. Ruut; all the professional workers with the deaf; and last but not least to all the deaf themselves, singletons, twins and triplets and their relatives. Without the active interest, cooperation and forbearance of these families, the present study could not have been accomplished.

# APPENDIX 1
## Questionnaire No. 1

### New York State
### Psychiatric Institute
722 WEST 168TH STREET, NEW YORK 32

LAWRENCE C. KOLB, M. D.
DIRECTOR OF INSTITUTE
DEPARTMENT OF MEDICAL GENETICS
FRANZ J. KALLMANN, M. D.
PRINCIPAL RESEARCH SCIENTIST

MENTAL HEALTH PROJECT
FOR THE DEAF
TELEPHONE: LOrraine 8-4000
EXT. 108

February 15, 1958

To help in planning more and better health services for the deaf, we are asking all deaf people who live in New York to answer the questions below and to send this letter back to us in the enclosed stamped envelope. Please answer as soon as you can because your answer will help in the planned health program for the deaf (early hearing impairment).

1. Have you a brother or sister (<u>twin</u>) who was born the same day as you were? Yes_____ No_____

2. If you have, is your twin a brother?_____ sister?_____

Is your twin living?_____ If he or she died, at what age?_____
(Yes or No)

3. Are your name and address correct as shown above?_____
(Yes or No)
If not, the right form is as follows:

Name_____

Address_____

4. What is your date of birth?

Month_____ Day_____ Year_____

5. How many other people in your family are twins?_____
"  "  "  "  "  "  "  " deaf?_____

6. Are there any deaf twins among your friends?_____
(Yes or No)

7. Do you think the deaf need more health services?_____
(Yes or No)

If you should get more than one letter like this, please fill out and return each one. We thank you very much for your help in this health program.

Sincerely yours,

*Franz J. Kallmann*

Franz J. Kallmann, M.D.

FJK:SP
Encl.

## Letter sent with Questionnaires Nos. 2 and 3

New York State
### Psychiatric Institute
722 WEST 168TH STREET, NEW YORK 32

LAWRENCE C. KOLB, M.D.
DIRECTOR OF INSTITUTE

DEPARTMENT OF MEDICAL GENETICS
FRANZ J. KALLMANN, M.D.
CHIEF OF PSYCHIATRIC RESEARCH
(MEDICAL GENETICS)

MENTAL HEALTH PROJECT
FOR THE DEAF
EIGHTH FLOOR, ROOM 858
TELELPHONE: LORRAINE 8-4000
EXT. 105

In connection with our project for the deaf, we
need the answers to the questions on the attached
sheet from all deaf persons in New York State.
Would you please help us?

Your answer will, of course, be kept strictly con-
fidential.

Sincerely yours,

*Franz J. Kallmann*

Franz J. Kallmann, M.D.

Encl.
FJK/jr

## Questionnaires Nos. 2 and 3

### SPECIAL RESEARCH QUESTIONNAIRE
#### Mental Health Project for the Deaf
NEW YORK STATE PSYCHIATRIC INSTITUTE
AND UNITED STATES OFFICE OF VOCATIONAL REHABILITATION

Mother ☐ Deaf
☐ Hearing

Father ☐ Deaf
☐ Hearing

(Please correct above address if incorrect)    Were your parents cousins? Yes ☐    No ☐    *

Date of birth .............................................

☐ White
☐ Other

Check one    ☐ Born deaf

☐ Became deaf at age ...........

☐ R. Catholic
☐ Jewish
☐ Protestant
☐ Other

Have you ever been married?

☐ Yes

☐ No, never married

More than once?    ☐ Yes
☐ No

Year of 1st marriage...............

☐ Now divorced    Year of divorce...............

☐ Now widowed    Year widowed ...................

HOW MANY CHILDREN HAVE YOU HAD? ..............

If ever married

Name of (husband, wife).....................................

Date of birth...........................................

Check one    ☐ Hearing
☐ Born deaf
☐ Became deaf at age.........
☐ Hard of hearing

☐ White

☐ Other

☐ R. Catholic
☐ Jewish
☐ Protestant
☐ Other

If married more than once, please give above information and dates of each marriage on other side.

*This question was included in some of the questionnaires No. 3

- 2 -

## CHILDREN

|  | Name | Sex M or F | Year of birth | Hearing | Deaf | Still living | Dead |
|---|---|---|---|---|---|---|---|
| 1st | | | | | | | |
| 2nd | | | | | | | |
| 3rd | | | | | | | |
| 4th | | | | | | | |
| 5th | | | | | | | |
| 6th | | | | | | | |
| Others | | | | | | | |

### Please list ALL your brothers and sisters

| Name | Sex M or F | Age | Hearing | Deaf | Living | Dead |
|---|---|---|---|---|---|---|
| | | | | | | |
| | | | | | | |
| | | | | | | |
| | | | | | | |
| | | | | | | |
| | | | | | | |

### Other DEAF Relatives

| Name | Relationship |
|---|---|
| | |
| | |
| | |
| | |
| | |
| | |

## APPENDIX 2

**Audiometric test responses in twin index pairs measured in decibels of hearing loss**
**(nr = No response at maximum intensity of instrument for given frequency)**

| Family no. & zygosity | Twin | Sex | Ear tested | 125 | 250 | 500 | 750 | 1000 | 1500 | 2000 | 3000 | 4000 | 6000 | 8000 |
|---|---|---|---|---|---|---|---|---|---|---|---|---|---|---|
| | | | | | | | Frequency in cycles per second (cps) | | | | | | | |
| 1 DZ | A | M | R | 65 | 60 | 85 | 85 | 85 | 95 | 95 | 95 | 90 | nr | nr |
| | | | L | 30 | 60 | 60 | 75 | nr | 100 | 90 | 100 | 100 | nr | 80 |
| | B | F | R | 15 | 5 | 5 | 5 | 0 | 5 | -5 | -5 | -10 | -10 | -10 |
| | | | L | 5 | 5 | 5 | 0 | -5 | -10 | -10 | -10 | -10 | -10 | -10 |
| 2 MZ | A | M | R | 45 | 50 | 45 | 50 | 55 | 65 | 65 | 55 | 65 | 75 | 70 |
| | | | L | nr | 65 | 70 | 85 | 95 | nr | nr | nr | nr | nr | nr |
| | B | M | R | 65 | 75 | 80 | 80 | 90 | nr | nr | nr | nr | nr | nr |
| | | | L | 60 | 65 | 75 | 85 | 95 | 85 | 85 | 75 | 85 | 75 | 70 |
| 3 MZ | A | F | R | nr | nr | nr | nr | nr | nr | nr | nr | nr | nr | nr |
| | | | L | nr | nr | nr | nr | nr | nr | nr | nr | nr | nr | nr |
| | B | F | R | 15 | 10 | 0 | 0 | 0 | 0 | 0 | 5 | 5 | 15 | 45 |
| | | | L | 30 | 25 | 20 | 25 | 35 | 10 | 5 | 25 | 20 | 35 | 45 |
| 4 DZ | A | M | R | nr | 70 | 85 | 95 | 95 | 100 | nr | nr | nr | nr | nr |
| | | | L | 65 | 75 | 95 | 95 | 100 | 100 | nr | nr | nr | nr | nr |
| | B | M | R | 10 | 5 | 5 | 5 | 0 | 0 | 15 | 10 | 0 | 15 | 25 |
| | | | L | 10 | 5 | 5 | 0 | 0 | 5 | 10 | 10 | 5 | 10 | 20 |

(Continued)

## APPENDIX 2 (Continued)

| Family no. & zygosity | Twin | Sex | Ear tested | 125 | 250 | 500 | 750 | 1000 | 1500 | 2000 | 3000 | 4000 | 6000 | 8000 |
|---|---|---|---|---|---|---|---|---|---|---|---|---|---|---|
| | | | | | | | | Frequency in cycles per second (cps) | | | | | | |
| 5 MZ | A | F | R | nr | 75 | 70 | | 85 | | 75 | | 95 | | 80 |
| | | | L | nr | 80 | 90 | | nr | | nr | | nr | | nr |
| | B | F | R | 45 | 45 | 45 | | 40 | | 20 | | 0 | | 35 |
| | | | L | 35 | 30 | 30 | | 5 | | 5 | | 5 | | 20 |
| 6 MZ | A | M | R | 40 | 65 | 65 | 75 | 65 | 65 | 65 | 65 | 60 | 85 | 80 |
| | | | L | 35 | 65 | 70 | 75 | 75 | 75 | 70 | 65 | 70 | 80 | 80 |
| | B | M | R | 50 | 60 | 70 | 70 | 80 | 80 | 75 | 75 | 70 | 95 | nr |
| | | | L | 45 | 65 | 85 | 90 | 95 | 95 | 90 | 65 | 75 | nr | nr |
| 7 MZ | A | F | R | 65 | 70 | 85 | 85 | 95 | 95 | nr | nr | nr | nr | nr |
| | | | L | 45 | 50 | 70 | 75 | 70 | 80 | 85 | 85 | 85 | nr | nr |
| | B | F | R | 50 | 60 | 75 | 80 | 85 | 90 | 100 | 95 | nr | nr | nr |
| | | | L | 60 | 65 | 75 | 85 | 95 | 95 | 95 | 100 | nr | nr | nr |
| 8 MZ | A | F | R | nr | 75 | 80 | 90 | 95 | 95 | 95 | 90 | 90 | nr | nr |
| | | | L | nr | nr | 90 | 95 | nr | nr | nr | nr | nr | nr | nr |
| | B | F | R | nr | 65 | 75 | 90 | 95 | 95 | 100 | 95 | 95 | 85 | nr |
| | | | L | nr | 75 | 80 | 95 | 95 | 95 | 85 | 85 | 85 | 100 | nr |
| 9 MZ | A | F | R | nr | nr | 95 | 95 | nr | nr | nr | nr | nr | nr | nr |
| | | | L | nr | nr | 100 | 95 | 95 | 100 | 100 | 100 | 95 | nr | nr |
| | B | F | R | nr | nr | 95 | nr | nr | nr | nr | nr | nr | nr | nr |
| | | | L | nr | 75 | 95 | 95 | 95 | nr | nr | 100 | 100 | nr | nr |

(Continued)

## APPENDIX 2 (Continued)

| Family no. & zygosity | Twin | Sex | Ear tested | Frequency in cycles per second (cps) | | | | | | | | | | |
|---|---|---|---|---|---|---|---|---|---|---|---|---|---|---|
| | | | | 125 | 250 | 500 | 750 | 1000 | 1500 | 2000 | 3000 | 4000 | 6000 | 8000 |
| 10 MZ | A | F | R | 50 | 65 | 85 | 75 | 95 | 100 | nr | nr | nr | nr | nr |
| | | | L | 75 | 80 | nr | | nr | 85 | nr | nr | nr | nr | nr |
| | B | F | R | 30 | 30 | 25 | 15 | 15 | 25 | 30 | 50 | 45 | 20 | 10 |
| | | | L | 10 | 10 | 5 | 10 | 10 | 40 | 30 | 45 | 35 | 20 | 5 |
| 11 DZ | A | F | R | 40 | 40 | 50 | 55 | 65 | 95 | 100 | nr | 100 | 85 | 80 |
| | | | L | 25 | 35 | 45 | 55 | 70 | 75 | 95 | 95 | 95 | 90 | nr |
| | B | F | R | -5 | -10 | -10 | -10 | -10 | -5 | -5 | 0 | 0 | -5 | 0 |
| | | | L | 5 | 5 | -10 | -10 | -10 | -5 | -10 | -10 | -10 | -10 | -10 |
| 12 DZ | A | F | R | nr | 75 | 75 | 80 | 85 | 85 | nr | nr | nr | nr | nr |
| | | | L | 65 | 65 | 70 | 85 | 85 | 95 | 100 | nr | nr | nr | nr |
| | B | M | R | 5 | 0 | -5 | 0 | 0 | 5 | 5 | 5 | -10 | 10 | 10 |
| | | | L | 15 | 15 | 10 | 0 | 0 | -5 | 5 | 0 | -10 | 0 | 5 |
| 13 MZ | A | M | R | 55 | 70 | 95 | nr | nr | nr | nr | nr | nr | nr | nr |
| | | | L | nr | nr | nr | nr | nr | nr | nr | nr | nr | nr | nr |
| | B | M | R | nr | nr | nr | nr | nr | nr | nr | nr | nr | nr | nr |
| | | | L | nr | nr | nr | nr | nr | nr | nr | nr | nr | nr | nr |
| 14 DZ | A | F | R | 65 | 80 | nr | 100 | nr | nr | 100 | nr | nr | nr | nr |
| | | | L | nr | nr | 100 | nr | nr | 100 | nr | nr | 100 | 90 | 80 |
| | B | F | R | 65 | nr | nr | nr | nr | nr | nr | nr | 100 | nr | nr |
| | | | L | 50 | 70 | 85 | 90 | 100 | nr | nr | 100 | nr | 100 | nr |

(Continued)

## APPENDIX 2 (Continued)

| Family no. & zygosity | Twin | Sex | Ear tested | 125 | 250 | 500 | 750 | 1000 | 1500 | 2000 | 3000 | 4000 | 6000 | 8000 |
|---|---|---|---|---|---|---|---|---|---|---|---|---|---|---|
| 15 DZ | A | F | R | 35 | 65 | 75 | 80 | 90 | 85 | 85 | 75 | 70 | 75 | 80 |
|  |  |  | L | 45 | 65 | 75 | 95 | 100 | nr | nr | nr | nr | nr | nr |
|  | B | F | R | 20 | 10 | 5 | 5 | 5 | 40 | 50 | 50 | 50 | 60 | 55 |
|  |  |  | L | 5 | -5 | -5 | 5 | 0 | 30 | 40 | 50 | 50 | 55 | 60 |
| 16 DZ | A | M | R | 10 | 15 | 20 | 35 | 40 | 45 | 50 | 40 | 75 | 90 | 75 |
|  |  |  | L | 20 | 25 | 15 | 65 | 75 | 90 | 95 | nr | nr | nr | nr |
|  | B | M | R | 10 | -5 | 0 | -5 | -5 | 0 | 5 | -5 | 0 | 10 | 20 |
|  |  |  | L | 0 | -10 | -5 | 0 | -5 | -5 | -10 | -10 | -10 | -5 | 5 |
| 17 DZ | A | M | R | 65 | 65 | 75 |  | 100 |  | nr |  | nr |  | nr |
|  |  |  | L | 60 | 65 | 70 |  | 100 |  | nr |  | nr |  | nr |
|  | B | F | R | 60 | 70 | 85 |  | nr |  | nr |  | nr |  | nr |
|  |  |  | L | 50 | 70 | 85 |  | 100 |  | nr |  | nr |  | nr |
| 18 MZ | A | M | R | nr | 65 | 65 | 75 | 80 | 85 | 80 | 85 | 85 | 85 | 80 |
|  |  |  | L | nr | nr | 90 | 95 | 90 | 95 | 100 | 100 | nr | nr | nr |
|  | B | M | R | 15 | 10 | 10 | 5 | 5 | 0 | 0 | 5 | 10 | 10 | 20 |
|  |  |  | L | 20 | 15 | 5 | 5 | 5 | -5 | 0 | 0 | 0 | 20 | 20 |
| 19 DZ | A | F | R | nr | 75 | 80 | 90 | 95 | 95 | 95 | 95 | 95 | nr | nr |
|  |  |  | L | nr | 75 | 80 | 90 | 95 | 90 | 95 | 100 | 90 | nr | nr |
|  | B | M | R | nr | 80 | 80 | 80 | 75 | 85 | 85 | 75 | 80 | 80 | 70 |
|  |  |  | L | 60 | 65 | 80 | 85 | 85 | 85 | 85 | 85 | 90 | nr | nr |

(Continued)

## APPENDIX 2 (Continued)

| Family no. & zygosity | Twin | Sex | Ear tested | Frequency in cycles per second (cps) | | | | | | | | | | |
|---|---|---|---|---|---|---|---|---|---|---|---|---|---|---|
| | | | | 125 | 250 | 500 | 750 | 1000 | 1500 | 2000 | 3000 | 4000 | 6000 | 8000 |
| 20 MZ | A | M | R | nr | nr | 90 | 90 | 90 | nr | nr | 100 | nr | nr | nr |
| | | | L | nr | 70 | 85 | 95 | 100 | nr | nr | nr | nr | nr | nr |
| | B | M | R | nr | nr | 85 | 95 | nr | nr | nr | nr | nr | nr | nr |
| | | | L | nr | nr | nr | nr | nr | nr | nr | nr | nr | nr | nr |
| 21a DZ | A | M | R | nr | 70 | 80 | 85 | 85 | 75 | 75 | 95 | 95 | nr | nr |
| | | | L | nr | 75 | 75 | 85 | 85 | 75 | 70 | 85 | 95 | 100 | nr |
| | B | F | R | 20 | 15 | 5 | 10 | 0 | 0 | 0 | 5 | 0 | -5 | 0 |
| | | | L | 5 | 5 | 0 | -5 | -10 | 5 | -10 | -10 | -10 | 0 | 15 |
| 21b DZ | A | M | R | nr | 70 | 80 | 85 | 85 | 75 | 75 | 95 | 95 | nr | nr |
| | | | L | nr | 75 | 75 | 85 | 85 | 75 | 70 | 85 | 95 | 100 | nr |
| | B | F | R | 25 | 15 | 5 | -10 | -5 | -5 | -5 | 0 | -10 | -10 | 10 |
| | | | L | -10 | 0 | -5 | -5 | -5 | -10 | -10 | -10 | -10 | -10 | 5 |
| 22 MZ | A | M | R | nr | nr | nr | nr | nr | nr | nr | nr | nr | nr | nr |
| | | | L | nr | nr | nr | nr | nr | nr | nr | nr | nr | nr | nr |
| | B | M | R | nr | nr | nr | nr | nr | nr | nr | nr | nr | nr | nr |
| | | | L | nr | nr | nr | nr | nr | nr | nr | nr | nr | nr | nr |
| 23 MZ | A | F | R | nr | nr | 95 | 95 | 95 | 100 | nr | nr | nr | nr | nr |
| | | | L | nr | nr | 90 | 100 | 95 | 95 | 95 | 95 | 100 | 95 | nr |
| | B | F | R | 0 | 0 | -5 | 0 | 0 | -10 | 0 | 5 | 0 | 5 | -10 |
| | | | L | 35 | 30 | 50 | 60 | -5 | -10 | -10 | -10 | -10 | -10 | 0 |

## APPENDIX 2 (Continued)

| Family no. & zygosity | Twin | Sex | Ear tested | 125 | 250 | 500 | 750 | 1000 | 1500 | 2000 | 3000 | 4000 | 6000 | 8000 |
|---|---|---|---|---|---|---|---|---|---|---|---|---|---|---|
| 24 DZ | A | F | R | 20 | 30 | 40 | 55 | 75 | 75 | 80 | 90 | 80 | 90 | 80 |
| | | | L | 15 | 30 | 50 | 65 | 65 | 75 | 90 | 85 | 90 | 85 | 80 |
| | B | | R | 10 | -5 | -5 | 0 | 0 | 0 | -5 | 0 | 0 | 5 | 10 |
| | | | L | 10 | 10 | -5 | 0 | 5 | 5 | -5 | 0 | 5 | 10 | 20 |
| 25 MZ | A | F | R | 65 | 60 | 55 | 75 | 85 | nr | nr | nr | nr | nr | nr |
| | | | L | 55 | 55 | 55 | 70 | 80 | 90 | 95 | nr | nr | nr | nr |
| | B | | R | nr | 75 | 70 | 75 | 85 | 95 | nr | nr | nr | nr | nr |
| | | | L | 60 | 60 | 65 | 80 | 85 | 95 | 100 | 100 | nr | nr | nr |
| 26 DZ | A | F | R | nr | 75 | 85 | 95 | nr | nr | nr | nr | nr | nr | nr |
| | | | L | nr | 80 | 90 | 95 | 95 | 85 | 80 | 75 | 75 | 85 | nr |
| | B | | R | 15 | -10 | 0 | -5 | 0 | -5 | -5 | 0 | 0 | 5 | 5 |
| | | | L | 0 | 0 | 0 | 0 | 0 | -5 | -10 | -10 | -10 | 0 | 5 |
| 27 DZ | A | F | R | 60 | 70 | 95 | nr | nr | nr | nr | nr | nr | nr | nr |
| | | | L | 55 | 65 | 100 | nr | nr | nr | nr | nr | nr | nr | nr |
| | B | | R | 10 | 0 | -5 | -10 | -5 | -5 | 5 | 0 | 0 | 5 | 0 |
| | | | L | 10 | -10 | -5 | -5 | -5 | -10 | -10 | -10 | -10 | -5 | 0 |
| 28 DZ | A | M | R | 50 | 55 | 85 | 95 | 95 | 90 | 80 | 85 | 80 | 75 | nr |
| | | | L | 35 | 35 | 70 | 85 | 80 | 70 | 60 | 60 | 70 | 70 | 70 |
| | B | | M | R | 15 | 15 | 20 | 15 | 10 | 5 | 0 | 5 | 0 | 0 | -5 |
| | | | L | 20 | 20 | 15 | 15 | 15 | 15 | 15 | 0 | 10 | 10 | 10 |

*Frequency in cycles per second (cps)*

(Continued)

## APPENDIX 2 (Continued)

| Family no. & zygosity | Twin | Sex | Ear tested | 125 | 250 | 500 | 750 | 1000 | 1500 | 2000 | 3000 | 4000 | 6000 | 8000 |
|---|---|---|---|---|---|---|---|---|---|---|---|---|---|---|
| | | | | | | | | Frequency in cycles per second (cps) | | | | | | |
| 29 DZ | A | M | R | 55 | 70 | 80 | 100 | nr | nr | nr | nr | nr | nr | nr |
| | | | L | nr | nr | 80 | 90 | 100 | nr | nr | nr | nr | nr | 80 |
| | B | F | R | 15 | 10 | 15 | 15 | 10 | 15 | 10 | 5 | 15 | 5 | 0 |
| | | | L | 5 | 5 | -5 | -5 | -5 | -5 | -10 | -10 | 0 | -10 | -5 |
| 30 DZ | A | M | R | 60 | 55 | 60 | 70 | 80 | 80 | 85 | 85 | 85 | 95 | 75 |
| | | | L | 25 | 55 | 75 | 85 | 90 | 85 | 85 | 85 | 85 | 75 | nr |
| | B | F | R | nr | 80 | 70 | 85 | 85 | 85 | 90 | 80 | 75 | 90 | 75 |
| | | | L | nr | nr | 85 | 85 | 85 | 85 | 90 | 80 | 85 | 95 | 75 |
| 31 DZ | A | F | R | nr | 65 | 75 | 75 | 75 | 80 | 75 | 75 | 90 | nr | nr |
| | | | L | 65 | 65 | 75 | 80 | 85 | 75 | 75 | 70 | 70 | 70 | 75 |
| | B | F | R | 25 | 15 | 10 | 0 | 0 | -5 | -5 | 0 | 5 | 20 | 25 |
| | | | L | 65 | 65 | 80 | 75 | 60 | 60 | 80 | 75 | 70 | 90 | nr |
| 32 MZ | A | F | R | 50 | 50 | 50 | 60 | 85 | nr | nr | nr | nr | nr | nr |
| | | | L | 20 | 40 | 70 | 90 | 85 | 90 | 95 | 95 | nr | 95 | nr |
| | B | F | R | 30 | 30 | 25 | 55 | 70 | 95 | 95 | 95 | 95 | 100 | 80 |
| | | | L | 15 | 15 | 5 | 5 | 5 | -10 | 0 | -10 | 5 | 10 | 0 |
| 33 DZ | A | M | R | nr | 80 | nr | nr | nr | nr | nr | nr | nr | nr | nr |
| | | | L | nr | 80 | 95 | nr | nr | nr | nr | nr | nr | nr | nr |
| | B | F | R | 15 | 10 | 5 | -10 | -5 | 0 | 5 | -10 | -10 | 5 | -5 |
| | | | L | 0 | 10 | -5 | -10 | -5 | -10 | 0 | -10 | -10 | -10 | -5 |

(Continued)

## APPENDIX 2 (Continued)

| Family no. & zygosity | Twin | Sex | Ear tested | 125 | 250 | 500 | 750 | 1000 | 1500 | 2000 | 3000 | 4000 | 6000 | 8000 |
|---|---|---|---|---|---|---|---|---|---|---|---|---|---|---|
| 34 MZ | A | M | R | 60 | 70 | 100 | 100 | nr | nr | nr | nr | nr | 95 | nr |
|  |  |  | L | 65 | 80 | 90 | 100 | 100 | nr | nr | nr | nr | nr | nr |
|  | B | M | R | 10 | 5 | 5 | 0 | 0 | -5 | 5 | 0 | 5 | 0 | 5 |
|  |  |  | L | 10 | -5 | -5 | -5 | -5 | -10 | 0 | -5 | 10 | -10 | 5 |
| 35 MZ | A | M | R | nr | nr | nr | nr | nr | nr | nr | nr | nr | nr | nr |
|  |  |  | L | nr | nr | 100 | 95 | 95 | 100 | 100 | nr | nr | nr | nr |
|  | B | M | R | nr | nr | nr | nr | nr | nr | nr | nr | nr | nr | nr |
|  |  |  | L | nr | 75 | 90 | 95 | 95 | 95 | nr | nr | nr | nr | nr |
| 36 DZ | A | F | R | nr | nr | 85 | 90 | 95 | nr | nr | nr | nr | nr | nr |
|  |  |  | L | nr | 80 | 75 | 70 | 70 | 75 | 95 | 95 | 100 | 85 | nr |
|  | B | F | R | 20 | 20 | 15 | 15 | 10 | 5 | 5 | 5 | 5 | 10 | 5 |
|  |  |  | L | 30 | 25 | 30 | 25 | 25 | 15 | 10 | 10 | 15 | 15 | 5 |
| 37 DZ | A | M | R | nr | nr | 90 | nr | nr | nr | nr | nr | nr | nr | nr |
|  |  |  | L | nr | 80 | 90 | 85 | nr | nr | nr | nr | nr | nr | nr |
|  | B | F | R | 20 | 20 | 10 | 5 | 5 | 15 | 25 | 25 | 40 | 45 | 40 |
|  |  |  | L | 10 | 15 | 5 | 10 | 10 | 15 | 30 | 45 | 50 | 80 | 55 |
| 38 MZ | A | F | R | nr | nr | nr | nr | nr | nr | nr | nr | nr | nr | nr |
|  |  |  | L | nr | nr | nr | nr | nr | nr | nr | nr | nr | nr | nr |
|  | B | F | R | nr | 75 | 95 | 75 | 80 | 95 | 65 | 85 | nr | nr | nr |
|  |  |  | L | 20 | 15 | 20 | 20 | 20 | 30 | 30 | 70 | nr | nr | nr |

Frequency in cycles per second (cps)

(Continued)

## APPENDIX 2 (Continued)

| Family no. & zygosity | Twin | Sex | Ear tested | Frequency in cycles per second (cps) | | | | | | | | | | |
|---|---|---|---|---|---|---|---|---|---|---|---|---|---|---|
| | | | | 125 | 250 | 500 | 750 | 1000 | 1500 | 2000 | 3000 | 4000 | 6000 | 8000 |
| 39 DZ | A | F | R | nr | nr | nr | nr | nr | nr | nr | nr | nr | nr | nr |
| | | | L | nr | nr | 95 | nr | nr | nr | nr | nr | nr | nr | nr |
| | B | M | R | nr | nr | nr | nr | nr | 95 | nr | nr | nr | nr | nr |
| | | | L | nr | 65 | 70 | 75 | 75 | 65 | 75 | 80 | nr | nr | nr |

# Chapter 4

## INTELLIGENCE TESTS IN DEAF TWINS

ROSE M. SALZBERGER and LISSY FEINGOLD JARVIK

Theoretically, a comparative study of twins is an ideal way to assess the effects of deafness on measurable intellectual performance. It has been established that on standard intelligence tests the scores of one-egg twin partners (identical hereditary endowment) are as similar as those of a single individual tested on more than one occasion, while members of two-egg pairs (genetically no more alike than ordinary siblings) tend to differ in test scores about as much as brothers and sisters of dissimilar age (67, 103, 104, 158, 250).

Mean intra-pair differences in the test scores of one-egg pairs (monozygotic) discordant for deafness compared with those of corresponding two-egg pairs (dizygotic) might be a measure of the retarding influence of deafness.

The twins selected for psychological testing were drawn from the series of twins described in Chapter 3. An attempt was made to test all those 40 pairs in whom both partners were living and could be audiometrically examined. However, three pairs were unavailable at the time when the psychologists visited their homes. Another two pairs, though tested, were excluded from the analysis because they were found to be schizophrenic. They will be described later, together with the test results obtained from a set of triplets (treated as two discordant dizygotic pairs in Chapter 3).

The remaining 33 pairs consisted of 16 one-egg and 17 two-egg sets (Table 1), ranging in age from three to 67 years. Concordance for deafness was established for 12 pairs and discordance for 13, while eight were classified as partially concordant. The criteria for classification as to concordance have been described elsewhere. Thus *hard of hearing* was defined as a hearing loss of at least 35 decibels at three or more frequencies in one or both ears. *Profound deafness of early onset* referred to inability to hear or recognize meaningful sounds during childhood, usually necessitating instruction in a special school for the deaf. In concordant pairs both partners suffered profound deafness of early onset, while in partially concordant or discordant pairs the cotwin was classified as either hard of hearing or having normal hearing.

Most of the younger twins, in the age range three to 14 years, were examined by means of the Arthur Point Scale (14). To test this group the

**TABLE 1**

Classification of 33 twin pairs in psychometric series
as to concordance for deafness

| Type of twin pair, and sex | | Concordant | Partially concordant | Discordant | Total |
|---|---|---|---|---|---|
| One-egg | Male | 5 | 0 | 2** | 7 |
| | Female | 3* | 6*** | 0 | 9 |
| Two-egg Same sex | Male | 0 | 0 | 3** | 3 |
| | Female | 1* | 2 | 4 | 7 |
| Two-egg | Opposite sex | 3* | 0 | 4* | 7 |
| All pairs | | 12 | 8 | 13 | 33 |

*Includes one pair tested with the Arthur Point Scale.
**Includes two pairs tested with the Arthur Point Scale.
***Includes three pairs tested with the Arthur Point Scale.

examiner* used natural signs and pantomime, because the children had not yet developed skills of reading, lip reading, or sign language.

The limitations imposed by deafness were most apparent in these younger subjects. Contact could be made only on the most primitive level, as shown by the children's difficulties in communicating their responses to projective material. In one case, the twins pointed out certain illustrations in a picture book to explain what they meant.

The wide differences between discordant twin partners in this younger group were reflected in their intelligence quotients (Table 2). While the mean I.Q. of the five hearing twins was 115, that of the 14 deaf twins was 95. Interestingly, the hard of hearing cotwins had an average I.Q. of 96, thus placing themselves close to the deaf rather than the hearing group. Since this average was derived from only three cases in the partially concordant group, and in two of them the profoundly deaf twin scored considerably lower than the hard of hearing partner, evaluation will have to await the accrual of further data.

A larger sample of *one-egg* pairs might also be expected to elucidate the effects of early profound deafness on intellectual retardation. In the present series of younger one-egg twins, only one concordant and two discordant pairs could be examined. The intra-pair difference in I.Q. for the concordant set was two points, and for the discordant pairs, 10 and 31 points. The

---

* Grateful acknowledgment is hereby made to Dr. Hans Furth who administered the tests during the first two years of this study. Subsequent tests were administered by one of the writers (R.M.S.). In all instances (including the older twins) both members of a pair were tested by a single examiner.

## TABLE 2
### Arthur Point Scale I.Q.'s of 11 twin pairs
according to concordance for deafness

| Type of twin pair | Concordant | | Partially concordant | | Discordant | |
|---|---|---|---|---|---|---|
| | Twin 1* | Twin 2 | Twin 1 | Twin 2 | Twin 1 | Twin 2 |
| One-egg | 113 (6)** | 115 | 72 (13) 72 (10) 114 (7) | 91 81 115 | 73 (9) 99 (8) | 104 109 |
| Two-egg Same sex | 69 (13) | 66 | – | | 112 (6) 129 (3) | 104 125 |
| Two-egg Opposite sex | 112 (6) | 123 | – | | 64 (14) | 132 |

*Twin 1 and twin 2 were designated arbitrarily in the concordant group. In the partially concordant and in the discordant group, the twin with early profound deafness was always designated as twin 1 and the hard of hearing or normally hearing cotwin as twin 2.

**Age at testing in years.

three partially concordant one-egg pairs showed an average difference of ten points.

An adequate series of one-egg pairs might also help in appraising the various methods of educating the deaf. If it is assumed that the I.Q. of the hearing twin suggests the *potential* intellectual level of the deaf cotwin, the educational techniques resulting in the closest approximation of the scores of both twins could be regarded as the most effective. Here it should be stipulated, however, that the hearing one-egg cotwin, in order to serve as an indicator of the partner's potential, should meet the criterion of having been raised under optimal environmental conditions.

The difficulties inherent in procuring a statistically representative sample of monozygotic twins are almost prohibitive, of course. For instance, a survey of a deaf population approximating 15,000 persons yielded but two discordant monozygotic pairs. Including all ages, 16 one-egg sets were tested by us.

Twins over age 14 (20 pairs) were examined by means of the Wechsler-Bellevue Intelligence Scale, Form 1 (236), as were two pairs who were 12 and 13 years old. The hearing subjects were tested according to standard procedure, but a modified version was used in the deaf twins. In this revised form, developed by Levine (135), questions in the verbal part of the test are rephrased in simple language readily translated into signs. These questions were mimeographed so that the subjects could write their responses. No vocabulary test was given either to hearing or deaf subjects. In this way, most of the 22 pairs could be tested on both the verbal and the performance scale. In only four pairs were communication skills so poor (including sign language) that examination had to be limited to the performance tests.

Analysis of the test results* (Appendix) yielded mean *full scale* I.Q.'s of 103 for the eight subjects with normal hearing, 90 for the 24 deaf subjects, and 105 for four hard of hearing twins. The handicap of the deaf subjects was even more marked with respect to the *verbal scale* where the corresponding mean I.Q.'s were 99 for the hearing, 77 for the deaf, and 97 for the hard of hearing. On the *performance scale* the differences among the three groups were less pronounced (108, 106, and 114, respectively). Inclusion of the scores of the eight twins (four pairs) who were tested only with the performance scale would reduce the mean I.Q.'s to 102 and 108 for the deaf and hard of hearing, respectively. The difference observed in our twin subjects between verbal and performance I.Q.'s is substantially in agreement with the findings of the only other study of deaf persons employing the Wechsler-Bellevue Intelligence Scale (135).

The mean *intra-pair differences* observed in the present study were computed in two ways (Table 3). The first method was the one conventionally used in twin studies and consisted of calculating the differences without taking into consideration whether the first or the second twin had the higher score. It is open to question, however, whether this method truly reflects differences between discordant twin partners in the light of the postulate that the effects of deafness are unidirectional. If deafness invariably results in a lowering of the I.Q., the direction of the difference has to be taken into account.

For this reason, mean differences were recomputed by deducting the score of the first twin from that of the second. The first twin (twin 1) was always the index case and, therefore, the twin partner with early profound deafness. In concordant pairs, the second twin (twin 2) also qualified as an index case and the designation as twin 1 or twin 2 was arbitrarily based on the alphabetical order of their first names. In the partially concordant group, twin 2 was hard of hearing, while in discordant pairs, twin 2 had normal hearing.

As expected, the latter technique led to a reduction in the average intra-pair differences. Yet the overall relationships failed to be materially affected.

* The assistance of Dr. Jane Weiss and Mrs. Carmen Woodbury is hereby gratefully acknowledged.

## TABLE 3

Mean intra-pair differences in I.Q.'s for 22 twin pairs given the Wechsler-Bellevue Intelligence Scale*
and classified as to concordance for deafness

| Type of twin pair | Full scale | | | Verbal scale | | | Performance scale | | |
|---|---|---|---|---|---|---|---|---|---|
| | Concordant | Partially concordant | Discordant | Concordant | Partially concordant | Discordant | Concordant | Partially concordant | Discordant |
| | Absolute intra-pair differences (without regard to sign) | | | | | | | | |
| One-egg | 6.0 (5)** | 4.7 (3) | — | 7.0 (5) | 10.3 (3) | — | 9.3 (7) | 5.0 (3) | — |
| Two-egg | 7.0 (1) | 13.0 (1) | 18.6 (8) | 4.0 (1) | 28.0 (1) | 27.8 (8) | 11.5 (2) | 5.0 (2) | 10.0 (8) |
| | Differences recomputed by deducting score of twin 1 from that of twin 2 (see text) | | | | | | | | |
| One-egg | 6.0 | 3.3 | — | 1.8 | 7.0 | — | 3.0 | -1.0 | — |
| Two-egg | -7.0 | 13.0 | 18.6 | -4.0 | 28.0 | 27.8 | 2.5 | -5.0 | 5.3 |

*Modified form administered to deaf subjects (see text for explanation)
**Figures in parentheses refer to number of twin pairs

For *one-egg pairs* neither method demonstrated the disadvantages of early profound deafness when compared with later onset or partial hearing loss. The intra-pair differences in full scale I.Q. (Table 3), though usually favoring the twin partner with some hearing, were no larger for the three pairs that showed only partial concordance for deafness than for the completely concordant group. It may be noted in this connection that the three partially concordant one-egg cotwins in the younger group also resembled the deaf rather than the hearing subjects.

It is possible that the scores of twin partners with greater residual hearing were lowered under the influence of a totally deaf cotwin. However, this explanation appears implausible in view of their actual I.Q.'s. The other possibility would be that given adequate hereditary endowment and good educational opportunities, the profoundly deaf cotwins were able to compensate for their handicap. Comparison of discordant one-egg twin partners would be of great value in this regard, but no such pairs were available in the older group.

Regardless of the method used, the retarding effects of total deafness were more marked on the verbal than the performance scale (Table 3). Thus, while the mean intra-pair difference on the verbal scale was 1.8 for the five concordant one-egg pairs, compared with 7.0 for the three partially concordant one-egg pairs, corresponding differences on the performance scale were 3.0 and $-1.0$ (minus sign indicates that the deaf twin partners had higher scores than hard of hearing twins).

Intra-pair differences derived from *two-egg sets* indicated similar trends. However, comparisons of this kind have but limited value in small samples, since the effects of deafness and unequal hereditary endowment are combined in such pairs. Only in truly representative samples would the assumption be warranted that the intellectual potential of the deaf and hearing partners would be the same in the absence of any direct relationship between the factors responsible for deafness and those that produce variations in intellectual endowment.

For example, in any given discordant dizygotic pair, a small difference between the I.Q.'s of the twin partners could be due to a small retarding effect of deafness on one of two similar intellectual potentials, or a moderately retarding effect of deafness on moderately dissimilar intellectual potentials, or a markedly retarding effect of deafness on markedly dissimilar intellectual potentials. Depending on the direction of the inherent difference, the resulting difference in I.Q. might be expressed either as an advantage of the hearing or of the deaf twin without elucidating the degree of handicap imposed by deafness.

In the case of our eight-year-old triplets, the deaf partner (male) obtained an Arthur Point I.Q. of 102, while his two hearing sisters scored 104 and 107. Obviously he may have been endowed with greater intellectual potential than his sisters, although its expression was curtailed by his early deafness. Another possibility would be that he had similar endowment, but that the manifestation of it was not sufficiently affected to provide measurable differences on this test.

Likewise, little is known concerning the relative potential abilities of the 20-year-old dizygotic A. twins, partially concordant for deafness. On the Wechsler-Bellevue Scale, the deaf twin obtained scores of 97, 123, and 112 for the verbal, performance, and full scale, respectively. The corresponding scores for the hard of hearing cotwin were 82, 77, and 78. How much of the I.Q. difference in favor of the deaf twin was due to differences in native endowment and how much was attributable to variations in disturbance of personality integration was difficult to determine. The hard of hearing twin, diagnosed as schizophrenic, was hospitalized on several occasions, while the deaf twin, despite many emotional problems, continued to function outside of institutions with psychiatric help.

By contrast, the one-egg O. twins, concordant for deafness as well as for schizophrenia, obtained similar test scores. On the Wechsler-Bellevue Intelligence Scale (revised for the deaf), one of these 27-year-old twins was given scores of 90, 102, and 96 for the verbal, performance, and full scale, respectively. His cotwin's corresponding I.Q.'s were 90, 116, and 103.

Although these twins were excluded from the statistical analysis because of their psychotic conditions, the 7.0-point-difference in their I.Q.'s (full scale) was in line with the average difference of 6.0 observed in the other five concordant one-egg pairs (Table 3). The latter figure agreed with intrapair differences reported for hearing one-egg pairs.

The one-egg R. twins, partially concordant for deafness, served to illustrate that genotypically identical individuals tend to display marked behavioral similarities despite considerable variation in the degrees of deafness. When these twins were first reported at the age of three years they were considered one of those rare pairs of the discordant monozygotic variety. Both parents and an older sister were deaf, while a younger brother seemed to have normal hearing. One of the twins had been profoundly deaf since birth, while the other functioned as a normally hearing child. One year later the deaf twin was classified as having a mental age of 50 months (I.Q. of 104) on the Merrill-Palmer Scale (omitting verbal tests). Her cotwin's mental age was almost identical (49 months, I.Q. of 102). On the Vineland Social Maturity Scale both girls scored exactly the same on all items, achieving an age equivalent of five years with a social quotient of 125.

At the age of seven, the twins were tested again, this time with the performance part of the Wechsler-Bellevue Intelligence Scale for Children (WISC) and the Arthur Point Scale. On the WISC the deaf twin scored 99, while on the Arthur Point Scale (Table 2) her I.Q. was 114. Her cotwin's respective I.Q.'s were 94 and 115. Although the latter twin continued to function as a normally hearing child, she was found audiometrically to have a considerable hearing loss. Hence reclassification from the normal to the hard of hearing category became necessary, putting the pair in the partially concordant group. However, their intellectual similarities have continued to be pronounced, and it will be interesting to see how long it will persist.

In general, it has been confirmed by the various results of this unique twin study that early profound deafness is apt to curtail significantly intellectual performance as conventionally measured. Thus, the mean difference between verbal and performance I.Q.'s was 29 for the deaf twins (77.1 versus 106.3) compared with almost 9 for the twins with normal hearing (99.5 versus 108.1)—a discrepancy of 20 points (Table 4). Similarly, the mean verbal I.Q. of the hearing twins exceeded that of the deaf ones by 22 while the corresponding difference on the performance scale was only 2 points. For the two discordant one-egg pairs, who because of their youth were tested with the Arthur Point Scale rather than with the Wechsler-Bellevue Intelligence Scale, the mean difference in I.Q. was 20.5 in favor of the hearing partner (Table 2).

The close agreement between these three estimates of the effects of deafness indicates that the early onset of severe deafness lowers I.Q.'s on language dependent tests by approximately 20 points. Further investigations of discordant one-egg pairs will be required for confirmation. Moreover, it should be emphasized that this estimate has been of the average rather than the maximum effect of deafness.

On performance scale alone, the hearing cotwins tend to achieve higher scores than their deaf dizygotic partners, as reflected by a mean intra-pair difference of 5.3 in favor of the hearing twins (Table 3). Their average score (108.1) also exceeded the mean score of the total group (106.3) of deaf twins (Table 4). Although the deaf obtain performance scores comparable to those of hearing subjects, they should not be expected to compensate to such a degree as to surpass the hearing group.

**TABLE 4**

Mean I.Q.'s of 38 twins with profound deafness of early onset
and 13 cotwins with normal hearing*

| Hearing status | Wechsler-Bellevue | | | Arthur performance scale |
|---|---|---|---|---|
| | Full scale | Verbal scale | Performance scale | |
| Deaf | 90.3 (24)** | 77.1 (24) | 106.3 (24) | 95.2 (14) |
| Hearing | 103.5 (8) | 99.5 (8) | 108.1 (8) | 114.8 (5) |

*Seven hard of hearing twins were omitted from this table, as were eight twins who received only the performance part of the Wechsler-Bellevue Scale. For details, see Appendix.

**Figures in parentheses refer to number of twin individuals.

The limitations imposed by deafness become more and more apparent with time. Only those deaf children given a chance to develop socially and to acquire some means of communication can begin to function linguistically like their hearing peers. It is therefore recommended that the deaf child of preschool age be given training as early as possible. Otherwise, isolation from the hearing community is inevitable. Taking care of the child's physical needs is not enough. For his intellectual and psychological growth, contact with the hearing world is essential.

Although early exposure to education and hearing companions is desirable, it is not suggested that the deaf child be thrust into a competitive situation in the hearing environment where he is bound to be repeatedly frustrated. Rather, it is recommended that his early education be supplemented by experiences in a hearing milieu.

Similarly, educational facilities for the development of manual skills should be made available to the deaf, provided care is taken not to exert pressure on the child to exceed his capacity. Too much stress might exact the sacrifice of language development.

Finally, further research is called for on the hard of hearing. If our finding that the twin with some degree of hearing loss tends to resemble the deaf rather than the hearing can be fully substantiated, it would mean that special attention will have to be devoted to this borderline group.

## APPENDIX
### Wechsler-Bellevue I.Q. scores of 22 twin pairs with deafness

| Type of twin pair | Age at testing | Full Scale | | Verbal Scale | | Performance Scale | |
|---|---|---|---|---|---|---|---|
| | | Twin 1* | Twin 2 | Twin 1 | Twin 2 | Twin 1 | Twin 2 |
| One-egg, concordant, male | 20 | 74 | 74† | 62 | 62 | 91 | 91 |
| '' | 16 | 79 | 89 | 53 | 65 | 109 | 116 |
| '' | 34 | – – | – – | – – | – – | 102 | 98 |
| '' | 67 | 110 | 116 | 107 | 109 | 107 | 116 |
| '' | 29 | 89 | 95 | 80 | 88 | 101 | 104 |
| One-egg, concordant, female | 15 | – – | – – | – – | – – | 86 | 68 |
| '' | 22 | 72 | 80 | 59 | 46 | 92 | 116 |
| One-egg, partially concordant, female | 64 | 123 | 121 | 110 | 105 | 133 | 135 |
| '' | 37 | 105 | 115 | 95 | 110 | 115 | 119 |
| '' | 33 | 98 | 100 | 79 | 90 | 120 | 111 |
| Two-egg, concordant, opposite sex | 12 | – – | – – | – – | – – | 86 | 100 |
| '' | 50 | 110 | 103 | 105 | 101 | 114 | 105 |
| Two-egg, partially concordant, female | 16 | 72 | 85 | 55 | 83 | 98 | 90 |
| '' | 23 | – – | – – | – – | – – | 85 | 83 |
| Two-egg, discordant, male | 16 | 72 | 79 | 52 | 71 | 99 | 93 |
| Two-egg, discordant, female | 37 | 103 | 125 | 90 | 115 | 125 | 130 |
| '' | 16 | 86 | 98 | 71 | 94 | 106 | 102 |
| '' | 20 | 82 | 82 | 69 | 77 | 100 | 91 |
| '' | 15 | 93 | 115 | 79 | 109 | 110 | 119 |
| Two-egg, discordant, opposite sex | 36 | 97 | 112 | 94 | 111 | 100 | 112 |
| '' | 30 | 79 | 101 | 70 | 108 | 90 | 101 |
| '' | 13 | 67 | 116 | 49 | 111 | 93 | 117 |

*In concordant pairs designation of twins as 1 or 2 was arbitrary; in partially concordant pairs deaf partner was designated as twin 1 and hard of hearing partner as twin 2; in discordant pairs deaf partner was designated as twin 1 and hearing partner as twin 2.

†Scored independently by three psychologists.

# Chapter 5

## SEXUAL PATTERNS AND FAMILY RELATIONSHIPS

### Kenneth Z. Altshuler

In this chapter and the two which follow (Chapters 6 and 7), there are set forth the findings obtained through detailed interviews of the deaf individuals and their families who were selected from the total resident deaf population of New York State by means of sampling procedures previously described (Chapter 1). Interviews were conducted according to an outline designed to elicit information on adjustive patterns in several areas of behavior. Patterns and preferences regarding marriage, community participation, education and vocational adjustment were of particular interest. With the interviews performed by psychologically trained research workers skilled in manual communication, data were obtained which included statements of attitude as well as factual information. All correlations are statistically significant ($P = .05$ or lower) unless otherwise stated.

It is not surprising that unusual difficulties should have been encountered in gathering information regarding certain aspects of general life patterns among the deaf. Considerations of privacy, propriety, and prestige are intensified in the sexual area where social custom and a sense of pride dictate reticence and the denial of any aberration. Also, the preferences a person once held regarding marriage and children may not coincide with the attributes of his actual spouse or children. In view of these limiting features, one must interpret the data with care, remaining alert to the possible importance of small variations.

### Sexual Aspects and Dating Patterns

Tables 1 and 2 present data regarding the acquisition of sexual knowledge and type of sexual experience, if any, during the school years, according to the sex of the respondent. As might be expected, the largest percentages of both males and females picked up their information from friends. Of those who did not, females were more likely to learn about sex at home, while males did so at school or through reading books.

None of the women questioned admitted having had any sexual experience during her school years. Whether these answers were true or were attributable to modesty or the presence of other family members during the interview remained uncertain. It may be noted, however, that a large number of men also disclaimed any sexual experience during their school years (commonly extending into the late teens). This observation lends weight to the impression that the deaf differ from their hearing peers with respect to the prevalence and nature of sexual experimentation and activity that usually go with adolescence.

### TABLE 1
#### Sources of sex information

| Learned about sex: | Total | | Male | | Female | |
|---|---|---|---|---|---|---|
| | Number | Per cent | Number | Per cent | Number | Per cent |
| Total responses | 351 | 100.0 | 191 | 100.0 | 160 | 100.0 |
| At home | 21 | 6.0 | 4 | 2.1 | 17 | 10.6 |
| In school | 38 | 10.8 | 28 | 14.7 | 10 | 6.2 |
| From friends | 197 | 56.1 | 120 | 62.8 | 77 | 48.2 |
| Combination of above | 73 | 20.8 | 25 | 13.1 | 48 | 30.0 |
| From books | 22 | 6.3 | 14 | 7.3 | 8 | 5.0 |
| No answer | 288 | xxx | 143 | xxx | 145 | xxx |

### TABLE 2
#### Sex experience during the school years

| Kind of experience | Total | Male | Female |
|---|---|---|---|
| None | 305 | 147 | 158 |
| Homosexual | 20 | 20 | 0 |
| Heterosexual | 12 | 12 | 0 |
| Both | 4 | 4 | 0 |
| Did not answer | 298 | 151 | 147 |

Additional evidence in this direction may be seen in the finding that homosexual activity tends to be more common than heterosexual behavior among those males who admitted some sexual experience during this phase of life. Including those who gave no answer about their own experiences, 19.6 per cent of the respondents stated that there was homosexual activity known to them while at school. The possible implications of these findings will be discussed in the section on mental health in the deaf, where it is noted that homosexuality was a problem in fully 10 per cent of cases seen in the outpatient clinic of the Project (Chapter 10).

The information on dating while of school age is consistent with that on sexual experience. As can be seen in Table 3, less than 20 per cent had the experience of dating other than in group situations—usually supervised school functions or parties. More than one-half had had no experiences which could be described as dates. A full 10 per cent had had no friendly relationships whatever with the opposite sex, almost half of them having also had no friends among their own sex either throughout the school years.

Information about the sexual experience of unmarried persons 16 years old or over is presented in Table 4. Less than one-quarter admitted having had any such experience, and here the similarity between the answers of men and women is unexpected and striking. It is even more remarkable that close to 40 per cent of men (or 62 per cent of men who answered the question) reported that they had no sexual activity at all. The most plausible explanation for this finding would seem to be due to a combination of unreported homosexuality and limitations in heterosexual experience.

Of those who married, 70 per cent had a special boy friend or girl friend prior to dating the person chosen as spouse, while 16 per cent dated only in groups before meeting their mates (Table 5). During the school years, the only difference in dating behavior between those who married and

### TABLE 3
#### Dating and friends during the years at school

| Kind of date | Per cent of answers |
|---|---|
| All answers (n = 450) | 99.9 |
| Dated alone only | 1.7 |
| Dated in groups only | 19.2 |
| Dated alone and in groups | 17.4 |
| No dates, but had friends of both sexes | 51.8 |
| No dates; had friends only of same sex | 5.6 |
| No dates, no friends | 4.3 |

### TABLE 4
#### Sexual experience in unmarried deaf persons 16 years or older

| Sexual experience | Total (154) | Male (104) | Female (50) |
|---|---|---|---|
| | Per cent | Per cent | Per cent |
| Total | 100 | 100 | 100 |
| Some heterosexual experience | 23 | 23 | 24 |
| No heterosexual nor homosexual experience | 36 | 38 | 34 |
| No answer | 40 | 39 | 42 |

**TABLE 5**
**Previous dating in the married deaf**

| Kind of date | Per cent |
|---|---|
| Total (n = 480) | 100.0 |
| Had girl (boy) friends other than spouse | 69.6 |
| – And had sex frequently | 3.3 |
| – And had sex occasionally | 17.5 |
| – And had no sex | 22.3 |
| – No information on sex | 26.5 |
| Dated only in groups before he (she) met spouse | 16.3 |
| No dates at all | 14.2 |

those who did not (see Table 2) was that the latter students were more likely to have had no friends of either sex.

Fourteen per cent of responding married persons had no dates other than with their own mates. All the men and more than two-thirds of the women in this group were over 40 years at the time of interview. Apparently, the absence of previous social dating has become less common in the courtship patterns of today's young deaf people.

Other features that distinguish persons who married may be seen in Table 6. There is a significant difference in the marital status of congenitally deaf males and those with acquired deafness: two-thirds of the acquired deaf men are married as compared with only one-third of the congenitally deaf. Since there is no evidence to indicate that congenitally deaf persons marry later in life than do the other deaf, this difference appears to be a real one. It is not related to the hearing status of the parents, nor to the presence of deaf or hearing sibs. In addition, only one-quarter of only children married, whereas two-thirds of children with hearing or deaf sibs married.

Since some of those in the only-child category who did not find a spouse were males with congenital deafness and a conspicuous lack of friends at school, these two variables may not be entirely independent. It would seem, at any rate, that congenitally deaf boys who are the only child in their family are subject to special limitations. Therefore, they may be in special need of counseling and guidance with respect to marriage.

Attitude toward one's deafness and skill in communication are the result of complex living experiences and without doubt associated with the distinguishing features mentioned above. As can be seen in Table 7, more respondents who are disturbed by their deafness remain single than is true for those who express stoical acceptance. Subjects who denied any handicap were too few to warrant clear inferences. Regarding communication, the less skill there is present, the less likelihood there is of marriage.

Length of courtship was found to be related to marital adjustment as is shown in Table 8. Although courtship may last anywhere from less than

## TABLE 6
### Hearing status of spouse, according to sex, type of deafness, and hearing status of sibs

| Hearing status of respondent's spouse | Respondent's deafness | | | | Hearing status of respondent's sibs | | |
|---|---|---|---|---|---|---|---|
| | Congenital | | Acquired | | All hearing | One or more deaf | No sibs (only child) |
| | Male | Female | Male | Female | | | |
| Total responses | 129 | 127 | 166 | 151 | 384 | 172 | 39 |
| Per cent | 100.0 | 100.0 | 100.0 | 100.0 | 100.0 | 100.0 | 100.0 |
| Respondent not married, or spouse hearing | 86 | 50 | 48 | 50 | 146 | 64 | 29 |
| Per cent | 66.7 | 39.4 | 28.9 | 33.1 | 38.0 | 37.2 | 74.4 |
| Respondent married | 43 | 77 | 118 | 101 | 238 | 108 | 10 |
| Per cent | 33.3 | 60.6 | 71.1 | 66.9 | 62.0 | 62.8 | 25.6 |
| Spouse deaf | 43 | 77 | 118 | 97 | 230 | 108 | 10 |
| Per cent | 33.3 | 60.6 | 71.1 | 64.2 | 59.9 | 62.8 | 25.6 |
| Spouse hard of hearing | 0 | 0 | 0 | 4 | 8 | 0 | 0 |
| Per cent | 0 | 0 | 0 | 2.7 | 2.1 | 0 | 0 |

three months to over three years, the vast majority of the deaf (80%) court for more than a year before they marry, and approximately one-third court for periods greater than three years. The few persons that married within three months or less either were very fortunate or were still in the early years of marriage, for they reported uniformly good marriages. Apart from this group, marital adjustment appears directly related to length of courtship, with over 90 per cent of those with the longest courtships reporting good adjustment. In other words, poor adjustment, separations and divorces are apt to decrease as length of courtship increases.

Of particular interest would seem to be the finding that premarital concern about sex and the presence or absence of sexual experience apparently have no bearing on subsequent adjustment among those who did marry. Equally remarkable is the observation that excellent communicators are more likely to report poor marital adjustment (including separation or divorce) than those rated midway on the communication scale. Persons whose ability to communicate is poorest are not only the least likely to marry at all, but are as liable to post-marital discord as are those with excellent communication.

### TABLE 7A
#### Marital status by respondent's attitude toward his own deafness, for respondents 18 years and over

| Marital status | | Attitude toward deafness | | | | |
|---|---|---|---|---|---|---|
| | | Total responses | Denies handicap | Stoical acceptance | Disturbed by deafness | No information on attitude |
| Total responses on marriage | 512 | 433 | 34 | 273 | 126 | 57 |
| Per cent | 100.0 | 100.0 | 100.0 | 100.0 | 100.0 | xxx |
| Never married | 131 | 97 | 4 | 48 | 45 | 12 |
| Per cent | 25.5 | 22.3 | 11.8 | 17.5 | 35.7 | xxx |
| Ever married | 381 | 336 | 30 | 225 | 81 | 45 |
| Per cent | 74.5 | 77.7 | 88.2 | 82.5 | 64.3 | xxx |

Note:   Not included are 45 interviews in which there was no information on marriage nor on attitude toward deafness.

### TABLE 7B
#### Marital status by respondent's skill in communication for respondents 18 years or over

| Marital status | | Skill in communication | | | | |
|---|---|---|---|---|---|---|
| | | Total answers | Excellent | Satisfactory | Poor | No information on skill |
| Total responses on marriage | 512 | 508 | 204 | 246 | 58 | 4 |
| Per cent | 100.0 | 100.0 | 100.0 | 100.0 | 100.0 | xxx |
| Never married | 131 | 131 | 25 | 67 | 39 | 0 |
| Per cent | 25.5 | 25.7 | 12.3 | 27.3 | 67.4 | xxx |
| Ever married | 381 | 377 | 179 | 179 | 19 | 4 |
| Per cent | 74.5 | 74.3 | 87.7 | 72.7 | 32.6 | xxx |

Note:   Not included are 44 interviews for which there was no information on marriage nor on skill in communication.

## TABLE 8
### Length of courtship and marital adjustment

| Length of courtship before marriage | Total including no answer on adjustment | Total responses on adjustment | Marital adjustment | | | | Remarried | | No answer |
|---|---|---|---|---|---|---|---|---|---|
| | | | Excellent and good | Poor | Separated and divorced | Widowed | Good | Poor | |
| **All courtships** | | | | | | | | | |
| Number | 371 | 331 | 255 | 27 | 21 | 4 | 17 | 7 | |
| Per cent | 100.0 | 100.0 | 77.1 | 8.2 | 6.3 | 1.2 | 5.1 | 2.1 | |
| **Under 3 months** | | | | | | | | | |
| Number | 12 | 12 | 12 | 0 | 0 | 0 | 0 | 0 | |
| Per cent | 3.3 | 100.0 | 100.0 | 0 | 0 | 0 | 0 | 0 | |
| **3 - 6 months** | | | | | | | | | |
| Number | 19 | 15 | 11 | 0 | 4 | 0 | 0 | 0 | 4 |
| Per cent | 5.3 | 100.0 | 73.3 | 0 | 26.7 | 0 | 0 | 0 | xxx |
| **7 - 12 months** | | | | | | | | | |
| Number | 43 | 40 | 29 | 8 | 3 | 0 | 0 | 0 | 3 |
| Per cent | 11.9 | 100.0 | 72.5 | 20.0 | 7.5 | 0 | 0 | 0 | xxx |
| **1 - 3 years** | | | | | | | | | |
| Number | 163 | 148 | 104 | 16 | 14 | 0 | 10 | 4 | 15 |
| Per cent | 45.2 | 100.0 | 70.3 | 10.8 | 9.5 | 0 | 6.8 | 2.7 | xxx |
| **Over 3 years** | | | | | | | | | |
| Number | 134 | 116 | 99 | 3 | 0 | 4 | 7 | 3 | 18 |
| Per cent | 34.3 | 100.0 | 85.4 | 2.6 | 0 | 3.4 | 6.0 | 2.6 | xxx |

## Preferred Hearing Status of Mates and Children

Indications of preference regarding the type of deafness or hearing status of prospective mates and future children are important on several counts. For one thing, such preferences may be expected to demonstrate the degree to which accurate knowledge about hereditary deafness has been assimilated by the deaf. More particularly, they may reveal the amount of concern harbored by the deaf about genetic consequences. Furthermore, investigating preference data of this kind may throw light upon the relation between life experience and the different choices and indicate the extent to which caste status is associated with the various types of deafness.

Data relevant to the type of spouse desired are summarized in Table 9. Of the 453 persons that answered, 409 wanted to marry or had married. Thirty-one individuals wished to marry a hearing person and 27 had no preference about the hearing status of their mates. The vast majority (351, or 86%) preferred a deaf spouse.

It is hard to find a pattern of mate preference which would explain in all details the motivation for this potentially important choice. Certainly, social and cultural factors seemed to be more important than any knowledge of genetics in influencing the preferences for type of mate which were expressed. For example, among deaf men a preference for a hearing wife was expressed by 50 per cent of those who completed higher education. Success in such marriages is not unusual in this well-educated group. Apart from speech being more likely to be practiced there, a hearing wife can be an asset to individual achievement by fostering identity and relationship with the hearing world.

Among deaf women, on the whole, there was a more widespread expression of preference for a hearing husband, but here it was found mainly in the least educated group. Of the 31 people who preferred a hearing mate, 21 were women, 14 of whom had not graduated from grade school. Since such marriages are rare, it would seem that in the case of deaf women education helps to reconcile their spouse preference with existing possibilities.

As for preferring congenital or acquired deafness in one's potential spouse, 90 per cent of those who preferred a deaf spouse had no choice regarding type of deafness. Among those who did express a choice, or for that matter in those who wanted to marry a hearing person, their own type of deafness did not seem to play a consistent role.

The presence of other deaf people in the family, whether sibs or parents, bore little relation to the type of spouse desired. The proportion of those that wished to marry deaf or hearing persons, or that did not want to marry at all, did not vary, whether the parents were both deaf, both hearing, or one of each. If there were no other deaf persons in the family, the respondent was more likely to be uncertain about whether he would marry. Apparently a trend existed (though not of statistical significance) for more

## TABLE 9A

Type of spouse desired, by sex and type of deafness of respondent, for respondents 15 years or over

| Type of spouse desired | Total | | Sex and deafness of respondent | | | | | |
| --- | --- | --- | --- | --- | --- | --- | --- | --- |
| | | | Male | | | Female | | |
| | Number | Per cent | Cong'al | Acq'd | Not ascertained | Cong'al | Acq'd | Not ascertained |
| Total responses on spouse* | 430 | 100.0 | 71 | 134 | 7 | 89 | 110 | 19 |
| Hearing | 31 | 7.2 | 4 | 4 | 0 | 7 | 14 | 2 |
| Deaf | 351 | 81.7 | 63 | 102 | 7 | 78 | 88 | 13 |
| – born deaf | 8 | 1.9 | 0 | xxx | xxx | 8 | xxx | xxx |
| – acquired deafness | 24 | 5.6 | xxx | 4 | xxx | 10 | 10 | xxx |
| – either** | 319 | 74.2 | 63 | 98 | 7 | 60 | 78 | 13 |
| Hearing or deaf (no preference) | 27 | 6.3 | 0 | 19 | 0 | 0 | 4 | 4 |
| Uncertain about wishes to marry | 21 | 4.8 | 4 | 9 | 0 | 4 | 4 | 0 |
| Prefers not to marry | 23 | xxx | 9 | 4 | 4 | 4 | 2 | 0 |
| No answer on type of spouse desired | 62 | xxx | 22 | 14 | 4 | 7 | 15 | 0 |

*Excludes cases that prefer not to marry, or that give no answer on type of spouse desired.
**Includes cases where the respondent did not understand the distinction.

## TABLE 9B

Type of spouse desired, by education of respondent, for respondents 15 years or over

| Type of spouse desired | Total | | Did not graduate | | Graduated | | Some higher education | | Education not ascertained |
|---|---|---|---|---|---|---|---|---|---|
| | Number | Per cent | Male | Female | Male | Female | Male | Female | |
| Total responses on spouse* | 430 | 100.0 | 81 | 91 | 104 | 115 | 19 | 12 | 8 |
| Hearing | 31 | 7.2 | 0 | 14 | 4 | 9 | 4 | 0 | 0 |
| Deaf | 351 | 81.7 | 68 | 69 | 89 | 102 | 11 | 8 | 4 |
| − born deaf | 8 | 1.9 | 0 | 0 | 0 | 8 | 0 | 0 | 0 |
| − acquired deafness | 24 | 5.6 | 0 | 0 | 4 | 16 | 0 | 4 | 0 |
| − either** | 319 | 74.2 | 68 | 69 | 85 | 78 | 11 | 4 | 4 |
| Hearing or deaf (no preference) | 27 | 6.3 | 8 | 4 | 11 | 0 | 0 | 4 | 0 |
| Uncertain about wishes to marry | 21 | 4.8 | 5 | 4 | 0 | 4 | 4 | 0 | 4 |
| Prefers not to marry | 23 | xxx | 11 | 0 | 4 | 6 | 0 | 0 | 2 |
| No answer on type of spouse desired | 66 | xxx | 25 | 4 | 15 | 14 | 0 | 0 | 8 |

*Excludes cases that prefer not to marry, or that give no answer on type of spouse desired.
**Includes cases where the respondent did not understand the distinction.

**TABLE 9C**

Type of spouse desired, by other deaf in family of respondent, for respondents 15 years or over

| Type of spouse desired | Respondent | | | | | | | |
|---|---|---|---|---|---|---|---|---|
| | Total | | Had one or more deaf parents or sibs | | Had no deaf parent nor deaf sib | | No answer about parents or sibs | |
| | Number | Per cent | Number | Per cent | Number | Per cent | Number | |
| Total responses on spouse* | 430 | 100.0 | 106 | 100.0 | 296 | 100.0 | 28 | |
| Hearing | 31 | 7.2 | 4 | 3.8 | 27 | 9.1 | 0 | |
| Deaf | 351 | 81.7 | 90 | 84.9 | 233 | 78.8 | 28 | |
| – born deaf | 8 | 1.9 | 4 | 3.8 | 4 | 1.4 | 0 | |
| – acquired deafness | 24 | 5.6 | 2 | 1.9 | 18 | 6.1 | 4 | |
| – either** | 319 | 74.2 | 84 | 79.2 | 211 | 71.3 | 24 | |
| Hearing or deaf (no preference) | 27 | 6.3 | 11 | 10.4 | 16 | 5.4 | 0 | |
| Uncertain about wishes to marry | 21 | 4.8 | 1 | .9 | 20 | 6.7 | 0 | |
| Prefers not to marry | 23 | xxx | 6 | xxx | 17 | xxx | 0 | |
| No answer on type of spouse desired | 62 | xxx | 20 | xxx | 34 | xxx | 8 | |

*Excludes cases that prefer not to marry, or that give no answer on type of spouse desired.
**Includes cases where the respondent did not understand the distinction.

**TABLE 9D**

Type of spouse desired, by attitude toward respondent's own deafness,
for respondents 15 years or over

| Type of spouse desired | Total | | Denies handi-cap | Stoical accept-ance | Disturbed by deafness | No answer on attitude |
|---|---|---|---|---|---|---|
| | Number | Per cent | | | | |
| Total responses on spouse* | 430 | 100.0 | 35 | 239 | 101 | 55 |
| Hearing | 31 | 7.2 | 7 | 8 | 16 | 0 |
| Deaf | 351 | 81.7 | 23 | 219 | 66 | 43 |
|   – born deaf | 8 | 1.9 | 0 | 8 | 0 | 0 |
|   – acquired deafness | 24 | 5.6 | 4 | 12 | 8 | 0 |
|   – either** | 319 | 74.2 | 19 | 199 | 58 | 43 |
| Hearing or deaf (no preference) | 27 | 6.3 | 4 | 4 | 15 | 4 |
| Uncertain about wishes to marry | 21 | 4.8 | 1 | 8 | 4 | 8 |
| Prefers not to marry | 23 | xxxx | 0 | 9 | 10 | 4 |
| No answer on type of spouse desired | 62 | xxxx | 0 | 26 | 8 | 28 |

*Excludes cases that prefer not to marry, or that give no answers on type of spouse desired.

**Includes cases where the respondent did not understand the distinction.

persons from families with no other deaf members to prefer a hearing spouse than for respondents with either deaf sibs or parents.

Attitude toward one's own deafness was found to be related to preference for spouse. While the majority in all groups prefer a deaf mate, this preference is most closely associated with the attitude of stoical acceptance. At either extreme, those that deny that deafness is a handicap, as well as those that are frankly disturbed by their deafness, are somewhat more likely to prefer a hearing spouse. Thus, it would appear that denial actually serves to cover up a real concern about deafness rather than reflect a comfortable acceptance. This explanation was borne out by the finding that not a single respondent who disavowed deafness as a handicap wanted to have children who were deaf (Table 10).

Table 10 relates the preference for deaf or hearing children to the same categories which have already been discussed in regard to spouse preference.

**TABLE 10A**

Type of children desired, by sex and type of deafness of respondent, for respondents 15 years or over

| Type of children desired | Total | | Sex and deafness of respondent | | | | | |
|---|---|---|---|---|---|---|---|---|
| | | | Male | | | Female | | |
| | Number | Per cent | Congenital | Acq'd | Not ascertained | Congenital | Acq'd | Not ascertained |
| Total answers on children | 430 | 100.0 | 63 | 133 | 7 | 95 | 113 | 19 |
| Wants no children | 34 | 7.9 | 4 | 7 | 4 | 7 | 8 | 4 |
| Wants children | | | | | | | | |
| Deaf | 28 | 6.5 | 8 | 4 | 0 | 8 | 4 | 4 |
| Hearing | 193 | 44.9 | 21 | 67 | 0 | 44 | 59 | 2 |
| Deaf or hearing (no preference) | 136 | 31.6 | 22 | 54 | 3 | 27 | 25 | 5 |
| No answer, or uncertain about deafness of children | 39 | 9.1 | 8 | 1 | 0 | 9 | 17 | 4 |
| No answer on children, or prefers not to marry | 136 | xxx | 46 | 26 | 12 | 14 | 18 | 20 |

## TABLE 10B

### Type of children desired, by education of respondent, for respondents 15 years or over

| Type of children desired | Total | | Did not graduate | | Graduated | | Some higher education | | Education not ascertained or still in school |
|---|---|---|---|---|---|---|---|---|---|
| | Number | Per cent | Male | Female | Male | Female | Male | Female | |
| Total answers on children | 430 | 100.0 | 72 | 95 | 107 | 118 | 15 | 12 | 11 |
| Wants no children | 34 | 7.9 | 0 | 7 | 15 | 12 | 0 | 0 | 0 |
| Wants children | | | | | | | | | |
| Deaf | 28 | 6.5 | 4 | 8 | 4 | 8 | 4 | 0 | 0 |
| Hearing | 193 | 44.9 | 22 | 46 | 59 | 51 | 7 | 8 | 0 |
| Deaf or hearing (no preference) | 136 | 31.6 | 46 | 23 | 29 | 30 | 4 | 4 | 0 |
| No answer, or uncertain about deafness of children | 39 | 9.1 | 0 | 11 | 0 | 17 | 0 | 0 | 11 |
| No answer on children, or prefers not to marry | 131 | xxx | 48 | 7 | 19 | 20 | 4 | 0 | 33 |

**TABLE 10C**
Type of children desired, by other deaf in family of respondent,
for respondents 15 years or over

| Type of children desired | Respondent | | | | |
|---|---|---|---|---|---|
| | Total | | Had one or more deaf parents or sibs | Had no deaf parent nor deaf sib | No answer about parents or sibs |
| | Number | Per cent | | | |
| Total answers on children | 430 | 100.0 | 117 | 281 | 32 |
| Wants no children | 34 | 7.9 | 4 | 27 | 3 |
| Wants children | | | | | |
| Deaf | 28 | 6.5 | 8 | 16 | 4 |
| Hearing | 193 | 44.9 | 36 | 142 | 15 |
| Deaf or hearing (no preference) | 136 | 31.6 | 49 | 80 | 7 |
| No answer, or uncertain about deafness of children | 39 | 9.1 | 20 | 16 | 3 |
| No answer on children, or prefers not to marry | 128 | xxxx | 24 | 78 | 26 |

Presenting in detail the choices of those who were certain that they want to marry, this table shows a relationship between the attitude toward one's own deafness and to the preference for deaf or hearing children only in the paradoxical way noted above. As might be expected, persons with some higher education are more likely to be desirous of having hearing children and less likely to be without a preference in this respect than are individuals who have not completed even a primary school education.

Of the 430 persons who wished to marry, eight per cent did not want to have children. Interestingly enough, this preference was expressed more clearly by individuals from all hearing families than by those from families with a deaf sibling or parent. Also, people with excellent communication showed a higher preference rate in favor of a childless marriage. Most of the persons whose communication was rated as poor did not wish to marry.

The reasons for these preferences are uncertain. A feeling of not being up to parenthood may be fostered in deaf persons who are raised in a hearing family made anxious and confused by their affliction. Also, with recognition of the difficulties encountered in attaining good communication there may be an unwillingness to impose a similar burden on future offspring. Or the preferences could simply reflect an individual's more comfortable degree of

**TABLE 10D**
Type of children desired, by attitude toward respondent's
own deafness, for respondents 15 years and over

| Type of children desired | Total | | Denies handi-cap | Stoical accept-ance | Disturbed by deafness | No answer on attitude toward deafness |
|---|---|---|---|---|---|---|
| | Number | Per cent | | | | |
| Total answers on children | 430 | 100.0 | 35 | 243 | 108 | 44 |
| Wants no children | 34 | 7.9 | 0 | 19 | 15 | 0 |
| Wants children | | | | | | |
| Deaf | 28 | 6.5 | 0 | 16 | 8 | 4 |
| Hearing | 193 | 44.9 | 16 | 98 | 56 | 23 |
| Deaf or hearing | | | | | | |
| (no preference) | 136 | 31.6 | 15 | 91 | 21 | 9 |
| No answer, or uncertain about deafness of children | 39 | 9.1 | 4 | 19 | 8 | 8 |
| No answer on children, or prefers not to marry | 136 | xxxx | 0 | 36 | 18 | 82 |

adjustment to his handicap in families where close relatives are similarly affected. This possibility is supported by the finding that most persons from deaf families do not care one way or the other about the hearing status of their children. On the other hand, individuals from hearing families who do wish to have children are more likely to express a preference for hearing children.

For those who do want children, it is shown by the data in Table 10 that more women than men prefer hearing children. In deaf women this preference is not related to the nature of their own deafness; in the men a preference for hearing children tends to be associated with acquired deafness.

Regardless of these differences, however, only 6.5 per cent of people who wish to marry prefer to have deaf children. With the category "Either deaf or hearing' probably representing in many cases a post-facto modification of their actual choice, and with close to 50 per cent of those who wish to have children expressing a definite preference for hearing ones, it may be assumed that the majority hold this preference regardless of other existing attitudes. At the same time, 86 per cent, as has been noted, desire deaf mates.

Unfortunately, there is a pronounced lack of knowledge among the deaf about the workings of heredity, as may be inferred from the data in Table

11. Although preference for a mate with acquired deafness is found only among those who wish to have hearing children, it is expressed by only 15 per cent of the congenitally deaf that would like their children to hear. Fully 74 per cent of persons with congenital deafness who profess a desire for hearing children appear unconcerned about their mate's deafness. Among the acquired deaf, including some that are not altogether certain of the origin of their deafness, there is a similar lack of concern. Even among persons who prefer their children to be deaf, there is no attempt to select the type of mate most likely to produce the desired result! These data strongly affirm the need for specialized counseling services through which genetic knowledge might be effectively disseminated among those members of the deaf community who seek advice in matters of marriage and parenthood.

## Family Relationships

Lacking awareness of genetic principles, many deaf persons produce similarly afflicted children, as is shown in Table 12. Almost 25 per cent of deaf parents have at least one deaf child. In an effort to define the attitudes and problems that exist in rearing children, parents were questioned about difficulties in obedience or control, and educational and vocational goals for their children, either hearing or deaf. Since families having both deaf and hearing children were too few in number for valid comparison, the data summarized in Table 13 constitute a comparison of the attitudes and aspirations of parents with deaf children and parents with hearing children. These data are probably biased to some extent. No respondent will be eager to make admissions that might be construed as personal failure, such as difficulty in controlling his own children. A tendency, nevertheless, is reported for deaf parents to have more problems of control and obedience with hearing children than with deaf ones.

Educational expectations for hearing children were considerably higher than for deaf ones, and usually included specifically continuation of formal education beyond high school. For deaf children the parents seemed to allow a greater degree of self-determination.

When it came to vocational goals, the story was somewhat different. While 56 per cent of all parents had specific vocational goals for their deaf children, only 46 per cent of the deaf parents of hearing children had made similar plans, including six per cent where vocational expectations were obviously too high to be realized. There were no instances in which unrealistic goals had been set for deaf children. A related finding in the same direction was that all the male deaf respondents whose parents were also deaf expressed the belief that their own parents had had specific vocational goals for them. The corresponding rate in the group of respondents with hearing parents was less than 45 per cent.

These observations, along with the interviewers' impression of the respondents, would seem to indicate that the deaf approach their deaf

### TABLE 11
### Type of children desired, by type of deafness of respondents
### 15 years or over, and type of spouse desired

| Deafness of respondent and type of spouse desired | Total number | Wants children | | | | Does not want children | No answer about children |
|---|---|---|---|---|---|---|---|
| | | Deaf | Hear-ing | Either way | No answer | | |
| Total responses on spouse | 527 | 28 | 186 | 143 | 32 | 34 | 104 |
| Respondent congenitally deaf | | | | | | | |
| Desires spouse – | | | | | | | |
| Hearing | 11 | 4 | 7 | 0 | 0 | 0 | 0 |
| Deaf | | | | | | | |
| – born deaf | 8 | 0 | 4 | 4 | 0 | 0 | 0 |
| – acquired deafness | 10 | 0 | 10 | 0 | 0 | 0 | 0 |
| – either | 123 | 8 | 44 | 49 | 4 | 11 | 7 |
| Hearing or deaf | 0 | 0 | 0 | 0 | 0 | 0 | 0 |
| Undecided about spouse | 2 | 0 | 0 | 2 | 0 | 0 | 0 |
| Undecided about mar-riage | 8 | 4 | 0 | 0 | 0 | 0 | 4 |
| Does not wish to marry | 13 | 0 | 0 | 0 | 0 | 0 | 13 |
| No answer about spouse | 43 | 0 | 0 | 0 | 7 | 0 | 36 |
| Respondent acquired deaf-ness | | | | | | | |
| Desires spouse – | | | | | | | |
| Hearing | 18 | 0 | 14 | 0 | 4 | 0 | 0 |
| Deaf | | | | | | | |
| – born deaf | 0 | 0 | 0 | 0 | 0 | 0 | 0 |
| – acquired deafness | 14 | 0 | 8 | 2 | 0 | 4 | 0 |
| – either | 176 | 8 | 82 | 62 | 13 | 11 | 0 |
| Hearing or deaf | 23 | 0 | 12 | 11 | 0 | 0 | 0 |
| Undecided about spouse | 3 | 0 | 3 | 0 | 0 | 0 | 0 |
| Undecided about mar-riage | 13 | 0 | 0 | 1 | 0 | 0 | 12 |
| Does not wish to marry | 6 | 0 | 0 | 0 | 0 | 0 | 6 |
| No answer about spouse | 30 | 0 | 0 | 4 | 0 | 0 | 26 |
| Respondent's deafness unknown | 26 | 4 | 2 | 8 | 4 | 8 | 0 |

## TABLE 12
### Hearing status of children of deaf respondents

| Hearing status of children | Number | Per cent |
|---|---|---|
| Total responses | 592 | 100.0 |
| Hearing only | 220 | 37.2 |
| Deaf only | 48 | 8.1 |
| Hearing and deaf | 21 | 3.5 |
| Unmarried or childless | 303 | 51.2 |

## TABLE 13
### Obedience of children, and respondent's vocational and educational goals for children, by hearing status of children, reported by deaf parents

| Obedience and goals | Hearing status of children | | | |
|---|---|---|---|---|
| | Hearing children | | Deaf children | |
| | Number | Per cent | Number | Per cent |
| Obedience | | | | |
| Total responses | 178 | 100.0 | 37 | 100.0 |
| No problems | 112 | 62.9 | 26 | 70.3 |
| Some problems | 46 | 25.8 | 11 | 29.7 |
| Many problems | 20 | 11.3 | 0 | 0 |
| No answer, or no children, or never married | 98 | xxx | 48 | xxx |
| Educational goals | | | | |
| Total responses | 122 | 100.0 | 27 | 100.0 |
| No special goals | 35 | 28.7 | 11 | 41 |
| Graduation from HS or school for deaf | 23 | 18.9 | 11 | 41 |
| More than the above | 64 | 52.5 | 5 | 18 |
| No answer, or no children, or never married | 98 | xxx | 15 | xxx |
| Occupational goals for children | | | | |
| Total responses | 132 | 100.0 | 34 | 100.0 |
| No specific goals | 71 | 53.8 | 15 | 44 |
| Specific goals | | | | |
| Consistent with reality | 53 | 40.2 | 19 | 56 |
| Inconsistent with reality | 8 | 6.1 | 0 | 0 |
| No answer, or no children, or never married | 88 | xxx | 11 | xxx |

**TABLE 14**

Treatment received from siblings and parents, as reported by deaf respondents

| From siblings or parents | Total | | Preferential treatment because of deafness | | Neither preferred nor rejected | | Shunned because of deafness | |
|---|---|---|---|---|---|---|---|---|
| | Number | Per cent | Number | Per cent | Number | Per cent | Number | Per cent |
| Hearing sibs | 293 | 100.0 | 18 | 6.0 | 257 | 88.0 | 18 | 6.0 |
| *Hearing parents | 360 | 100.0 | 80 | 22.2 | 264 | 73.3 | 16 | 4.4 |
| **Hearing mother | 465 | 100.0 | 114 | 24.5 | 319 | 68.6 | 32 | 6.9 |
| **Hearing father | 410 | 100.0 | 97 | 23.7 | 283 | 69.0 | 30 | 7.3 |
| *Deaf parents | 31 | 100.0 | 0 | 0 | 31 | 100.0 | 0 | 0 |

*Where respondent reported that both parents showed the same attitude.
**Where respondent reported differences in parents' attitudes.

children with less uncertainty, make fewer demands of them, and have a more realistic understanding of their potentials and limitations. Toward hearing children their attitudes are less sure, apparently bogged down by greater expectations and an overvaluation of the absence of impaired hearing. Unlimited potentials are attributed to the hearing child, wishfully thought of as capable of returning an enhanced personal (or narcissistic) value to the parents.

Other aspects of intra-family relationships among the deaf were examined by questioning respondents about the interaction between themselves and their siblings and parents. For purposes of tabulation, the various answers were divided into three groups, one in which the respondent said he was accepted like any other family member, and two in which he said he had received special treatment, either being preferred or shunned. Once again, noncommittal or evasive answers were not counted as falling into any category, so that the estimates must be regarded as minimal. The results are summarized in Table 14.

Interestingly, only where there were hearing parents did respondents report being treated unlike others in the family. In this group over 22 per cent said they had been overprotected, and over 4 per cent, that they had been shunned by both mother and father. The importance of these differentiating factors emerges in the light of additional data. For instance, respondents who were considered frankly neurotic by the interviewing doctor were indeed found more often among those who reported rejection or overprotection by parents, rather than equal treatment, and were more likely to come from families without other deaf members.

Finally, regarding communication methods, speech was more often preferred among respondents whose families were all hearing than among those with other deaf members. This preference may be due to such factors as the socio-economic status of the family, duration and quality of education, and age of onset of deafness, as well as the fact, revealed by our data, that in only 12 per cent of hearing families with a deaf child does anyone other than the child learn to use manual communication.

# Chapter 6

## PATTERNS OF SOCIALIZATION AND COMMUNITY INTEGRATION

### George S. Baroff

The effect of severe communication handicap on group and community interaction was of considerable interest in the study of this deaf population. Data were obtained on social relationships, utilization of community resources and on participation in activities that are a normal part of contemporary urban life.

### Social Relationships

Social adjustment is a crucial factor in evaluating the limitations that may be imposed by any handicap. When, as in deafness, the disability may produce a serious degree of intellectual and emotional isolation during the formative years, its long-range effects on socialization potential are of obvious concern. The main question is whether deaf adults are withdrawn, isolated personalities, or maintain reasonably effective social relationships in spite of developmental lacks and the omnipresent communication barrier.

Both the interview data and clinical impression indicate that the deaf are certainly capable of establishing effective personal contacts. More than three-quarters of the persons interviewed claimed that they had close friends, and, of these, 80 per cent reported socializing on at least a once a week basis. Fortifying the impression of a fair degree of interaction was the finding that 67 per cent were either present or former members of deaf fraternal organizations.

Not only were we interested in the amount of socialization in the deaf, but also in the type of persons with whom they formed friendships. Almost one-half (45%) reported hearing as well as deaf friends, while one-third (34%) stated that their friendships were limited to the deaf. Although prestige factors may have played a role, especially with regard to hearing friends, the general impression was that the deaf are not lacking in socialization.

An interesting finding regarding friendships was the lack of any meaningful correlation between the likelihood of having friends and the individual's conception of the attitude of hearing persons toward the deaf. Almost one-third of the deaf felt that hearing people have negative feelings toward them. Since a large majority of them also claimed many friends, the infer-

113

ence was drawn that the deaf person who believes hearing people dislike the deaf does not necessarily thereby disclose the presence of paranoid-like thinking.

The data on club membership yielded some significant findings regarding the advantages accruing to the deaf person with unusually good communication skills. When past and present officers of these clubs were categorized in terms of age of onset of deafness, a disproportionately high percentage of officers was found among those whose deafness occurred after eight years of age. Such persons would be expected to have had well-developed language skills prior to the onset of hearing loss and, in fact, are least likely to identify themselves psychologically with the deaf population.

## Health Services

How does language handicap affect the use of services that are generally based on verbal communication? Superficially, the respondents' replies indicated that impaired speech does not prevent regular use of medical and dental facilities. Approximately 50 per cent reported that they had visited a physician and dentist in the preceding year. It would, however, be erroneous to assume that the speech barrier does not affect the quality of such services to some degree. Certainly, in the mental health specialty where verbal communication is a therapeutic as well as diagnostic agent, the deaf person seeking psychiatric assistance is at a disadvantage. Indeed, one of the chief factors in the organization of the mental health clinic for the deaf and in the training of mental health workers in manual language was to try to meet this heretofore unmet need.

Like the hearing, the deaf value health services, and only ten per cent expressed a negative attitude toward them. Educational achievement appears to have played some part in determining this attitude. The ten per cent who did not feel that health services were important included the greatest number of individuals who had failed to complete the minimum educational program for the deaf.

## Religious Activity

Here is another sphere in which the lack of verbal skills might be expected to have some limiting effect. A deaf member of a hearing church would have great difficulty in following those aspects of religious services which are neither repetitive nor written. In fact, in order to meet the needs of some of the deaf, Protestant and Catholic clergymen have been trained in manual language and services are regularly conducted in this manner. Among our population, 84 per cent reported some degree of religious activity, while more than one-third (39%) claimed regular attendance at either hearing or deaf churches. Slightly more than one-third (36%) of those who were regular participants in religious activity exclusively attended hearing churches and synagogues, while 27 per cent were members of congregations limited to the deaf.

## Voting

Data on the voting habits of the deaf are consistent with the impression that they take a good deal of interest in affairs which are not necessarily confined to their own special needs. Almost seven-tenths (69%) of the subjects claimed to have voted within the last three years, and only 24 per cent stated that they had never voted.

## News Interest

Cut off by his handicap from two major contemporary news media, radio and television, and frequently limited in general reading skills, the deaf person must lean heavily on the newspaper as a primary information source. In fact, 79 per cent stated that they read a newspaper every day, and only three per cent claimed they never read the newspaper. It is probable that the latter group represents individuals with extremely poor reading skills.

In the present study of the deaf, it soon became apparent that the communication handicap is often not limited to the speech zone. The whole area of language and symbol development may be affected, with written language frequently characterized by primitive grammatical construction. This tends to be a subject, object, and verb language which to some degree mirrors the simplified technique of manual language.

Since manual language is a pictorial representation of symbols, it is most effective in communicating the tangible or concrete—that which can be visualized. Manual language is ill-suited for communication of abstract ideas—that which is primarily symbolic. Yet it is through the use of abstraction that much of our information is formulated and disseminated. In view of the manifold effects of deafness, the straightforward style of newspaper writing makes it the most generally useful news medium for this population.

## Police

We did not expect that our interview would elicit reliable data on the extent of antisocial behavior in the deaf, but we were hopeful of assessing the general attitude to legally constituted authority. Almost 95 per cent denied ever having any run-in with the law, and the predominant attitude toward the police was favorable. Only 14 per cent considered the police unfair to the deaf. This group, quite naturally, constituted the highest proportion of individuals who admitted having difficulty with the law.

## Summary

The data indicate that persons with early total deafness can establish adequate socialization patterns and are able to participate in and utilize general community services. However, qualitative and quantitative differences between the deaf and the hearing in the nature of their social and community integration exist.

# Chapter 7

## EDUCATIONAL BACKGROUND AND VOCATIONAL ADJUSTMENT

### KENNETH Z. ALTSHULER and GEORGE S. BAROFF

*Education*

The deaf child usually attends a special residential or day school. Early enrollment is advised and speech training is generally stressed. Graduation from such a school in the late teens is often the end of formal education. If a student qualifies, he may continue in a vocational school, or he may go on to a hearing high school from which he may eventually be admitted to a regular college. As an alternative, he may take a special postgraduate course in preparation for enrollment at Gallaudet College for the Deaf.

Tables 1 and 2 show the general educational status of the deaf population of New York State, with the age at the beginning of schooling given in Table 3. Accordingly, almost all the deaf have had some formal schooling, and 3.7 per cent have had more than a high school education. Comparing these findings with Best's data of 1920 (22), it is of interest to note that in his population 91.4 per cent were reported to have had some education, but only 0.3 per cent had gone beyond the high school level. This change over the past few decades indicates that the deaf community has shared in the general trend toward increasing educational achievement. Yet in spite of this trend, more than 16 per cent of the current deaf population have left school before the age of 16 without graduating. It goes without saying that such premature termination and the factors leading to it may have a limiting effect on subsequent adjustment, even greater among the deaf than in the hearing.

According to Best, few if any classes were available in 1920 to deaf children below the age of five. More recently, however, the emphasis has been on early schooling. It is shown in Table 3 that more than 45 per cent of individuals surveyed began school prior to the age of six. That this trend is more or less a current one is emphasized by the fact that 59 per cent of those who started school prior to four years of age are still in school. Among early starters (below age 4) who have completed their education, the percentage achieving college level is considerably higher (16.7%) than it is for persons whose education began at a later age.

In Table 4, data on educational achievement are presented according to

116

## TABLE 1
### Type of school attended
### 607 respondents

| | |
|---|---|
| All respondents | 100.0% |
| School for the deaf | 83.2 |
| School for hearing only | 1.6 |
| School for hearing and school for the deaf | 15.2 |

## TABLE 2
### School level attained
### 530 respondents

| | |
|---|---|
| All respondents | 100.0% |
| Never attended school | .8 |
| Attended but did not graduate | |
| Left school before age 10 | 5.1 |
| Left school at ages 11-15 | 11.7 |
| Left school after age 16 | 26.8 |
| Graduated | |
| From hearing elementary school, or from school for deaf | 50.6 |
| From hearing high school | 1.3 |
| Some college education | 1.5 |
| Graduated from college | 2.2 |

## TABLE 3
### Scholastic achievement by age of entering school
### 536 respondents

| Age at entry | Total | | Did not graduate | *Graduated but no higher education | Higher education |
|---|---|---|---|---|---|
| All ages | 100.0% | 100.0% | 41.9% | 51.4% | 6.7% |
| Before age 4 | 10.8 | 100.0 | 33.3 | 50.0 | 16.7 |
| Age 4 or 5 | 34.5 | 100.0 | 45.5 | 52.1 | 2.4 |
| Age 6 or over | 54.7 | 100.0 | 41.6 | 50.8 | 7.6 |

*Graduation means graduation from school for the deaf or its equivalent.

## TABLE 4
### Scholastic achievement by type of deafness

| Type of deafness and age of onset | Total | | | Did not graduate | | *Graduated but no higher education | | Higher education | |
|---|---|---|---|---|---|---|---|---|---|
| | Male plus female | Male | Female | Male | Female | Male | Female | Male | Female |
| Total deaf | 473 | 248 | 225 | 118 | 82 | 111 | 131 | 19 | 12 |
| Per cent | xxx | 100.0 | 100.0 | 49.5 | 36.4 | 42.5 | 58.3 | 8.0 | 5.3 |
| Born deaf | 203 | 100 | 103 | 52 | 41 | 37 | 54 | 11 | 8 |
| Per cent | xxx | 100.0 | 100.0 | 52.0 | 39.8 | 37.0 | 52.5 | 11.0 | 7.7 |
| Acquired: | | | | | | | | | |
| Under 1 year | 61 | 36 | 25 | 25 | 7 | 11 | 18 | 0 | 0 |
| Per cent | xxx | 100.0 | 100.0 | 69.5 | 28.0 | 30.5 | 72.0 | 0 | 0 |
| Age 1-3 | 133 | 75 | 58 | 33 | 20 | 38 | 34 | 4 | 4 |
| Per cent | xxx | 100.0 | 100.0 | 44.0 | 34.5 | 50.7 | 58.5 | 5.3 | 6.9 |
| Age 4-7 | 46 | 25 | 21 | 4 | 6 | 17 | 15 | 4 | 0 |
| Per cent | xxx | 100.0 | 100.0 | 16.0 | 29.5 | 68.0 | 71.5 | 16.0 | 0 |
| Age 8 or over | 30 | 12 | 18 | 4 | 8 | 8 | 10 | 0 | 0 |
| Per cent | xxx | 100.0 | 100.0 | 33.3 | 44.4 | 66.7 | 55.6 | 0 | 0 |

*Graduation means graduation from school for the deaf or its equivalent.

whether deafness was congenital or acquired, together with the age of onset if acquired. There were no significant differences in achievement, except among those who became deaf after age four. This group is distinguished by a greater chance of graduating from a grade school or school for the deaf. In all likelihood, this difference is due to the advantages of greater development of language before the onset of deafness.

Among the congenitally deaf and those whose deafness was acquired before the age of four, girls are more apt than boys to graduate from a grade school or go on for further education. In line with this finding, Table 5 discloses that women were rated as "bright" more often than men. This estimate is based on impressions during the course of the interview and may be influenced by sex differences in preferred mode of communication, women being more likely to use speech (Table 6).

The relationship between preferred means of communication and scholastic attainment is also shown in Table 6. Differences in type of communi-

### TABLE 5
#### Intelligence as estimated by interviews

| Intelligence | Male | | Female | |
|---|---|---|---|---|
| | Number | Per cent | Number | Per cent |
| All deaf | 266 | 100.0 | 263 | 100.0 |
| Bright | 82 | 30.8 | 103 | 39.2 |
| Average | 144 | 54.1 | 115 | 43.7 |
| Dull | 28 | 10.6 | 37 | 14.1 |
| Defective | 12 | 4.5 | 8 | 3.0 |

### TABLE 6
#### Scholastic achievement by means of communication

| Means of communication | Did not graduate | | Graduated from school for deaf or its equivalent | | Higher education | |
|---|---|---|---|---|---|---|
| | Male | Female | Male | Female | Male | Female |
| Total | 106 | 95 | 127 | 134 | 19 | 12 |
| Mainly speech | 23 | 17 | 32 | 52 | 11 | 8 |
| Mainly signs | 58 | 50 | 79 | 42 | 4 | 4 |
| Equal use of speech and signs | 14 | 24 | 12 | 36 | 4 | 0 |
| Other | 11 | 4 | 4 | 4 | 0 | 0 |

cation emerge only with higher levels of education. Oralists or those with equal facility in speech and signs comprised 46 per cent of the total population, but represented 73 per cent of those who obtained education beyond graduation from a school for the deaf. Here it should be emphasized that the use of signs does not serve as a deterrent to graduation from a school for the deaf. The proportion of speakers and signers who graduate from a school for the deaf (excluding those who seek further education) are very similar, 54 and 51 per cent. It should also be noted that almost one-half of the population were exclusively signers, despite the educational emphasis on the oral method.

The attitude of the respondents towards school and their teachers was positive to a high degree. Although memory may have embellished the truth, 76 per cent reported that they had liked their school as well as their teachers. That small minority of people who had been expelled from school (4%) obviously represent a group that deserves detailed individual study (see Chapter 9).

Of special interest in the total educational picture are the recollected aspirations of deaf people at the completion of their education, and their estimate of its usefulness in the light of subsequent vocational experience. Approximately 40 per cent felt that their school training, vocational as well as academic, had been helpful in obtaining employment.

Table 7 discloses that 30 per cent of those interviewed either had no plans at all or had no specific work plans after leaving school. Those with no plans included 11 per cent of all persons classified as "bright". Thus, while a considerable number of deaf persons thought that their education had been of material vocational benefit, a substantial group of handicapped persons, many with high potential, entered the competitive job market with the feeling of being poorly prepared and with ill-defined goals. In a population whose handicap limits occupational opportunity even under good conditions, these data strongly indicate the need for expanded programs of counseling and guidance during the school years.

## Vocation

*1. Occupation and Job-status:* Table 8 shows the distribution into occupational classes of the deaf labor force in the State of New York, employed at the time of interview. Although clerical workers comprised only six per cent of the employed, this group included all the males in the labor force who were college graduates. Less than three per cent of the total were employers or businessmen, and a similarly small percentage provided custodial services.

The vast majority (87.5%) performed some kind of manual labor. More than one-half of the entire force were skilled workers in the printing, mechanical or other trades, and another 30.4 per cent fell into the unskilled category. No relationship was found between completion of grade school or school for the deaf and classification as a skilled or unskilled worker. Per-

**TABLE 7**

**Future plans for work or for education, by intelligence**

| Intelligence | Total | | Planned further academic or vocational training | | Had specific plans for work | | Had no specific plans | | Had no plans at all | | Planned to marry and live with parents | |
|---|---|---|---|---|---|---|---|---|---|---|---|---|
| | Number | and per cent | Number | and per cent | Number | and per cent | Number | and per cent | Number | and per cent | Number | and per cent |
| Total | 444 | 100.0 | 87 | 100.0 | 190 | 100.0 | 91 | 100.0 | 45 | 100.0 | 31 | 100.0 |
| Per cent | 100.0 | | 19.6 | | 42.8 | | 20.5 | | 10.2 | | 6.9 | |
| Bright | 174 | 39.2 | 47 | 54.1 | 72 | 37.9 | 31 | 34.0 | 20 | 44.4 | 4 | 12.9 |
| Per cent | 100.0 | | 27.0 | | 41.4 | | 17.8 | | 11.5 | | 2.3 | |
| Average | 228 | 51.4 | 36 | 41.5 | 106 | 55.8 | 48 | 52.8 | 15 | 33.3 | 23 | 74.2 |
| Per cent | 100.0 | | 15.8 | | 46.5 | | 21.0 | | 6.6 | | 10.1 | |
| Dull or defective | 42 | 9.4 | 4 | 4.6 | 12 | 6.3 | 12 | 13.2 | 10 | 22.3 | 4 | 12.9 |
| Per cent | 100.0 | | 9.5 | | 28.6 | | 28.6 | | 23.8 | | 9.5 | |

### TABLE 8
#### Occupational class of the employed deaf

| Occupational class | Total | | Male | | Female | |
|---|---|---|---|---|---|---|
| | Number | Per cent | Number | Per cent | Number | Per cent |
| All classes | 382 | 100.0 | 239 | 100.0 | 143 | 100.0 |
| Office-worker | 23 | 6.0 | 4 | 1.7 | 19 | 13.3 |
| Skilled | 218 | 57.1 | 145 | 60.6 | 73 | 51.0 |
| Unskilled | 116 | 30.4 | 69 | 28.9 | 47 | 32.9 |
| Custodial | 15 | 3.9 | 11 | 4.6 | 4 | 2.8 |
| Own business | 10 | 2.6 | 10 | 4.2 | 0 | 0 |

### TABLE 9
#### Weekly income of wage-earners by sex

| Weekly income | Total | | Male | | Female | |
|---|---|---|---|---|---|---|
| | Number | Per cent | Number | Per cent | Number | Per cent |
| Total | 264 | 100.0 | 178 | 67.4 | 86 | 32.6 |
| $ 1 – 19 | 8 | 3.0 | 4 | 1.5 | 4 | 1.5 |
| $ 20 – 39 | 22 | 8.3 | 7 | 2.7 | 15 | 5.7 |
| $ 40 – 59 | 67 | 25.4 | 19 | 7.2 | 48 | 18.2 |
| $ 60 – 74 | 71 | 26.9 | 55 | 20.8 | 16 | 6.1 |
| $ 75 – 99 | 53 | 20.1 | 50 | 18.9 | 3 | 1.1 |
| $100 – 149 | 39 | 14.8 | 39 | 14.8 | 0 | 0.0 |
| $150 or over | 4 | 1.5 | 4 | 1.5 | 0 | 0.0 |

### TABLE 10
#### Cumulative distribution of weekly income by sex
#### 264 respondents

| Income | Male | Female |
|---|---|---|
| Under $ 20 | 2.2% | 4.7% |
| Under $ 40 | 6.2 | 22.1 |
| Under $ 60 | 16.9 | 77.9 |
| Under $ 75 | 47.8 | 96.5 |
| Under $100 | 75.8 | 100.0 |
| Under $150 | 97.8 | 100.0 |
| Total | 100.0% | 100.0% |

haps a laborer's or craftsman's vocational choice and skill are more closely related to the quality and area of vocational training received in school than to his general level of education.

Practically all of the men had full-time jobs, as only 3.9 per cent were classifiable as part-time employees. Among wage earning females, the frequency of part-time employment was higher; namely, 17.2 per cent.

Although this tabulated group comprised no professional people, there were a few such persons among the deaf as a whole. These "achievers" will be discussed individually in another chapter (Chapter 8). Also not included in Table 8 were those members of the labor force who were unemployed at the time of interview. They represented only 2.6 per cent of the total employable population, exclusive of housewives, students and retired persons.

*2. Income:* Table 9 compares the weekly earnings of men and women who were employed either on a full or part-time basis. Only a small proportion of male workers earned less than $60 a week, while the reverse was true for female workers. This difference is even more apparent in Table 10 which depicts the cumulative distribution of weekly income. More than three-quarters (77.9%) of the females reported earnings of less than $60 weekly, while only 16.9 per cent of males had earnings in this range. More than one-half the men but only 3.5 per cent of the women stated that their weekly incomes exceeded $75. No woman had earnings of more than $100 per week, an income claimed by a fourth of the male respondents.

Income level among the deaf was also found to be related to education. Deaf persons who continued their education upon graduating from a school for the deaf were more likely to secure higher incomes (over $75 a week).

*3. Job Stability:* As a measure of vocational adjustment, job stability is a parameter which lends itself to different interpretations. On the positive side, deaf workers, especially males, are shown in Table 11 to represent excellent employment risks; more than 93 per cent of men and 69 per cent of women held the same job for more than three years. The lesser degree of

**TABLE 11**
Longest time in one job, by sex

| Longest time in one job | Total | Male | Female |
|---|---|---|---|
| All responses | 416 | 126 | 290 |
| Per cent | 100.0 | 100.0 | 100.0 |
| 3 years or more | 82.9 | 93.2 | 69.6 |
| 1 to 2 years | 8.9 | 3.4 | 16.0 |
| 6 to 11 months | 6.3 | 1.7 | 12.2 |
| Less than 6 months | 1.9 | 1.7 | 2.2 |

stability in females was probably attributable to their higher frequency of part-time employment and to interruption of work by marriage and pregnancy.

Another positive feature is that only two per cent of deaf working people reported to have been fired from their last job, or during the five years preceding the interview if more than one job was held in this period. Although this estimate is necessarily a minimum one because of the emotional implications of the question and possible euphemistic employer practice ("laid off" may be equivalent to discharge), it seemed to be consistent with the finding that only a negligible proportion had regularly failed to hold jobs for more than six months.

This high degree of stability may have some negative determinants. Limitations in occupational range and chances for promotion have been suggested as reenforcing stability by restricting free occupational movement (24). That job persistence is not wholly a matter of self-determination is clearly indicated by our data in Table 12. Although persons with the least job stability were most likely to feel discriminated against, 45% of the more stable workers also assumed that the deaf were always unfairly treated. While the gradations of discrimination reported may have been subjectively overestimated, actions based on such feelings were apt to result in the same degree of immobility that would have evolved if these opinions were objectively accurate.

The belief that deafness had deprived them of a job for which they considered themselves qualified was expressed by more than one-half of the office and unskilled factory workers. The advantage of having a trade was apparent. Only one-third of the people with such skills felt deprived of work in their particular field of proficiency.

Job stability may also be enhanced by the fact that within the given area of occupation only two per cent of all deaf workers had accidents that were attributable to deafness. In other words, the hearing loss did not appear to interfere with continuous and efficient vocational performance by inducing any great number of interruptions or job changes caused by accidents.

So far the emphasis has been on objective vocational parameters. At least

## TABLE 12
### Feelings of discrimination related to job stability
### 147 respondents

| Longest time on job | Says there is always discrimination against the deaf |
|---|---|
| More than 1 year | 45% |
| 6 months to 1 year | 56 |
| Under 6 months | 100 |

equal in significance are the feelings and attitudes that form the substrate from which the facts of observed behavior are derived and by which they may be determined. The importance of such subjective elements is matched by the difficulties inherent in their ascertainment and evaluation. Reported attitudes must be carefully weighed, since they may be colored by a desire to maintain status or please the interviewer, or by considerations of social correctness. Although the inquiry approached attitudes through a series of related check questions, conclusions had to be cautiously drawn and remained tentative.

4. *Attitudes toward Job, Coworker, Employer and Handicap:* The attitudes expressed by respondents toward job, coworkers and boss (Table 13)

### TABLE 13
#### Attitude toward boss, fellow workers, and job
#### 347 respondents

| Attitude toward boss and fellow workers | Total | Likes job | Does not like job |
|---|---|---|---|
| All responses | 347 | 298 | 49 |
| Per cent | 100.0 | 85.9 | 14.1 |
| Likes boss | 93.9 | 83.4 | 10.5 |
| Likes fellow workers | 87.9 | 81.7 | 6.2 |
| Has some trouble with fellow workers | 6.0 | 1.7 | 4.3 |
| Does not like boss | 6.1 | 2.5 | 3.6 |
| Likes fellow workers | 2.5 | 1.3 | 1.2 |
| Has some trouble with fellow workers | 3.6 | 1.2 | 2.4 |

would seem to indicate that almost 86 per cent liked their particular jobs. It should be noted, however, that this category was extended to include all replies that were not clearly negative; it was applied to neutral and noncommittal affirmatives, such as "okay," or "good," accompanied by a shrug of the shoulders. When compared with the previously mentioned experiences of discrimination and job deprivation, this classification should not be construed as a true estimate of job satisfaction in the deaf. The open statement of dissatisfaction by 14 per cent was undoubtedly an underestimate. Dissatisfaction with the job would be most likely to occur in people who also expressed more than the usual degree of disturbance over their handicap (Table 14).

Answers to the question "How do you feel about your deafness?" were of considerable interest. The replies of as many as 62 per cent could be categorized as stoical acceptance. Significantly, almost 10 per cent denied that deafness was any handicap. Women were most likely to be of this opinion, perhaps because they are less exposed to social competition. Also, they had a greater proficiency in speech, which is associated with the tendency to deny deafness as a handicap. Nevertheless, the emphatic denial of handicap probably signified as deep a dissatisfaction as an admission of disturbance.

People who are frankly unhappy over their deafness are more prone to interpersonal job difficulties than those who are not (Table 14). Also, they are more likely to believe that their deafness deprived them of jobs which they were qualified to perform (Table 14). Thus, emotional disturbance

## TABLE 14
### Attitude toward deafness among those that dislike job, by presence or absence of interpersonal job difficulties

| Aspects of work-adjustment (Not mutually exclusive) | Total | | Denies handicap | Stoical acceptance | Disturbed by deafness |
|---|---|---|---|---|---|
| | Number | Per cent | | | |
| All the deaf that responded on attitude toward deafness | 349 | 100.0% | 8.4% | 62.2% | 29.4% |
| A. Dislikes job | 46 | 100.0 | 8.7 | 39.1 | 52.2 |
| B. Interpersonal job difficulties | 34 | 100.0 | 0.0 | 47.0 | 53.0 |
| No interpersonal job difficulties | 275 | 100.0 | 9.5 | 64.0 | 26.5 |
| C. Not deprived of job because of deafness | 175 | 100.0 | 12.0 | 65.7 | 22.3 |
| Deprived of job because of deafness | 144 | 100.0 | 4.9 | 53.5 | 41.6 |

over deafness itself may be expected to be central in many problems requiring vocational counseling.

5. *Preference for Coworkers:* The deaf generally work with hearing people. Hence, many were the only handicapped person at their place of work, while others had the experience of working with other deaf employees. The individuals interviewed were questioned regarding their preference for work with deaf or hearing fellow employees, and the reasons for their choice. According to the data in Table 15, 45 per cent preferred only hearing coworkers, while 41 per cent either had no preference or would like to work with a mixed group. Less than 11 per cent expressed the desire to work exclusively with deaf people.

Almost a quarter of the respondents stated they had no preference. For

### TABLE 15
#### Preference for fellow employees
#### 378 respondents

| | |
|---|---|
| Prefers hearing only | 44.8% |
|    Some constructive reason | 10.3 |
|    Trouble when other deaf are present | 6.9 |
|    The deaf talk too much | 12.5 |
|    No reason given | 15.1 |
| Prefers deaf only | 10.8 |
| Prefers mixed group | 17.7 |
| Satisfied with either hearing or deaf | 23.5 |
| No opinion | 3.2 |

the most part these individuals were the better educated. Apparently, their opinions were more reasoned than emotional. They also regarded hearing persons as generally lacking in understanding rather than simply liking or disliking the deaf. Emotional bias apparently had a greater bearing in the 11 per cent that preferred only deaf coworkers. No one in this group expressed the opinion that hearing people might like the deaf or be interested in them.

The substantial number of respondents (45%) who preferred being the only deaf person in their working group would seem to call for further comment. As to the replies summarized in Table 15, it may be noted that reasons interpreted as "constructive" were related to situations where another deaf worker could conceivably interfere with work performance because of the need for manual communication. Interestingly, the reasons given by almost one-half of this group were that other deaf people were inclined to talk too much or somehow might make for job difficulties. Such explanations included the notions that other deaf workers were inferior or lazy and would cause employers to frown on all deaf people, or that their presence would otherwise interfere with the respondent's easy mingling with non-deaf workers. Although these feelings may have been partly justifiable, they would seem to indicate that the deaf themselves were not free of the prejudicial stereotypes usually attributed to the hearing. Apart from any realistic limitations, their self-esteem and concepts of self, as in other minority groups, tend to be lowered by society's attitudes. Negative in-group feelings, as indicated by an increased preference for hearing coworkers only, were intensified in persons who were the sole deaf members in their families; yet, 27 per cent of individuals brought up with other deaf relatives also expressed this preference.

6. *Feelings of Discrimination and Those Regarding Attitudes of Hearing People:* Closely associated with minority group stereotypes are feelings of discrimination. Table 16 shows the frequency and intensity of these feelings

**TABLE 16**
Opinions regarding vocational discrimination

| Sex of respondent | All responses | | No discrimination against the deaf Per cent | Some discrimination Per cent | Always discrimination Per cent |
|---|---|---|---|---|---|
| | Number | Per cent | | | |
| Male | 188 | 100.0 | 30.3 | 33.0 | 36.7 |
| Female | 138 | 100.0 | 29.7 | 13.8 | 56.5 |

in the New York State population. Approximately one-third of men and women reported no discrimination against the deaf. This opinion was held mostly by persons who had no trouble obtaining employment and by those with more education.

Of the total sample, 68 per cent believed that there was some discrimination against the deaf, and more than one-half of this group thought of it as prevailing generally. Deaf persons who were rated as brighter than average more often gave qualified answers as to the existence of some discrimination, while the opinion of those rated average in intelligence was likely to be of an over-simplified and exaggerated nature. This tendency was found in men and women alike.

It was previously established that fewer of the skilled workers expressed a belief in personal vocational deprivation because of deafness than did those who were unskilled. However, there was no significant difference in opinion about the intensity of discrimination that presumably operated against the deaf as a whole. Thus it would appear that many deaf persons are capable of separating personal experiences from their opinions regarding attitudes toward their group. An exception was that small group of people who had been unable to hold a job for six months. All of them agreed on having been discriminated against (Table 12). Conversely, the tendency to feel discriminated against seemed to decrease with increased job stability.

The perception of the attitude of the hearing toward the deaf and the relationship of such perception to feelings of being discriminated against are summarized in Tables 17 and 18. The deaf expressed no clearcut majority opinion about how the hearing feel towards them. Exponents of the notion that negative feelings are most prevalent were almost equal in number to those stating that the hearing feel positively towards them. However, a large number denied that they had formed any opinion at all.

Table 18 demonstrates a direct relationship between the two notions that hearing people dislike the deaf and that there is general vocational discrimination. The belief in general discrimination and the perception of negative feelings might be likened to the two sides of the same coin, were

**TABLE 17**

Opinions regarding attitude of hearing people toward the deaf

| Responses regarding attitude of hearing people toward the deaf | Number | Per cent |
|---|---|---|
| 1. Total | 430 | 100.0 |
| 2. Hearing people like the deaf | 62 | 14.4 |
| 3. Some hearing people like the deaf | 28 | 6.5 |
| 4. Some hearing people like the deaf, and some hearing people pity the deaf | 10 | 2.3 |
| 5. Hearing people pity the deaf | 14 | 3.3 |
| 6. Hearing people dislike the deaf | 102 | 23.7 |
| 7. Some hearing people dislike the deaf, and some pity them | 8 | 1.9 |
| 8. Hearing people are not interested in the deaf | 6 | 1.4 |
| 9. Hearing people do not understand the deaf | 41 | 9.6 |
| 10. Don't know or no opinion | 124 | 28.8 |
| 11. Other | 35 | 8.1 |

**TABLE 18**

Opinions regarding vocational discrimination by attitudes perceived in hearing people

| Attitude perceived in hearing people toward the deaf | No vocational discrimination against the deaf | Some vocational discrimination | Always vocational discrimination |
|---|---|---|---|
| Hearing people feel positively toward the deaf* | 27 | 24 | 25 |
| Hearing people feel negatively toward the deaf** | 60 | 20 | 8 |
| Hearing people do not understand the deaf*** | 11 | 8 | 15 |

*Lines 2, 3, 4, and 5 in Table 17
**Lines 6, 7, and 8 in Table 17
***Line 9 in Table 17

it not for the fact that a third of deaf persons who declare that hearing people like the deaf nevertheless think that there is general discrimination.

It is a moot point whether this discrepancy is explained by social factors surrounding the interview or was due to differences among respondents in their capacities for abstract reasoning. The latter possibility seems to be the less plausible one, since those who state that the hearing do not understand the deaf are least likely to feel discriminated against and comprise many of the more educated group. Apparently, the more intelligent deaf tend to be more moderate in their opinions, with more education helping them perceive the attitudes of the non-deaf in less emotional terms.

# Chapter 8

## DEAF PERSONS OF OUTSTANDING ACHIEVEMENT

Lissy Feingold Jarvik, Rose M. Salzberger, and Arthur Falek

On the basis of our data on the educational and vocational achievements of the deaf population in New York State as previously described, it may be assumed that the early onset of profound deafness tends to exert a restrictive influence upon subsequent accomplishments. Of course, there is the extraordinary example of Helen Keller, handicapped by both loss of vision and hearing, who attained an astounding degree of international fame. Her accomplishment is underscored by the fact that nowhere in the general literature on eminence and creativity do the names appear of any persons designated as manifesting severe auditory impairment since childhood.

With outstanding success in life in the presence of early total deafness being extremely rare, a separate study of deaf persons of unusual achievement seemed to be of value for the identification of pertinent variables.

### Selection of Subjects

An attempt was made to ascertain individuals who had acquired status, prestige or recognition considerably greater than that accorded the average deaf person. To secure the names of such individuals, contact was made with organizations and educators of the deaf. Newspapers and magazines, including those specifically addressed to the deaf, were examined and their editors personally approached. Our search for deaf persons of unusual achievement was made known generally throughout deaf and hearing circles in New York State.*

Potential subjects were selected on the basis of three criteria:

1. Verified deafness from early childhood, which had to be so severe as to preclude normal means of communication; when it occurred later in childhood, it had to be sufficiently pronounced to require attendance at a school for the deaf.

2. Attainment of adulthood, as persons under the age of 21 could not be expected to have established successful careers.

3. Residence in New York State or the Greater Metropolitan Area of New York City.

The histories of the 44 persons who met these three criteria were obtained

* The contribution of Dr. Martin Wodin in ascertaining and interviewing the subjects is gratefully acknowledged.

by personal interview and then were presented for evaluation of the degree of achievements to an independent committee especially appointed for this purpose.* The committee made its decisions on the basis of the following operational definitions of unusual achievement:

1. In the professional category, a person had to maintain professional status. To be included in this group, a teacher of the deaf had to be known for outstanding talent in the field.
2. In the business world, a person had to demonstrate executive ability combined with a better than average education.
3. In the arts, a person had to have gained recognition from his peers (official agencies, galleries, and the like) and shown his ability to support himself by the fruits of his artistic endeavors.
4. In the deaf community, a leader had to have attained national recognition.

It bears repetition that cases were judged solely on the basis of these requirements without consideration of family background, social standing or personal characteristics.

Of the total of 44 cases, 17 were rejected for any of the following reasons: failure to meet standards in the professional category, lack of responsible position in business, insufficient demonstration of leadership qualities, subject's refusal to cooperate in the verification of achievement. For example, detailed examination of the functions performed by several candidates from the world of business revealed the euphemistic nature of their titles. Another person proposed for the professional category qualified only as a student.

### Characteristics of Subjects

The 27 deaf individuals accepted by the committee as having achieved unusual success ranged in age from 28 to 78 years, with a median of 47 years (mean 48).

While the preponderance of males (23 men to 4 women) was far greater than the ratio of 113 males : 100 females found in the total deaf population (see Chapter 2), it was clearly in line with reported sex differences among eminent and creative hearing persons (33, 35, 124, 190).

*Vocational Accomplishments:* A list of the most eminent men of all times (34) comprised a far larger number of persons renowned in military or political affairs than in the professions. However, 78 per cent of deaf achievers were classified as such by reason of their professional status. The categories of business, arts, and deaf community leadership yielded eleven,

* Grateful acknowledgment is hereby made of the generous services rendered by Dr. W. Edwards Deming, Consultant in Sampling Statistics to the Mental Health Project for the Deaf, the late Professor Carney Landis of Columbia University, and Dr. Jakob Rutschmann, Associate Research Scientist (Psychology) at the New York State Psychiatric Institute, Columbia University.

seven and four per cent, respectively, of the deaf group with unusual achievement. By contrast, the ten men ranked most eminent by Cattell included three artists, no scientists, and the philosophers Aristotle, Bacon and Plato. Cattell's selections have been mentioned here only for want of comparable statistical data of more recent origin. Their usefulness is impaired by various methodological imperfections (65) as well as the fact that the subjects all gained renown prior to the 20th century.

During the present century there has been an enormous increase in the number of scientists. This trend is reflected in *American Men of Science* which included about 4,000 scientists in the first edition (1906) and in the tenth edition (1961) listed over 95,000 for the corresponding sections on physical and biological sciences. The latter edition contains the names of two of our five deaf scientists (a biochemist, a biologist, and three chemists).

The wide variety of occupations represented by the 21 professionally active deaf achievers is impressive (Table 1). In regard to such linguistically demanding vocations as editor, teacher and translator, it should be mentioned that the editor in this particular instance dealt largely with illustrative material, while the teachers specialized in physical education or the instruction of advanced deaf students.

### TABLE 1
#### Occupations of 21 deaf persons classified as professionals*

| Occupation | Number of persons | Occupation | Number of persons |
|---|---|---|---|
| Accountant | 2 | Draftsman | 1 |
| Architect | 1 | Editor | 1 |
| Biochemist | 1 | Engineer | 2 |
| Biologist | 1 | Minister | 2 |
| Chemist | 3 | Physical therapist | 1 |
| Curator (Museum) | 3 | Teacher | 2 |
| Dentist | 2 | Translator | 1 |

*Two persons with double professions have been active in both and were therefore listed twice.

The translator, although deafened at the age of seven, was proficient in eight languages. Even when dealing with highly technical material, he exhibited a degree of competence rarely equaled by hearing persons. Here exceptional endowment together with appropriate educational and social opportunities overcame a severe handicap. However, an outstanding accomplishment of this kind should not be interpreted as encouraging the deaf in unrealistic vocational goals. Aspirations toward occupations contingent upon verbal facility are likely to remain unfulfilled and would merely lead to frustration and feelings of inadequacy. Accordingly the major professions of law, medicine and social science are not represented in our series, although one of the achievers did attend law school for a short while.

Of the three persons judged successful in business, one had established his own advertising agency and another his own printing plant. The third entered a relative's insurance agency where his efforts were so fruitful that he is now a leading agent for one of the world's largest insurance companies.

The two painters in the category of the arts had exhibits in European and American galleries. The paintings of one are found in permanent collections of museums throughout the United States, while the other's murals decorate the lobbies of several of New York's famous buildings.

The qualities of one of the two individuals classified as community leaders are substantiated by the fact that the offices held by him included that of president of an international association of the deaf. The other founded a well-known organization for the deaf and has been a "prime mover for associational and religious interests among the deaf, skillfully enlisting the interest and aid of persons prominent in the community and so demonstrating the fact that deaf persons can have remarkable talent for leadership in behalf of their fellow men." The occasion for this citation, quoted in part, was the bestowal of an honorary doctorate by Gallaudet College.

It may be noted that the recipient of this academic distinction became deaf only at the age of 11 years, while the other recognized leader was born deaf, as were both artists. Similarly, deafness has been present since birth or infancy in four of the five scientists, but the dentists as well as the ministers became deaf after the establishment of speech patterns (between the ages of 5 and 9 years).

In other words, the ages reported for onset of deafness varied from birth to 11 years (Table 2). The proportion of congenitally deaf among the 23 male achievers (30.4%) was only slightly lower than that (36.9%) found for the New York State population of deaf men. The female achievers, four in all, were too few in number for comparative statistical purposes.

Of the 19 persons whose deafness occurred after birth, 11 attributed it to meningitis and one each to pertussis, rubella, or mastoiditis (complicating scarlet fever). Two persons gave a history of a progressive hearing loss, with total deafness established at the ages of five and ten years, respectively. Two others were unaware of any precipitating conditions. The one case of apparently traumatic etiology was that of a child brutally beaten by the Nazis.

Regardless of the cause of total deafness, the actual age of onset is held to be a critical factor in intellectual, emotional and social development (8, 132, 135). As noted in Chapters 5-7, loss of hearing prior to the establishment of language is detrimental in all three areas, and contributes to an imbalance between physiological and psychological maturity.

It is remarkable, therefore, that over one-third of this group of deaf achievers lost all hearing before the age of nine months, 80 per cent of them

## TABLE 2
### Educational background of 27 deaf achievers

| Case No. | Age in years | | Educational background | | | | Achievement category |
|---|---|---|---|---|---|---|---|
| | At time of evaluation | At onset of deafness | Elementary school | High school | College | Advanced degree | |
| 1 | 58 | 10 | C* | A* | A | Yes | Professional |
| 2 | 38 | 0.5 | A | A | A | Yes | Professional |
| 3 | 67 | 5 | A | A | A | Yes | Professional |
| 5 | 46 | 2 | B* | A | A | No | Professional |
| 6 | 78 | 11 | C | B | None | No | Business† |
| 7 | 47 | 11 | C | A | A | No | Professional |
| 8 | 51 | Birth | B | A | A | Yes | Professional |
| 9 | 70 | 7 | C | B | B | Yes | Professional |
| 10 | 40 | 2 | B | A | A | Yes | Professional |
| 11 | 48 | Birth | B | A | A | No | Professional |
| 12 | 61 | 5 | B | B | B | No | Professional |
| 13 | 35 | 7 | B | A | A | No | Professional |
| 14 | 64 | Birth | B | B | None | No | Professional |
| 15 | 47 | 9 | C | A | A | Yes | Professional |
| 16 | 41 | Birth | B | A | None | No | Business |
| 17 | 37 | Under 2 | B | A | A | No | Professional |
| 18 | 28 | 0.7 | B | B | A | No | Professional |
| 20 | 43 | Birth | B | B | None | No | Artist |
| 21 | 47 | Birth | B | A | A** | No | Business |
| 22 | 61 | Birth | None | None | None | No | Artist |
| 23 | 58 | 3 | B | B | B | No | Professional |
| 27 | 52 | 8 | C | B | B | No | Professional |
| 29 | 51 | 9 | C | B | B | No | Professional |
| 30 | 52 | Birth | B | B | None | No | Leadership |
| 32 | 28 | 7 | B | A | B | No | Professional |
| 33 | 29 | 1.5 | A | A | B | No | Professional |
| 37 | 36 | 5‡ | B | A | None | No | Professional |

\* A  attended school without special facilities for the deaf.
  B  attended school with special facilities for the deaf.
  C  attended both types of schools.

\*\* Attended only for one year, all others graduated.

† Also recognized leader of the deaf.

‡ Progressive loss of hearing, began at age two and was complete by age five.

having been born deaf. As mentioned previously, one of the nationally recognized leaders of the deaf never experienced auditory perception. If only the 19 individuals are considered who became deaf after birth, the median age for onset of total deafness was five years. This finding is in substantial agreement with the median age of seven years reported in a preliminary analysis of potential achievers (179). The median age drops to two years when the eight persons who were born deaf are included. As a matter of fact, more than one-half (55.6%) of the entire group of 27 achievers were totally deaf by the age of three years, i.e. before speech patterns had become well established.

These accomplishments in no way minimize the stultifying effects of deafness. Rather, they reflect the extraordinary endowment which the given achievers must have had to overcome the handicap of complete hearing loss. Among the factors that led to achievement in this group were those based on intellectual and personality traits, family background, and educational opportunities. While it was not feasible to administer psychological tests to them, personal interviews conducted by trained investigators classified these individuals as above average intelligence. They also furnished evidence of those strong features of personality that make for success. Despite limited academic opportunities for persons so handicapped, the majority of the given subjects completed a college education.

*Educational Background:* Although only one-quarter (25.9%) obtained advanced degrees (3 Ph.D.'s, 2D.D.S.'s, 2 M.A.'s), more than two-thirds (70.4%) of the 27 deaf achievers were college graduates (Table 2). Gallaudet College contributed seven graduates, one of whom subsequently earned an advanced degree at a ranking university. The remaining 12 achievers attended colleges without special facilities for the deaf, six completing their graduate education. Columbia, Fordham, Illinois, Princeton, Yale, and New York University were among the institutions represented.

Moreover, four of the achievers pursued studies at leading universities in their chosen areas of specialization, without remaining long enough to receive an advanced degree. Another six attended specialized institutes of art, architecture or design, while still another was awarded an honorary doctorate even though his regular education had terminated in high school. Two persons who became totally deaf at the ages of two and ten years, respectively, were elected to Phi Beta Kappa. One of them was also a member of Sigma Xi (national honorary scientific society), and had been valedictorian of his hearing high school graduating class.

To examine the relationship between age at onset of deafness and educational achievement (Table 2), the subjects were divided into the following three groups: (1) *born deaf* (8 achievers), (2) *became deaf in early childhood* (three years or younger), before language and speech patterns had been well established (7 achievers), and (3) *became deaf in later childhood* (12 achievers).

The proportion of persons with advanced degrees was 13 per cent of those deaf since birth; 29 per cent of those deaf since early childhood; and 33 per cent of those deaf since later childhood. This distribution suggests a positive correlation between age at onset of deafness and academic achievement. Because non-professional groups rarely comprise people with advanced degrees, the proportions were recomputed for the professionals alone in each onset category. Here the association between age at onset and completion of graduate training was less distinct, the corresponding rates being 33, 29 and 36 per cent for those deaf since birth, since early childhood, and since later childhood respectively.

As for undergraduate training (Table 2), comparison of the number of college graduates among achievers deaf since birth (25%) with those deaf since early childhood (100%) or later childhood (83%) again seemed to point to the retarding effects of congenital deafness. Limiting the comparison to professionals failed to change this trend (67%, 100% and 91%, respectively). Notable was the completion of college education by all seven achievers who became deaf between the ages of six months and three years.

At some time during their pre-college training, all but four of the achievers attended schools with special facilities for deaf students (Table 2). The four exceptions were made possible by the use of private tutors, in one instance without formal education. The other three attended hearing schools, although one of them subsequently chose to attend Gallaudet College.

Otherwise, all the achievers who were born deaf or became so in early childhood received their primary education at schools designed for the deaf, as did four of those who became totally deaf in later childhood (between the ages of 5 and 7 years). The rest attended both types of elementary school, usually transferring to special schools after the onset of deafness. The only achiever trained exclusively at primary and secondary schools for the deaf, who entered a hearing college, went on to graduate in the top third of his class.

Of the 27 deaf achievers, 13 attended private primary or secondary schools, but eight of them received supplemental instruction. Private tutoring during school years was also reported by several others, and only two of the entire series stated that no additional help had been available to them. In 12 cases, aid was given by a parent, another relative, or friend. The mother of one such achiever founded a school for the deaf in an area where none had previously existed. If these 12 cases are combined with the 13 who reported private tutoring, over 90 per cent of the deaf achievers received supplemental educational aid during their school years.

*Family History:* In the families of the achievers, deafness occurred infrequently, a deaf relative being reported by only seven. One had two deaf parents as well as two deaf children; another a deaf sister; and a third a deaf grandmother and great-grandmother. In three other families, two second cousins and the child of a first cousin were deaf. One achiever had a brother whose hearing loss was limited to one ear.

The majority of the parents were in the middle or upper income bracket. More than three-quarters of the fathers (80.5%) were either business executives or professionals. While most of them were active in the business world, there was one physician, one teacher, and one religious leader.

As to marital status, it may be noted that one-third of the achievers remained single. All but two of them were over 35 years old at the time of interview, with two women falling into this category. Since general population rates differ for the sexes and our group of achievers contained but four women, our comparisons will be limited to the 23 male achievers. In this category, 30 per cent never married. This rate is not very different from the 28 per cent found for the New York State population of deaf men over age 25. However, it is much higher than the corresponding general population rate for New York State (14% single men). As was to be expected from data on the New York State population of the deaf, there were more bachelors among the congenitally deaf male achievers (43%) than among those who became deaf after birth (25%).

Among the 16 married men, the ages at first marriage ranged from 24 to 42 years, with a median and a mean of 29 years. The corresponding ages of their wives ranged from 17 to 38 years and were on the average two years lower (median and mean 27 years). Only two wives were older than their husbands (each by three years). One of them was hearing, the other deaf. The largest age difference was found between a hearing wife and her mate who was 13 years her senior.

Of the 18 marriages (including those of two female achievers), six were childless. The remaining 12 contributed 25 children, all but two of whom had normal hearing. Only one of the deaf achievers was divorced.

Of the 16 wives, five were hearing, two hard of hearing, and nine deaf. Thus 56 per cent of the men married deaf wives (the two married women also chose deaf husbands), and only 31 per cent had hearing wives. By comparison, an even smaller proportion of the males in the deaf population of New York State (10%) married hearing women. In other words, while three times as many married males in the achiever group, compared with all New York State deaf married males, had chosen hearing wives, still over two-thirds had deaf mates. Of the eight top professionals, four had hearing wives and three had deaf ones, and one remained single. Three of the four men with highest academic achievement who married hearing wives listed them as having contributed to their success. Only one other achiever credited his marriage partner in a similar way.

### Factors Contributing to Success

The achievers were asked what factors they regarded as essential in their success. Encouragement, guidance and the support of others were cited most frequently (Table 3), followed closely by the strength gained through their particular personal attributes. While 18 deaf achievers believed that the help of a close relative, such as a parent, sibling, uncle or aunt, con-

## TABLE 3
### Factors responsible for success according to the achievers themselves

| | | |
|---|---:|---:|
| 1. Encouragement, guidance and support by others | | 33 |
|     Relatives | 18 | |
|     Hearing contacts | 9 | |
|     Marriage partner | 4 | |
|     Specific teachers | 2 | |
| 2. Education | | 11 |
|     Proficiency in speech and lipreading | 6 | |
|     Good training at school for the deaf | 3 | |
|     College education | 2 | |
| 3. Personal attributes | | 25 |
|     Motivation, initiative and drive | 9 | |
|     Ability to rise above handicap | 3 | |
|     Willingness to expend extra effort | 3 | |
|     Willingness to forget deafness | 3 | |
|     Willingness to accept deafness | 2 | |
|     Individual capability | 2 | |
|     Courage | 1 | |
|     Extraversion | 1 | |
|     Social value of athletics | 1 | |
| 4. Miscellaneous | | 5 |
|     Proper contacts | 4 | |
|     Late onset of deafness | 1 | |
| | | 74 |

tributed a great deal, only four marriage partners and two teachers were so credited. Among the personal qualities considered as pertinent to unusual accomplishments, drive and initiative received prominent mention. Of particular interest were the statements of three subjects who seemed to be convinced that a willingness to forget one's deafness was necessary for success. However, two achievers were of the opposite opinion and actually suggested that acceptance of one's deafness was a requisite. Other factors included education, late onset of deafness, and possession of the "right" contacts.

On the whole, achievement in the hearing world has been ascribed to good family background, notably in terms of socioeconomic status with an intellectual and cultural home milieu (100, 145, 187, 191, 231). Personality factors including initiative, originality, motivation, and intellectual flexibility have also been described as important elements in achievement and creativity (19, 32, 87, 98, 215). Other investigators have emphasized the role of intellectual endowment and educational opportunity (36, 41, 77, 148). Thus, the factors considered important by deaf achievers for their own success corresponded generally to those derived from studies of achievement in the hearing population.

Defining outstanding achievement in the hearing world has proved a formidable task. Stein and Heinze (218) in their careful review of the literature on creativity included the following criteria: psychological measures, literature citations, acknowledgment by other professionals, general recognition of prominence, numerical counts of creative products, and engagement in artistic endeavors that require creativity. As expected, the diversified approaches to the study of creativity led to a variety of conclusions.

An interesting suggestion has been made to the effect that the dominant philosophy of a culture may actually be an important factor in either stimulating or impeding achievement (217). Therefore, the communication barrier in deafness may serve not only to limit the scope of vocational activities attainable by the deaf, but may also interfere with attempts to convey to the deaf person the value placed on achievement by the hearing. While the major goal of the deaf community seems to be that of winning equality with the hearing, adjustment to the sensory defect and contentment in life are obviously not equal to achievement as defined in the hearing world.

It cannot be denied that few if any of the 27 achievers listed would qualify as persons of outstanding attainment among the hearing. Yet the difference between the accomplishments of the selected subjects, academic or otherwise, and those of the average deaf is impressive. In fact, it is comparable to that between outstanding and average hearing persons.

### Conclusions

In conclusion, it may be stated that generally the factors associated with unusual achievement among the deaf tend to be similar to those described for the hearing. To overcome the markedly retarding effects of early total deafness, it appears that far greater effort, endowment and opportunity are required than for equivalent accomplishments of hearing persons.

Deaf children with high intellectual endowments should be given every encouragement to develop communication skills which will enable them to make both written and oral contacts with hearing people. They should be provided with tutors, in addition to formal education, and be guided towards accomplishment in those areas where they can best attain success.

Based on the findings of the present study, a variety of careers appear to be open to the gifted student with a complete hearing loss. In our series, art, architecture, engineering, chemistry, dentistry and accounting were among the fields selected by talented deaf persons of unusual achievement. Sustained efforts in these areas may prove to be rewarding for many others aiming at outstanding success.

# Chapter 9

## DELINQUENCY AND CRIME

### M. Michael Klaber and Arthur Falek

For a long time, the inability of hearing persons to communicate readily with hearing-impaired individuals led to the general assumption that the deaf were legally incompetent. Along with minors, the mentally retarded, and the mentally ill, deaf persons were accorded the special protection of the courts and were thereby deprived of the full privileges of citizenship (22, 243).

Only during the past few decades have workers for the welfare of the deaf succeeded in eliminating most if not all of the discriminatory laws. The present tendency is to regard deaf persons in court as very much like other citizens (22). From a legal point of view, the status of the deaf offender corresponds to that of a hearing person who commits an antisocial act.

Although many agencies are concerned with varying aspects of delinquency and crime, little information is available on offenses committed by deaf persons. The dearth of research in this area is in part a consequence of the reluctance among both the deaf and the many good people working with them to arouse animosity. What is often glossed over are the facts that deafness is a handicap and that some deaf persons do commit antisocial acts. The findings of the few studies devoted to the latter problem have been contradictory.

Data comparing a group of juvenile delinquents to a matched group of non-delinquent controls showed no difference in the incidence of hearing impairment in the two groups (80). In another study, however, based on teachers' ratings, boys in a residential school for the deaf were found to be more prone to outbursts of temper and habits of stealing than a group of hearing controls in public schools (213). Such variables as rating standards and the effects of prolonged dormitory life were not controlled in this study. After a review of the available literature, Barker and his associates (16) concluded that there was no strong association between delinquency and deafness.

Information has been lacking not only with respect to the types of offense committed by deaf persons, but also regarding the psychological determinants of antisocial acting-out tendencies among the deaf, and of the ways in which law enforcement agencies tend to deal with such offenders.

It was decided, therefore, in connection with our pilot study of the demographic, social, and psychiatric aspects of early total deafness, to undertake a special study of a series of individuals with profound hearing loss, who had come into contact with law enforcement agencies.

### Collection of Cases

In order to assess the frequency of offenses committed by deaf individuals in New York State, it was necessary to get in touch with local law enforcement agencies, corrective institutions, and state mental hospitals. All agencies approached assured us of their willingness to cooperate. However, it was especially the fact that they were not required to indicate the hearing status of the offender on their records, which caused considerable difficulty in collecting our case material. The impracticability of searching the case histories of every offender in the hope of finding deaf lawbreakers forced us to rely on the memory of those in authority for recalling the names of deaf offenders.

With data on the number of arrests or convictions of deaf persons unavailable, we could not collect statistically useful information on the incidence of criminal acts among the deaf. Instead, we focused our analysis on 51 deaf persons residing in New York State, whose criminal activities came to our attention during the period 1957-1961. These cases were derived from such diverse sources as penal institutions, state mental hospitals, parole and probation bureaus, and daily newspaper items, as well as from the files of our own outpatient services for the deaf. It can be seen from Table 1 that over one-half (59%) of the deaf offenders included in this study were referred by mental hygiene facilities, while approximately one-quarter (27%) of the group were reported by law enforcement agencies.

**TABLE 1**
Sources of ascertainment of 51 New York State deaf offenders

| Ascertainment | Number of cases |
|---|---|
| Penal institutions | 6 |
| Mental hospitals* | 13 |
| Division of Parole | 5 |
| Bureau of Probation | 3 |
| Daily newspapers | 7 |
| Psychiatric Clinic for the Deaf | 17 |
| **Total** | **51** |

*Under the jurisdiction of the State Departments of Mental Hygiene and Correction.

*Offenses Committed*

The offenses committed by this group ranged from vagrancy to first degree murder. In Table 2 the 51 deaf offenders are classified according to the type of legal violation and the age (under or over the age of 21) at the time of the offense. In those cases where more than one type of offense had been committed, the more serious violation was used for analysis.

As is seen from Table 2, the largest number of cases fell into the area

### TABLE 2
**Types of violations committed by 51 deaf offenders**

| Type of violation | Under age 21 | Over age 21 | Total |
|---|:---:|:---:|:---:|
| Assault | 5* | 3 | 8 |
| Bookmaking | – | 1 | 1 |
| Burglary and theft | 3 | 2 | 5 |
| Disorderly conduct | 1 | 6 | 7 |
| Forgery | 1 | 1 | 2 |
| Homosexuality | 2 | 5* | 7 |
| Indecent exposure | – | 1 | 1 |
| Manslaughter | – | 1 | 1 |
| Molesting females | 2 | 1 | 3 |
| Murder | – | 3 | 3 |
| Narcotics | 1 | 1 | 2 |
| Pedophilia | 1 | 4 | 5 |
| Persistent reckless driving | – | 1 | 1 |
| Promiscuity | 3** | – | 3 |
| Shoplifting | 1 | – | 1 |
| Vagrancy | 1 | – | 1 |
| **Total** | **21** | **30** | **51** |

*Includes one female
**All females

of sexual offenses, including pedophilia (5 cases), molesting females (3 cases), promiscuity (3 cases), indecent exposure (1 case), and homosexuality (7 cases). There were also eight cases of assault (15.7%), seven of disorderly conduct (13.7%), and five of burglary and theft (9.8%). Moreover, three murderers (5.9%) and one convicted of manslaughter were found in this group, as well as two forgers, two narcotics peddlers, and one case each of vagrancy, persistent reckless driving, shoplifting and bookmaking.

*Characteristics of the Offenders*

Sociologically, the deaf form a unique subculture, membership in which is determined solely by their physical disability. In a society dominated by the hearing, deaf persons of necessity frequently associate with one another, living apart from the world of the hearing yet having to conform to its laws.

Of special interest in considering the deaf offender was whether or not any other member of his immediate family was deaf. The majority of deaf offenders in this series (60.7%) came from homes with two hearing parents, and only a few (9.8%) had one or both parents deaf (Table 3). These minimum estimates apparently reflect the high frequency of hearing parents in this group, similar to that obtained for the general deaf population (see Chapter 2). On the other hand, 13 deaf offenders (25.5%) had one or more deaf siblings, whereas only ten (19.6%) were from homes where all the siblings were presumably hearing. The proportion of deaf offenders with at least one deaf sib seems unusually high.

As to marital status (Table 4) it may be noted that three-quarters of this series of deaf persons who committed antisocial acts were single at the time of their arrest. The most plausible or at least a partial explanation of this finding was the youthfulness of the entire group, since the mean age of the offenders when arrested was 24 years. The ages of the 46 men ranged from 14 to 65 years with a mean age of 25 years, while the average age of the five women was 17 years, ranging from 13 to 22 years. The one female in the group of offenders over the age of 21 came to our attention because of homosexual activities. The other four, between 13 and 17 years old, were arrested for some form of delinquency.

Like hearing offenders, most of the deaf lawbreakers came from lower socio-economic levels. If they happened to be employed at the time of the offense, the job was usually a menial one, such as dishwashing or grave digging. In a few instances, the offender was working at a highly skilled occupation, but the large majority were unemployed at the time when the offense was committed.

Information about school histories was available on 20 subjects. As may be seen from Table 5, nine of these individuals later committed sexual offenses, while 11 manifested other types of asocial behavior. The school records of all the non-sexual offenders and almost one-half of the sexual offenders indicated patterns of delinquency early in life, with expulsion from several schools in some cases.

### Attitudes of Law Enforcement Agencies

In conversations with members of law enforcement agencies, we gained the impression that the deaf offender, because of his difficulties in communication, is likely to be treated in a rather haphazard but sympathetic fashion. Seldom do the police arrest a deaf person for a minor offense. For instance, such an individual is rarely arraigned or convicted for peddling, although it is well known that many deaf persons perennially sell small articles from door to door.

A case history in point was that of Joe, an 18-year-old deaf boy convicted of "vagrancy." The only deaf child among five children of hearing

## TABLE 3
### Hearing status in relatives of deaf offenders

| Offenders | Parents | | | Spouse | | | Siblings | | | |
|---|---|---|---|---|---|---|---|---|---|---|
| | Both hearing | One or both deaf | Unknown | Hearing | Deaf | Unknown | All hearing | One or more deaf | Unknown | No sibs |
| Male | 31 | 4 | 11 | 2 | 2 | 7 | 8 | 13 | 14 | 11 |
| Female | 3 | 1 | 1 | 1 | 0 | 0 | 2 | 0 | 1 | 2 |
| Total | 34 | 5 | 12 | 3 | 2 | 7 | 10 | 13 | 15 | 13 |

### TABLE 4
Marital status of deaf offenders

| Sex | Single | Married | Separated or divorced | Unknown |
|-----|--------|---------|-----------------------|---------|
| Male | 35 | 5 | 3 | 3 |
| Female | 4 | 0 | 1 | 0 |
| Total | 39 | 5 | 4 | 3 |

### TABLE 5
Relation between nature of offense and
school behavior record in 20 deaf offenders

| Offense | Poor behavior record | Good behavior record | Total |
|---------|----------------------|----------------------|-------|
| Sex offenses | 4 | 5 | 9 |
| Other offenses | 11 | 0 | 11 |
| Total | 15 | 5 | 20 |

parents, he had never been treated as an equal at home, and did not get along well with either his parents or siblings. Although he was described as having been a "disruptive influence in the classroom," he was able to graduate from school. Afterwards, he sporadically attended a printing school. His performance on jobs assigned to him was poor and he never stayed on any one longer than a few months.

One day, while selling alphabet cards from door to door, he entered a beauty parlor and was asked to leave by the proprietress. In the argument that ensued he pushed her violently to the ground. When the police arrived, she refused to press assault charges because of his disability. Nevertheless, he was arrested for "vagrancy," convicted, and placed on parole for two years.

Evidently, Joe came to the attention of the court not because of his illegal sale of alphabet cards, but because of his unruly behavior. Furthermore, the injured woman refused to press assault charges against a deaf man.

Almost without exception, charges against the deaf are brought by municipal authorities rather than by private individuals. In court, the legal status of the deaf person is the same as that of any other citizen, except for the fact that manual communication is treated as a foreign language (69). An interpreter is assigned to the deaf defendant, or a friend or relative is asked to interpret for him. According to our observations, the courts usually deal quite leniently with the deaf offender in terms of conviction and length of sentence.

Since the modern judicial system is more interested in rehabilitation than punishment, the court prefers to put an offender on probation wherever possible, rather than sentence him to prison. Parole from prison is also granted with a view towards the benefits which the offender might derive from the guidance and counsel of the parole officer. Unfortunately, as the parole and probation authorities do not have officers trained in the use of the sign language of the deaf, difficulties in communication between the deaf offender and the rehabilitation officer often create an insurmountable barrier.

The following quotations from parole records may illustrate this point: A deaf thief—"Up to the present time there has been no difficulty in his supervision as far as his behavior is concerned, but the parole officer finds it quite difficult to communicate with him . . . "

A deaf man convicted of assault—"As far as parole supervision was concerned, the parole officer found that there was a complete lack of communication with him; he could not talk, was unable to write intelligibly . . . "

A murderer who served thirteen years in prison—"According to the record he has made a satisfactory adjustment, but the parole officer relates that he is a difficult person to supervise because he cannot understand the parole officer and the parole officer has similar difficulty with him. Communication is entirely through the use of written notes . . . "

It is not surprising, therefore, that despite lenient sentences frequently meted out by the courts, deaf offenders lack adequate supervision during their period of rehabilitation.

## Psychological Considerations

According to the results of various psychological studies, deaf persons rarely attain the degree of maturity found in hearing individuals. In particular, investigations using the Rorschach and other projective techniques have shown that the deaf tend to display emotional immaturity, personality constriction and deficient emotional adaptability (135). Also, tests with the Vineland Social Maturity Scale consistently reveal that deaf persons are less mature than hearing control subjects (16). Apparently, individuals deprived of the experience of hearing sounds and speech from an early age lag in their ability to conceptualize and synthesize ideas. With their capacity for abstract reasoning so limited, it is no wonder the deaf have difficulty adjusting to the complexities of modern society.

Generally speaking, individuals who are always getting into trouble with the law show certain psychological traits similar to those found in the deaf. Delinquents have been described as impulsive, immature and irresponsible (128). They, too, score lower on the Vineland Social Maturity Scale, and it is interesting to note that hearing offenders also manifest a deficit on verbal intelligence test items as compared with non-verbal ones (165).

Theoretically, criminal activities can be viewed as manifestations of varying degrees of immaturity, defined according to a scale of personality integration. Vagrancy, for example, often reflects a lack of personality integration which results in undirected and disorganized forms of behavior. Similarly, sex offenses are frequently the result of a circumscribed failure of maturation occurring in an otherwise well-functioning personality during the formative years. Less primitive are the impulsive acts. These undeliberated offenses are produced by deficiencies in the mechanism of control (conscience) developing later in personality maturation. Premeditated crimes, on the other hand, require a degree of foresight and restraint, a large measure of goal-directed action, and perhaps a higher level of integration. If deaf persons in general are less mature than hearing persons, the types of offenses rated according to maturity should have somewhat different frequencies for the deaf than the hearing.

To establish roughly an index of immaturity, we classified the offenses committed by our deaf according to the following ascending order of personality integration:

1. Disorganized behavior (disorderly conduct and vagrancy).
2. Sex offenses (homosexuality, pedophilia and abnormal heterosexual activities).
3. Impulsive acting out (unpremeditated acts of violence or theft).
4. Premeditated crime (planned criminal acts such as forgery and bookmaking).

On the basis of this index, there were in our series 8 cases of disorganized behavior offenses (disorderly conduct and vagrancy), 19 sex offenders, 14 impulsive acts of violence (murder, manslaughter, assault, reckless driving and shoplifting), and 10 cases of premeditated crime (forgery, narcotics, bookmaking, burglary and theft).

It may be of particular interest that in the general criminal population (159), sex offenders, even including prostitutes, constitute the smallest number of arraignments. In our series, however, sex offenders formed the largest group (37%), although no cases of prostitution were involved.

The usefulness of arraignment data for comparative purposes is decidedly limited. In our series, for example, only major offenses were classified. However, persons may be arraigned in court more than once during a given year for infractions of a particular law, with each arraignment counted separately. Furthermore, since court charges are frequently not identical with the committed offense and rarely clarify whether or not the act was premeditated, many difficulties are encountered in classifying offenses other than those recorded by the courts as sex violations.

Law officers, on the basis of years of experience, are known to report a large number of deaf sex offenders. It remains a moot point whether the prolonged period of residential education, the general level of social and psychological immaturity, the strict attitude of the police towards all sexual deviates, or all three factors combined contribute to this observation. Whatever the causes, it is certain that sex offenders represent a sizeable proportion of deaf persons brought to trial.

With psychosis being a manifestation of disorganized behavior patterns, psychiatric evaluation of the offenders also provides a measure in our rating scale. When the deaf offenders were classified according to the immaturity of the offense (Table 6), it was found that the frequency of diagnosed psychotics decreases as the level of maturity rises.

### TABLE 6
Frequency of psychosis in law violators classified according to category of offense

| Category | Number of offenders | Per cent psychotic |
|---|---|---|
| Disorganized behavior | 8 | 75.0 |
| Sex offenses | 19 | 31.6 |
| Impulsive acts | 14 | 21.4 |
| Premeditated crime | 10 | 10.0 |

A closer examination of some of the premeditated antisocial acts indicated that they may also be manifestations of immaturity. For example, a 17-year-old boy in our group stole a small transistor radio from an appliance store. Since he was deaf, the radio was the one item in the store of no use to him, especially since he had no plans for disposing of it. Still another deaf youngster was arrested while removing sideview mirrors from parked automobiles. Here, too, the act reflected a definite lack of judgment.

Patterns of gross immaturity were also discernible in the acts of violence committed by deaf offenders. The case of Paul is a good illustration. A deaf boy from a rural area, he came to our attention after having been sentenced to prison for manslaughter. His father, a chronic alcoholic, had deserted his wife, when Paul was only a few months old, and later committed suicide. The mother remarried twice.

Paul stayed in a residential school for four years before he was expelled as a serious problem. He had to leave another school after only six months because of similar difficulties. Both schools reported that he was uncontrollable and exerted a bad influence over the other students.

After dismissal from school, he held various jobs for short periods of time. At the age of 18, he married an ill-mannered deaf girl who bore him three children. Nevertheless, they continued to consort with questionable company, and a few years later, both had criminal records, he for burglary and she for promiscuity. They never had more than a makeshift home, and they soon were divorced.

Most of Paul's friends were also deaf and had poor school and work records. Among his cronies was a known "bully" who had been arrested several times on charges of assault. The two had met at school, but had long been rivals. One evening in a tavern patronized by the deaf, Paul shot his rival for no apparent reason.

At the trial Paul was described as emotionally unstable and lacking insight. Since most of the witnesses were deaf, and no complete history of the crime could be obtained from them, he was convicted of manslaughter and sentenced to five years in prison. He was paroled after a year, but he soon came again to the attention of the police because of assaultive behavior. He then was returned to prison and served his full sentence. Paul's history was similar to that of many hearing offenders and typical of the chronic sociopath. A behavior problem at school, he soon drifted into regular contacts with known criminals and accumulated a lengthy criminal record at an early age. The responsibilities of marriage had no effect on his career in crime.

The significant role of mental illness in the occurrence of some impulsive acts was exemplified by John, one of eleven children of an immigrant family. The mother was committed to a state hospital before he reached school age, and was never seen by him again. The father was described as an alcoholic who neglected his family. Placed in a residential farm school for the deaf, John remained there continuously until the age of 21.

As a professional boxer, he won local acclaim for his prowess in the ring, although his interest in fighting was strictly a financial one. Following his marriage to a local deaf girl, he never discussed his childhood experiences and kept largely to himself. According to his wife, he was basically a quiet man who felt cheated in life through his hearing loss and therefore withdrew more and more from social contact.

After winning the heavyweight championship in his local community, John retired from the ring at his wife's request and took a job as a laborer with a local company. Since he showed increasing evidence of a violent temper, he became the terror of the neighborhood. On one occasion, he destroyed the furniture and dinnerware in his own apartment. At other times, he assaulted neighbors and merchants.

He became well known to the local authorities, and was arrested a score of times after repeated warnings by the neighborhood police. However, as soon as he was arraigned before a judge, he managed to obtain his release because of his handicap. When his outbursts became even more violent, he had to be committed to a state hospital where he was diagnosed as a paranoid schizophrenic. Following his escape from the hospital, he presumably returned to the haunts of his boyhood in the Midwest.

Cases of this kind serve to illustrate the isolation of the deaf person from the community and its special services. At the same time, they testify to the importance of psychiatric facilities for the early recognition and treatment of mental illness in potential deaf offenders.

Even those deaf persons who committed apparently premeditated acts of law-breaking were found to be more immature than their hearing counterparts. There was no evidence to indicate that deaf persons in general are unable to plan criminal acts. Our impression was, however, that they are often the dupes of hearing individuals who involved them in premeditated offenses. For example, they were used as runners in policy rackets or in the distribution of narcotics.

## Recommendations

In view of these observations, the following recommendations may be made:

1. Law enforcement agencies would do well to establish a special category on their charts for recording physical handicaps of offenders. This step would permit the collection of a representative sample of cases, a prerequisite for studying the particular problems posed by law violators with a handicap such as deafness.

2. Law enforcement authorities working with deaf offenders require training in the use of sign language and in the special problems of the deaf. Qualified personnel to counsel deaf offenders is urgently needed for crime prevention and rehabilitation of offenders.

3. Special classes for deaf children with behavior disorders ought to be established in every state. Existing schools for the deaf are not equipped to work with these problem children. A special effort to help rather than expel them may be a strong preventive measure for combatting adult crime.

4. Agencies for the deaf should employ psychiatrically trained workers, alert to the signs of disordered behavior. Therapeutic and preventive measures can then be applied before serious acts of violence are committed.

PART TWO

PSYCHIATRIC CONSIDERATIONS: CLINICAL

OUTPATIENT PROGRAM

# Chapter 10

## OPERATIONAL DESCRIPTION OF PILOT CLINIC

KENNETH Z. ALTSHULER, GEORGE S. BAROFF, AND JOHN D. RAINER

While hospitalized, usually psychotic, persons represent an important special group, an overall view of the mental health problems and needs of the deaf could only be obtained through psychiatric study in the general deaf community. For this purpose, the project from its inception operated a pilot outpatient mental health clinic. Established as a limited part of the total research project, the clinic was manned by specially trained staff members and was open for consultation and treatment two days each week. Its main aims were to define common mental health problems among the deaf, and to develop and provide appropriate therapeutic methods and services.

Initial appointments were usually made through the mail or by telephone with the referring agency or individual. In each case, after thorough diagnostic evaluation, management recommendations were determined at staff conferences. Through regular multidisciplinary discussions, staff members were able to pool and broaden their own clinical experience, while offering necessary modifications in treatment plans where indicated.

In all, 217 persons applied to the clinic (Table 1). Fifty did not follow through after their initial approach, for the most part because proper evaluation could not be achieved by correspondence alone, and distance precluded direct consultations. Several patients, however, did travel from neighboring states and northern New York. A few applicants even offered to move their families thousands of miles for relocation in search of a successful resolution of their problems. In eight cases our research teams were able to evaluate patients outside the metropolitan area on special field trips.

The proportions of men and women in the clinic population were not significantly different, although there was a slight preponderance of males. The age distribution (Table 1) reflected the efforts of the clinic to limit services to persons over the age of 14 except in unusual situations. The concentration in the age range 13 to 31, while probably representing the greatest area of need, also resulted from increasing utilization of our services by schools for the deaf and by vocational and health agencies concerned with rehabilitation of young adults. In view of our relatively close association with these agencies, the 27 patients or 16.2 per cent over 40 years of

## TABLE 1
### The deaf clinic population by age and sex

| Group | Age | Male | Female | Total |
|---|---|---|---|---|
| Clinic patients | 0 - 12 | 3 | 2 | 5 |
| | 13 - 20 | 37 | 28 | 65 |
| | 21 - 30 | 27 | 18 | 45 |
| | 31 - 40 | 13 | 12 | 25 |
| | 41 - 50 | 7 | 8 | 15 |
| | 51+ | 6 | 6 | 12 |
| Applicants unable to attend clinic | All ages | 28 | 22 | 50 |
| Total | | 121 | 96 | 217 |

age probably underreflect the need for outpatient services among middle-aged or older persons.

As shown in Table 2, patients came from a variety of sources, with the largest number sent from groups directly interested in the deaf. The rest came from vocational, corrective or welfare agencies, private physicians or hospitals, or were self-referrals. The last group of persons had the initiative to seek out our project as a unique source of help for their special needs. Over the years, the size of this group grew considerably as a result of more widespread awareness of the clinic's existence. Had there been more publicity given the project, self-referrals would no doubt have been even more numerous, since the deaf community itself showed a keen appreciation of the need for such facilities.

The most common reasons for referral were acute psychiatric illness,

## TABLE 2
### Referral sources of deaf clinic population

| Source | Male | Female | Total |
|---|---|---|---|
| Division of Vocational Rehabilitation | 19 | 16 | 35 |
| Schools for the deaf | 21 | 9 | 30 |
| Organizations for the deaf | 14 | 22 | 36 |
| Correction and welfare agencies | 13 | 4 | 17 |
| Hospitals, clinics, private physicians | 16 | 18 | 34 |
| Family, friend or self-referred | 21 | 23 | 44 |
| Not indicated | 17 | 4 | 21 |
| Total | 121 | 96 | 217 |

homosexuality, poor work adjustment, social conflicts and family problems. The diagnostic distribution in Table 3 extends to virtually every form of psychiatric illness found in the hearing. Cases with more than one diagnosis were common. In addition, there were many atypical cases difficult to classify. Second only to schizophrenia (27.5%) in frequency was the diagnostic category of passive-aggressive personality disorder (20.4%) with a preponderance of the passive-dependent type.

Overt homosexuality, usually in the characterologic framework of such dependent personalities, was the predominant feature in 11.4 per cent of the total clinic population. To be sure, the types of patients seen by us were largely determined by the attitudes and considerations of the agencies referring them. Nevertheless, there is reason to believe that the frequency of homosexuality may be increased in dependent, handicapped, and sequestered groups such as the deaf.

Other common syndromes were antisocial reaction, intellectual subnormalcy, involutional disturbances, and situational reactions. For three patients we coined the term "primitive personality." Two were girls, 18 and 14 years of age, and the other a boy. In all three the clinical picture was characterized by a normal intellectual potential coupled with an almost total absence of language development. Conceptual and abstraction abilities remained undifferentiated and childlike. When approached on their level, the patients' emotional range was normal; they were warmly responsive and open, and their affective reactions appeared appropriate. In daily life, however, their behavior had the quality of emergency responses to an ever-present feeling of danger.

To illustrate, the 18-year-old girl was seen at the request of her parents who were thinking of having her committed to a school for the retarded. Her education, after a late start, had included several years at a school for the deaf, where she was classified as a slow learner. Her behavior had been erratic, with what the school authorities termed " . . . uncontrolled aggression and an ego structure in precarious balance." She proved to be unable to relate to either staff or peers, and was hostile to her mother at home, assaultive, and on occasion stealing. She frequently appeared to just "drag herself around" in stuporous fashion.

With this history, the form and content of her written communications seemed to point to defective intelligence or a schizophrenic process (Figure 1). However, comprehensive psychiatric interviews and psychological testing performed in sign language yielded no such evidence. Instead, the symptoms apparently resulted from the reaction of a primitive personality, undeveloped but capable of growth, to a world but vaguely apprehended.

On the basis of this diagnostic impression, she was placed on a program of rehabilitation. It consisted of further tutoring in communication, vocational training, and counseling for both the patient and her mother for whom the learning of signs was recommended. Over a two-year period of observation the patient did slowly but successfully pursue her vocational

## TABLE 3
### Diagnostic distribution of psychiatric disorders in deaf clinic patients

| Diagnosis | Number of cases |
|---|---|
| Psychotic disorders | |
|    a. Schizophrenic reaction | 46 |
|    b. Involutional psychotic reaction | 7 |
| Psychoneurotic disorders | |
|    a. Anxiety reaction | 5 |
|    b. Depressive reaction | 4 |
|    c. Phobic reaction | 2 |
|    d. Obsessive reaction | 2 |
|    e. Conversion reaction | 1 |
| Personality-pattern disturbances | |
|    a. Schizoid personality | 2 |
|    b. Inadequate personality | 1 |
|    c. Paranoid personality | 3 |
|    d. Other | 1 |
| Personality-trait disturbances | |
|    a. Passive aggressive personality | 34 |
|    b. Emotionally unstable personality | 2 |
|    c. Compulsive personality | 4 |
| Sociopathic personality disturbances | |
|    a. Antisocial reaction | 4 |
|    b. Sexual deviation | |
|      i. Transvestitism | 3 |
|      ii. Homosexuality | 19 |
| Transient situation personality disorder | |
|    a. Adjustment reaction of adolescence | 10 |
|    b. Adjustment reaction of adulthood | 10 |
| Psychophysiological autonomic and visceral disorders | 3 |
| Chronic brain syndrome | 3 |
| Mental deficiency | 15 |
| Primitive personality | 3 |
| No psychiatric illness | 9 |
| No diagnosis (incomplete study) | 9 |

## FIGURE 1

Schizophrenia-like communications of a non-psychotic deaf female

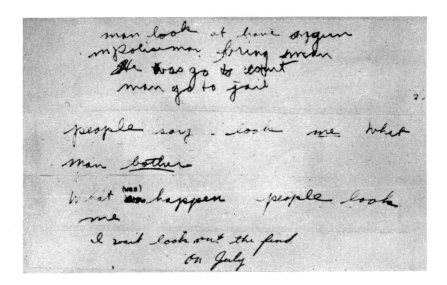

program, enhancing her communication skills and improving her relationship with her mother. More recently, she also started going out on dates.

The younger girl, too, had a limited education and was described as "behaving like an animal." The boy, who was referred by his school, was also a poor student. He seemed to be developing a phobic reaction to school, retreating more and more into personal ruminations. Similar therapeutic regimes were equally fruitful in these cases. The boy now holds a full-time job and has several friends, while the younger girl is continuing her educational training in school and under special tutelage, and is getting along well.

A striking example of the diagnostic pitfalls presented by deafness was the case of a 14-year-old girl with a history of temper tantrums and bizarre aggressive behavior. In school it was noted that "spinning like a top was a favorite pastime ... " One day she was found in a closet biting her arm. She had caused her nose to bleed by forcing her fingers into her nostrils. After she had several times assaulted schoolmates and relatives, using spoons as a weapon, she was expelled from school. She later ran away from home when asked to help with the dishes.

Ordinarily, behavior of this kind might suggest a schizophrenic process, and her fragmented language (Figure 2) would tend to confirm this diagnosis. However, careful clinical evaluation of this girl, who was almost

## FIGURE 2
### Fragmented language suggestive of schizophrenia

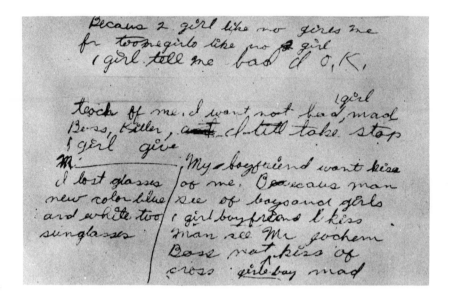

totally lacking in speech, failed to reveal any evidence of a psychosis. Our impression was that her maladjustment was due to family conflicts and painful social experiences associated with her handicap and, therefore, it was classified as a primary behavior disorder. Aided by appropriate recommendations, the patient was able to adjust sufficiently to be reinstated in a school for the deaf. The drawing shown in Figure 3 typifies her recent psychological test data which gave no evidence of psychotic distortion.

Such cases highlight some of the unique modifications imposed by deafness on phenomenology and on the interview process. Of course, their management requires skill in manual communication, as well as a general knowledge of the family settings and the special needs of the deaf. The necessity for special training is vividly illustrated in Table 4. The fair to good oralists with whom speech alone could be considered adequate for interviewing represented only 24.0 per cent of the cases seen. In the remaining 76.0 per cent, psychiatric evaluation could not even be approached without a thorough understanding of sign language. With the poorly skilled, fully 32.3 per cent, communication by any means would be ineffectual without the background of a broad study of deafness and its impact on life patterns and personality development.

Table 5 shows that these difficulties were not simply a matter of lack of

FIGURE 3

Figure drawing, showing no evidence of psychosis

**TABLE 4**
Communication skills of deaf clinic patients

| Means of communication | Skill in communication | | | | | | Total | | |
|---|---|---|---|---|---|---|---|---|---|
| | Good | | Fair | | Poor | | | | |
| | Male | Female | Male | Female | Male | Female | Male | Female | Both sexes |
| Manual only | 6 | 5 | 19 | 4 | 21 | 18 | 46 | 27 | 73 |
| Speech only | 8 | 10 | 11 | 12 | 6 | 7 | 25 | 29 | 54 |
| Combination of manual and speech | 11 | 10 | 11 | 6 | 0 | 2 | 22 | 18 | 40 |
| Total | 25 | 25 | 41 | 22 | 27 | 27 | 93 | 74 | 167 |

**TABLE 5**
Educational background of deaf clinic patients

| Educational background | Male | Female | Both sexes | |
|---|---|---|---|---|
| | | | Number | Per cent |
| No schooling | 1 | 0 | 1 | .6 |
| School for deaf | | | | |
| Not graduated | | | | |
| Retarded class | 4 | 3 | 7 | 4.2 |
| Expelled | 11 | 3 | 14 | 8.4 |
| Left school | 10 | 10 | 20 | 12.0 |
| Still in school | 13 | 6 | 19 | 11.4 |
| Graduated | 21 | 26 | 47 | 28.1 |
| Trade school | 7 | 5 | 12 | 7.2 |
| Hearing high school | 10 | 6 | 16 | 9.6 |
| Gallaudet College | 7 | 4 | 11 | 6.6 |
| Hearing college | 3 | 3 | 6 | 3.6 |
| Information not complete | 6 | 8 | 14 | 8.3 |
| Total | 93 | 74 | 167 | 100.0 |

intelligence or education. Only five patients had either no schooling or were in retarded classes, while the majority had at least graduated from one of the special schools for the deaf.

It is also worth noting that the percentage of our clinic population who had had some college education was greater than the comparable segment of the deaf population as a whole. As for those patients who were expelled from schools, it goes without saying that inability to maintain acceptable behavior in school is often a sign of serious emotional disturbance. However, greater than normal achievement also seemed to be accompanied by urgent problems. Apart from the usual range of psychotic or neurotic disorders, conflicts over vocational choice and mate selection tend to be intensified in this group.

Since there were no other mental health facilities specially equipped to deal with the deaf, our clinic was called on with increasing frequency for an ever-expanding range of services. In addition to somatic treatment and psychotherapy on a short or long-term basis, the clinic program provided many diagnostic evaluations for educational, correctional and vocational rehabilitation agencies, as well as counseling on marriage and parenthood. Table 6 shows the range and frequency of methods used in dealing with

## TABLE 6
### Types of therapeutic service rendered to deaf clinic patients

| Type of service | Number of cases |
|---|---|
| Psychotherapy | |
|     Supportive | 49 |
|     Insightful | 13 |
| Pharmacotherapy | 35 |
| Environmental modification (in conjunction with other agencies, home or school) | 42 |
| Counseling parents or relatives with regard to assistance to patient | 12 |
| Hospitalization and in-patient supervision of treatment | 31 |
| Formulation of vocational goals | 28 |
| Marriage counseling | 10 |
| Marital and parenthood counseling on genetic risks | 12 |
| Periodic observation | 8 |

clinic problems. Many clinic patients required more than one type of treatment. The theoretical considerations and practical techniques in applying these methods are discussed in Chapter 13.

For the most part, persons requesting counseling in anticipation of marriage and parenthood have been excluded from previous tables. Since the problems that they posed extended to those of hearing members of deaf families, they warrant special mention. For instance, advice was recently requested by a hearing man asking about the advisability of marrying a hearing girl with deaf parents. She is indicated by the arrow in the accompanying pedigree (Figure 4). On the basis of the family history, her mother's deafness was classified as hereditary, she being one of three deaf children of a first-cousin marriage. The father's deafness, on the other hand, might have been acquired. Counseling in such instances cannot be limited to estimates of the statistical risk of deafness in the couple's future children. It has to take into account the emotional stability of the two persons involved and their attitude toward acquiring deaf relatives with the attendant possibility of social stigma. In this particular case, both persons were relieved of anxiety by a frank discussion of the genetic aspects and other factors.

Equally complex are the problems of a deaf person who wishes to marry

## FIGURE 4
### Counseling problem in a family with early total deafness

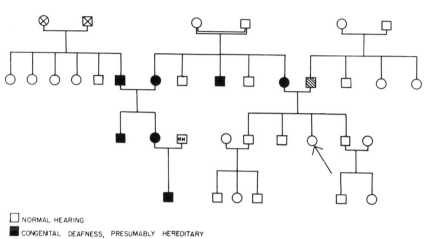

☐ NORMAL HEARING
■ CONGENITAL DEAFNESS, PRESUMABLY HEREDITARY
▧ ACQUIRED DEAFNESS
HH HARD OF HEARING
⊠ HEARING STATUS UNKNOWN

a hearing individual. Our records include data on several good marriages between exceptionally successful deaf men and hearing women. Other questions that call for special attention are the optimal conditions for rearing a deaf child in a hearing family, or, conversely, a hearing child of deaf parents.

Awareness of these problems is growing, along with the recognition that handicap-induced dependence and prolonged cloistered living with segregation by sexes lessen the chances for developing normal social relationships and make for poor adjustment. Various school authorities have recently requested the cooperation of our staff in inaugurating preliminary programs of sex education and preparation for marriage. Such a program would serve the needs of older students faced with severe restrictions in social opportunities and mate selection.

Altogether, there is an undeniable need for a full range of psychiatric, psychologic, and counseling services for deaf families who by no means constitute a negligible portion of the total population. For organizational and budgetary reasons it was necessary for our pilot clinic to limit the number of patients that it accommodated. Even on a full-time basis, however, a single outpatient clinic could not meet the psychiatric needs of the entire deaf population of New York State. Nor could our research staff render the multitude of inpatient services required by hospitalized cases.

More than one per cent of the total deaf population of New York State were seen as patients during the few years that this clinic has been in operation. If this ratio were applied to the general population of New York, it would be the equivalent of about 160,000 persons seeking help, despite the obstacles of distance, the absence of widespread publicity, and limitations in weekly hours of operation.

All age groups were represented, with a variety of educational and vocational backgrounds. Clinical investigation revealed disorders that fell into almost every known psychiatric category; some defied classification by ordinary criteria. Special training in communication, broad clinical experience, and a knowledge of the life conditions and special aspects of development associated with deafness, were prerequisites for accurate evaluation. Only when these requirements were met, could the proper flexible therapeutic measures be planned and executed so effectively as to provide much needed relief not only to individual deaf patients, but to their confused and anxious family members as well.

# Chapter 11

## PSYCHOLOGICAL TESTING: DEVELOPMENT AND PRACTICE

### Edna S. Levine

The problem of reaching minds trapped in silence was on the way to solution with the establishment of special methods of communication and the founding of the first public schools for the deaf. In this country, public education was made available to the masses of illiterate deaf in the early 19th century. But once the masses were assembled and the deaf mind was reached, the question that next arose was: What kind of mind was this that had lain dormant so long?

Was it indeed a "tabula rasa," a "perfect cipher," a "complete automaton" as contemporary authorities claimed? How could it be activated? How much of the world's custom and culture could it grasp? Could it be brought to understand the ethical standards of society, moral obligations, religious concepts? What could be done to enable the deaf mind to realize its own potentials? What in fact were its potentials?

The problem of establishing mental potential was a very real one to the early educator. The complex teaching task before him would be greatly facilitated if he could assess the intellectual capacities of his pupils and so separate them into homogeneous groups for teaching purposes. Interestingly enough, it was this same problem of mental classification that led to the construction of the Binet-Simon Intelligence Test, which in turn provided the impetus for the whole psychological testing movement as we know it today.

In the field of the deaf, it was the educator who tackled the problem. In 1889, almost two decades before the Binet-Simon Scale was constructed, David Greenberger (85), head of the Institution for the Improved Instruction of Deaf Mutes (now the Lexington School for the Deaf in New York City), published his procedures for "testing" the intelligence of deaf children.

Greenberger's work introduced a new concept into the mental rating of pupils, the concept of objectivity. Previously the assessment of mental ability was largely a matter of personal judgment. But Greenberger sensed the need for a less subjective approach. This he did by basing his appraisals

Portions of this chapter are reproduced, by permission of the author, from *Youth in a Soundless World*, Edna S. Levine, New York University Press, 1956.

on specified test tasks such as building blocks, reaction to picture books, and the like. All the tasks used and suggested by Greenberger can be found in current mental tests for young children. The one thing lacking was the high degree of objectivity presently obtainable through test standardization.

Although Greenberger's unique contribution aroused some interest in its day, its full significance was not grasped. Nevertheless, psychology was in the air, and the need to "understand" deaf pupils was considered essential to educational success. As early as 1894, Taylor (223) deplored the fact that although "the child is the most important creature on earth . . . (he) is perhaps the least understood." He pushed for greater recognition of the value of psychology to education; he urged a closer study of individual pupils. The main problem, however, was how to study deaf pupils without proper instruments of evaluation. A look at the regular schools indicated that the task was apparently accomplished through subject matter examinations. Hence, a similar approach was tried with the deaf. In 1897, Taylor (224) reported the results of the first sizable investigation of deaf pupils.

A group of 148 deaf pupils and a control group of hearing pupils were directed to write as many words as came to mind in 15 minutes. The results showed that although the deaf group averaged 151 words to the 153 of the hearing, the average percentage of errors made by the deaf was only 2.7 per cent as compared with the 4.3 per cent made by the hearing. Although no great significance can be attached to these findings, the study itself was the precursor of many other studies concerned with comparisons between deaf and hearing groups.

The next of the early studies was that of Mott, the results of which were published during 1899 and 1900 (48). Here, too, the aim was to compare deaf and hearing groups. Physical as well as psychological measures were used with nine-year-old deaf and hearing children. It was found that the deaf were as good or better than the hearing in physical measurements, manual dexterity, and athletic skills. In tests of memory and observation, the deaf appeared to be markedly superior.

It remained for the most thoroughgoing investigation of the period to present the less optimistic side of the picture. This was the study by Mac-Millan and Bruner published in 1906 (144). As representatives of the Child Study Department of the Chicago Public Schools, these workers were concerned with the problem of taking over the education of 184 deaf children then attending the regular schools. Part of their tasks involved examining the pupils' capacities. Accordingly the deaf students were subjected to a typical test battery of the day. Included were tests of hearing, visual acuity, lung capacity, strength of grip, tapping, cancellation of A's, perception of size and weight, identification of objects by touch, and visual memory span for digits. Height, weight, and head measurements were also recorded.

The results of the MacMillan-Bruner study classified the deaf as considerably poorer than the hearing in the prime intelligence measure of the day—the cancellation of A's—as well as in tests of size-by-touch. The investigators interpreted this finding as an indication of delayed rather than retarded development. They believed that "were the deaf child's instruction begun in infancy instead of at six years, the difference might be reduced or even eliminated." This possibility had not escaped the notice of the educator, for as early as 1893, a "Union of Kindergartners for the Deaf" had already been organized for the purpose of introducing preschool programs in all schools for the deaf (102).

A very important result of the MacMillan-Bruner study was the evidence which demonstrated the practical value of the psychological examination. The educator was ripe for such demonstrations and eager for the help that psychology promised. Thus, when the first English translation of the Binet-Simon Intelligence Test appeared in 1910, it was greeted with enthusiastic interest by educators of the deaf.

The emphasis on objective evaluation combined with the Binet frame of reference marked the beginning of a new era in psychological work with the deaf. In the forefront of this era was Rudolph Pintner. From the time of his first publication on the deaf in 1915 until the year of his death in 1942, this pioneer was directly or indirectly responsible for most of the psychological activity in the field.

The first important investigation of the Pintner Period was an attempt by Pintner and Paterson (171) to use the Binet Test with the deaf. The Goddard revision was administered to 22 pupils whose average chronological age was 12.5 years. The test was given in whatever methods of communication the subjects preferred, but even so four pupils were completely unable to take the test. In the remaining 18, the results showed an average mental age of 7.9 years and an average mental retardation of 4.58 years.

For various reasons, the investigators were by no means satisfied with their findings. They complained of the many difficulties which had been encountered in test administration. In addition, they regarded many of the Binet test questions as completely unsuited to the life situation of the deaf. On the whole, they concluded that verbal measures of the Binet type could not be used with the deaf. Instead, they recommended the use of performance tests.

Construction of the Pintner-Paterson Performance Scale in 1917 was the direct consequence of this recommendation. While a theoretical frame of construction had been provided by the Binet Scale, intelligence on the performance scale was measured through manipulative rather than verbal tasks. The appearance of this objective, nonlanguage scale for mental measurement opened a new avenue for the psychological study of the deaf.

The next 25 years witnessed a tremendous surge of investigation in the field. Areas of exploration included not only intelligence but also personality, learning ability, scholastic attainment, special abilities, and the like. Comparisons between deaf and hearing pupils became the major trend. New tests were tried; studies were conducted by experienced as well as inexperienced examiners; by those familiar with the deaf as well as by some who were not. The sum total of the various approaches used by all workers in that period was classified by Taylor (225) as follows:

I. Experimental Work
   1. Under accepted controlled conditions.
   2. Under conditions less favorable, by persons of experience with the deaf, but possibly without adequate technique in research.
   3. Under conditions still less favorable, by persons lacking in research technique and familiar with too small a group of the deaf to justify adequate generalizations.

II. Observation
   1. Under accepted controlled conditions.
   2. Not under controlled conditions by persons of education and experience with the deaf. At times this is difficult to evaluate but it is worthy of record and study.
   3. Casual observations, often of suggestive value.
   4. Elaborations of personal opinion for the purpose of indoctrination. These may contain suggestions in outlining investigations.

III. Next to observations we may mention the application of knowledge or information resulting from other investigations or borrowed from other fields, but an innovation in this particular field.

IV. The compilation of statistical and other information.

As for the investigations themselves, the experiences of Pintner and Paterson with the Goddard-Binet Scale resulted in an epoch of nonverbal and nonlanguage testing of intelligence and personality.

Studies in which the Pintner Nonlanguage Mental Group Test was used included those by Reamer (188); by Day et al. (50); by Goodenough and Shirley (84); and by MacKane (143). According to the results of the first two investigations, the average difference in mental ability between deaf and hearing children was between two and three years in favor of the hearing. However, Goodenough and Shirley reported that their deaf subjects averaged "very close to Pintner's standards for hearing children and much above the median scores for deaf children in the National Survey," although they added that the "reason for these discrepancies is not apparent." On the other hand, MacKane's study yielded no such discrepancy. His findings confirmed those of Day et al., that the deaf are two years retarded mentally when compared with the hearing. However, in his study MacKane found that the 12-year level was "superior to other age-levels of the deaf." Such were the results of investigations with a group test.

Among the individual intelligence tests employed during the period under discussion, the Drever and Collins, the Grace Arthur, and the Pintner-Paterson performance scales were used most frequently. The first of them was devised by James Drever and Mary Collins of the University of Edinburgh primarily for testing deaf children. The results obtained in their investigations indicated that "when the language factor is entirely eliminated from our tests, it is very doubtful whether the deaf child is retarded at all" (60). The Grace Arthur Point Scale of Performance Tests was used by Lyon (140); by Bishop (25); and by Burchard and Myklebust (31). While Lyon concluded that "deaf children are on the average below the hearing child in general intelligence," Bishop as well as Burchard and Myklebust reported that their respective groups proved to be of average intelligence.

In an attempt to evaluate the conflicting results of the various studies, MacKane employed a battery of scales with 130 deaf children ranging in age from ten to 12 years. Each of them was paired with a hearing subject of the same age, sex, national background, and economic status. The battery consisted of the Drever-Collins Scale, the Pintner-Paterson Scale, the Grace Arthur Scale, and the Pintner Nonlanguage Mental Test. The main conclusion reached in this thorough analysis was the following: "It seems evident from this study that the performance scale and the nonlanguage test measure different abilities, for the study plainly shows that the same deaf children may be less than a year retarded in their responses to performance scales and yet be two years retarded in their responses to the nonlanguage test" (143).

Among other tests applied in investigations of intelligence was the Goodenough "Draw a Man" test, which was used in a number of studies. Petersen and Williams (169) employed this measure in a series of 330 deaf pupils ranging in age from five to 14 years. While these investigators reported an average retardation of one year and ten months, another study of 406 pupils by Goodenough and Shirley (84) seemed to indicate that age for age they were only "somewhat below the standards of hearing children who are making normal progress in school." Employing the same test in a comparison of 330 deaf and 330 hearing students ranging in age from six to 12 years, Springer (211) observed that "at no age level did the deaf and hearing differ significantly."

The Porteus Maze test was used by Zeckel and van der Kolk (252) in 100 deaf and 100 hearing children whose age range extended from seven to 14 years. The average I.Q. reported for the deaf group was 86.1, and that for the hearing group, 99.4. Hence, deafness was assumed to create "a mental backwardness which impedes also the development of regions of intellect other than those developed by speech."

Employing the Kohs Block Designs, Petersen (168) also found a "definite retardation of the deaf as compared with hearing pupils." By contrast, Schick (199) used the Randall's Island Performance Series in 30 deaf and 39 speech-defective children ranging in age from two to six years and concluded that " . . . we must again call attention to the average intelligence quotient of 97 which is proof that the deaf and speech-defective children are not mentally retarded but only educationally because of their language handicap." Similar conclusions were reached by Lane and Schneider (129) who compared the intelligence of 133 deaf and speech-defective children with that of 106 normal children in the age group seven to 19 years by means of the Advanced Performance Series. They stated that their study gave "further evidence to support the conclusion that the deaf child is normal mentally if his ability is measured on a test that does not involve the use of language for directions or response."

Turning to personality studies of the Pintner Period, one may mention the one conducted by Lyon (140) using the Thurstone Personality Schedule. In a series of 87 deaf high school pupils examined in a state residential school, the percentage of deaf pupils classified in Groups D and E ("emotionally maladjusted; should have psychiatric advice") was found to be more than twice that of college freshmen of approximately the same age.

These findings were generally confirmed in a study by Lily Brunschwig (29) in which the testing device—the Brunschwig Personality Inventory for Deaf Children—was standardized on deaf pupils by the investigator herself. It was observed in all comparisons of deaf and hearing students that "the deaf averaged poorer adjustment scores than the hearing, differences between the means of the deaf and hearing being statistically significant in six out of twelve comparisons."

In another investigation conducted by Pintner et al. (172), the Bernreuter Inventory was used to determine the adjustment status of 50 deaf students of Gallaudet College and 126 deaf adults. In this series, the deaf were found to be "only slightly more emotionally unstable, only a little more introverted and not quite so dominant as the normal hearing."

The social maturity of the deaf was assessed in three studies conducted respectively by Bradway (27), Streng and Kirk (221), and Burchard and Myklebust (31). Using the Vineland Social Maturity Scale, Bradway found the deaf to be 20 per cent inferior to hearing subjects throughout all age levels examined. This finding was confirmed by Burchard and Myklebust; however, contrary results were obtained by Streng and Kirk who classified their subjects as average in social maturity.

In another group of personality investigations, the Haggerty-Olson-Wickman Behavior Rating Schedules were employed. Kirk's study (118) revealed a significantly greater number of problem tendencies among the deaf and hard of hearing group than among normally hearing children, and was in agreement with the observations of Burchard and Myklebust. However, Springer (212) used the same schedules and reported very little difference between the groups. In fact, he observed on certain items that the deaf rated more favorably than the hearing.

In a second study, Springer administered the Brown Personality Inventory for Children. According to the results of this study, "all the groups of deaf children were found to receive much higher neurotic scores than the hearing control children." These findings were confirmed in a later study reported by Springer and Roslow (214).

In an overall review of the findings of the Pintner Period, it may be stated that about the only areas of agreement among the investigators were those of the three-to-four-year language retardation of the deaf, and of their normative performance on tests of mechanical and motor ability. As for intelligence, some of the investigators concluded that deaf pupils are mentally retarded, others that they are not. Some blamed the tests for these conflicting results, while others maintained that deafness itself creates a mental backwardness. Scant insight has been afforded into the actual thinking and reasoning abilities of deaf individuals. Instead, the stress was placed on comparisons between deaf and hearing groups.

In research designs, little if any provision was made to control even the most obvious variables. The deaf-in-mass was the unit of concern. In regard to personality, the general consensus was that the deaf present more problem tendencies and maladjustments than the hearing. However, psychic components of deaf personality were not explored. The findings were based largely on deaf pupil populations of widely differing ages and backgrounds, on dubious test instruments, and on comparisons between the deaf and the hearing. And again, the group was the unit of concern.

As noted earlier in this volume, the enthusiasm with which the educator welcomed psychology into the field was considerably shaken by the vague and conflicting findings of the Pintner Period. Moreover, the educator was by no means alone in his faultfinding as serious technical questions were raised by other psychological investigators as well. One of the chief targets for their criticism was the questionnaire-inventory type of psychological instrument used in personality testing of the deaf. Of these tests, Welles (240) stated that they "are not probing the underlying drives which are the causal factors in any individual's emotional behavior, but are merely making a sampling of symptomatic material," while Habbe (88) declared "that the investigator is courageous who obtains a list of 'yes' and 'no' responses for several hundred personality inventories and proceeds therefrom to deduce conclusions relating to various individuals in the group thus studied." Other targets for criticism were the practices of group measurement and mass study of the deaf, as well as the lack of experience of numbers of investigators with both the basic problems of deafness and the methodology of research techniques.

Nevertheless, despite questionable procedures and indecisive results, the Pintner Period served to formulate the fundamental questions underlying all psychological investigations of the deaf. The main questions posed were the following (173):

1. Does the handicap of language carry with it the inability to develop abstract intelligence?

2. Must abstract intelligence in its highest form always depend upon language or other symbols?

3. Are the deaf because of their lack of hearing unable to develop a symbolic structure which seems to underlie abstract intelligence?

Satisfactory answers to these three questions required far deeper clinical information about the normative deaf personality than had yet been obtained. This state of affairs in turn called for new investigative approaches and more deeply probing psychological instruments.

The first major departure from traditional procedure in the search for normative information was the investigation conducted by Levine in 1948 (132). On the basis of previous psychological experience with deaf adults and adolescents, the author was aware that they had far more to "say" than could be tapped by nonlangauge and questionnaire measures. A prerequisite was that the investigator be sufficiently familiar with their communicative characteristics to effect meaningful communicative relations with them. At the outset, therefore, a search among the more dynamic psychological techniques was made for those that would fit into a deaf individual's frame of language comprehension and life experience. After much trial, the two most promising methods were chosen, namely, the Wechsler-Bellevue Intelligence tests for Adolescents and Adults, Form I (236) and the Rorschach Projective Technique.

Another problem was to control the possible effects of the numerous variables associated with deafness. Thus, the study was limited to a carefully selected group of subjects who were representative of an important section of the deaf population, homogeneous in regard to basic background factors, and of normative behavior in the judgment of selected raters experienced with the deaf and familiar with the subjects of the study. The manner of test administration was guided entirely by the language and communicative skills of the individual subjects, with whatever modification in test directions that had to be made to insure maximum comprehension of a test task. Since the tests had been selected and the necessary modifications were made to retain as far as possible the psychological equivalence of the instruments for the deaf as for the hearing, the responses of the deaf subjects were scored in accordance with the regular test norms.

The following results were obtained in this investigation: (1) evidence of pronounced underdevelopment of the deaf subjects in conceptual forms of mental activity, despite normative mental potentials; (2) indications of marked emotional immaturity; (3) substantial lags in the comprehension of interpersonal relations; (4) highly egocentric life perspective; (5) a markedly constricted life area; and (6) rigid adherence to the book-of-etiquette code as standards for behaving and even for feeling. Evidently Pintner's question concerning the effects on mental development of language retardation was also applicable to the personality development of a normal deaf group. By and large, these findings have been confirmed by all subsequent investigations (135).

Possibly of broader clinical usefulness than the comparative findings of the study were the investigative procedures used. The clinical promise of this new psychodiagnostic approach to the deaf led to its employment in the present project as well as in other centers concerned with the psychological appraisal of deaf adolescents and adults (135). In the younger deaf population and in those with seriously limited language and communicative abilities, we must still rely on nonlanguage and performance tests. With other deaf subjects, however, projective techniques and selected verbal tests continue to be promising and effective. Among such techniques currently used in intelligence and personality testing are: the Wechsler Scales; the House-Tree-Person Test (H-T-P); the Make a Picture Story (MAPS); the Thematic Apperception Test (TAT); the Rorschach Technique; sentence completion tests; figure drawings; and others. Elsewhere, Levine (135) presents a detailed discussion of psychological appraisal of the deaf together with illustrative batteries of tests in current use.

Despite the promising turn taken in testing the deaf, there are numerous clinical limitations and technical problems encountered in using the newer techniques, all of which have been devised for, or standardized on, the hearing. The rationale of administering them to the deaf must still be established statistically as well as clinically. At present their use is dictated largely by the lack of instruments designed for, and standardized on, the deaf.

It may also be noted that the psychological tests in current clinical use are not equally effective with all deaf subjects. This limitation, of course, applies to hearing subjects as well but the unusual heterogeneity of the population makes it a special problem. Among the deaf, for example, there are those who can speak and read the lips with amazing skill, others who can speak but who cannot read the lips, still others who can lipread but who cannot speak comprehensively, and some who can do neither. Furthermore, there are deaf persons whose education has been appropriate to their needs in all respects while others have suffered severe educational deprivation. Then there are those whose spoken language is inferior but whose reading and writing skills are excellent. Conversely, there are those whose language skills are limited largely to their small fund of spoken expression. Also, there are deaf persons whose school-life contacts with family and community may have been restricted to weekend or holiday visits, and others with close family and community relations, sometimes for better and sometimes for worse. Moreover, there are some who may have no contact with other deaf individuals, while others tend to enjoy a full, rich life with both the deaf and the hearing. There are deaf persons who cannot communicate with some of their deaf peers for lack of a mutually understood method, and others who cannot communicate with the members of their own families for the same reason.

Finally, there are the emotionally adjusted and the emotionally disturbed, the mature and the utterly immature; those of high mental endowment and those of limited capacity; the sick and the well; those with single and those with multiple handicaps. And within the range of these extremes are numerous variations and combinations of ability and degrees of adjustment and attainment.

The highly heterogeneous state of this exceptional population plus the dearth of psychological instruments devised for the deaf place unusual demands upon psychologists specializing in the field. Clinical competence and flexibility are as essential as are familiarity with the development and developmental hazards of the deaf, and knowledge of their varied modes of communication and language usage. It is a naive worker who expects a test to tell the whole story. Frequently, more significant information is obtained from the case history, from clinical observation, and the interview. For the purposes of a full psychodiagnostic appraisal, these additional data are always part of the examination battery.

However, the break with traditional procedures has given psychology renewed vitality in clinical work with the deaf. Once again, the field is turning hopefully to this specialty. More and more schools are adding psychologists to their staffs. Government-sponsored workshops are being conducted for psychologists planning to work in this area (135). There is a heavy demand for psychologists in specialized research projects so that university training facilities are making their appearance. Clearly, psychology is in the air once more, but still facing it are the old unanswered questions and unfulfilled needs of the past. Among them are the following, formulated at a recent conference on research needs in the vocational rehabilitation of the deaf (192):

1. Instruments for studying the conceptualization processes, abstract thinking, and learning processes of the deaf.

2. Instruments for psychological assessment in such areas as intellectual capacity; educational achievement; psychosocial adjustment; vocational aptitudes; vocational interests.

3. Instruments for measuring communication potential and ability.

4. Programmatic, interdisciplinary research.

5. Demographic area studies to obtain information concerning the deaf person's socio-economic, religious, familial, and political status; his methods of communication, occupational history, etc.

6. Investigations to determine the adequacy of interviewers and researchers of the deaf as well as the methods which have been successfully employed in previous research on the deaf.

7. Establishment of criteria of vocational success and failure among the deaf.

Other essential studies which were recommended by the conference have been mentioned earlier in this volume. Among the methods of investigation suggested were autobiographical and demographic studies; statistical surveys; case history evaluations; anthropological procedures; opinion research studies; and content analysis of literature by and for the deaf.

The present project anticipated many of the suggestions and methods recommended by the conference. Nevertheless, much remains to be done. If the work of this project should stimulate and facilitate further psychological research, one of its major aims will have been accomplished.

# Chapter 12

## RORSCHACH DATA AND CLINICAL OBSERVATIONS

### George S. Baroff

Because of their psychiatric problems, deaf patients seen in the setting of an outpatient clinic might be expected to show deviant personality characteristics in projective tests. Therefore, a group of deaf persons who were not psychiatric patients was included in this study with a view toward separating those facets of personality which may be primarily associated with deafness from those influenced by the added presence of psychiatric disorder.

From the standpoint of statistical analysis, the available data are limited and merely indicate trends that are subject to verification as further results are accumulated. The present test series consists of only 31 cases, 21 of which were drawn from the clinic population. The remaining 10 cases were taken from our sample of deaf twins evaluated in previous sections (Chapters 3 and 4). One of the criteria for selection in this latter group, which served as our "normal control," was an intelligence quotient of at least 85.

The clinic series consisted of two categories: 10 schizophrenics and 11 individuals manifesting neuroses and character disorders, with homosexuality a characteristic of many of them.

### Cognitive Aspects of Personality

One of the claims of the Rorschach method is that it permits scrutiny of thought processes as well as thought products. Interest is centered not only

---

Editors' Note: The clinical diagnostic criteria developed in the course of observation and treatment of deaf psychiatric patients are discussed in Chapters 10 and 13. The latter chapter also deals with methods of psychotherapy.

In the psychiatric examination of the deaf patient, clinical competence, familiarity with the life problems of the deaf, and knowledge of their language and communication is essential. As stated in Chapter 11, much significant information is obtained from the case history and the clinical interview, and no psychological test can give the whole story.

The observations in this chapter, made in the course of the project, incorporate valuable formulations regarding some psychological characteristics of the deaf. While the editors are not invariably convinced of the objective or subjective validity of interpretations made according to Rorschach test procedure, and do not mean to venture into the controversial or theoretical aspects of Rorschach research, the exploratory data presented in Chapter 12 may be considered as supplementary to impressions gained in interviews and clinical work with deaf persons. Matters regarding the scientific establishment of the test in diagnostic work with the deaf have not been within the scope of this project.

on what is perceived but also on how the blot material is organized to produce percepts.

One aspect of the organizing process refers to response distribution according to the relative frequencies of whole and part responses. The three groups studied (the two clinic groups plus the control) showed a pattern of response distribution which clearly deviated from the accepted norm. Among the 31 protocols only one conformed to the expected proportions. With the exception of three neurotic patients who revealed an obsessional trend, the deviation was in the direction of excessive D (large detail) and W (whole responses). The variation between groups was small.

With high D said to reflect an orientation to the most obvious aspects of reality, the present finding may indicate a concrete, practical and occasionally unimaginative approach. In most of the persons tested, high W did not appear to be associated with an integrative or organizational need, but rather to reflect a vague, undifferentiated, and childlike wholistic quality. Common to all but the obsessional individuals was a lack of interest in precision, detail, and nuance.

There was only one instance in which high W seemed clearly to be a function of a need for higher level integration. In the case of an adolescent girl with high intellectual aspirations who was suffering from an acute schizophrenic illness, the W drive appeared compulsive in intensity and compensatory for anxiety about intellectual ability.

On the whole, deafness does seem to effect a kind of perceptual orientation that differs somewhat from the normative pattern. However, the hearing loss is unlikely to limit seriously the capacity to produce the same number of responses on the average as in the non-deaf. With an expected response total (R) of 20 to 45, the control group showed little deviation, their lowest R being 17. Slightly greater deviation was observed in the neurotic group, while the psychotic series was extremely variant, with eight of the ten subjects having less than the expected minimum of 20. The reduced number of responses in the schizophrenic group apparently reflected the impoverishment of thought processes associated with the disorder.

Paralleling the findings for R were those for the frequency of popular responses (P). If five popular responses are considered the minimum expected frequency, only two of the ten normals had a lesser number. Slightly more than one-half of the neurotics had a reduced P, while eight of the ten schizophrenics were deviant in this respect. Hence, deafness does not seem to prevent the individual from seeing the world much like the non-deaf do. This indication, of course, refers only to gross consensual validation, because there is some variation in the apperceptive approach of the deaf. Schizophrenic deaf, like their hearing counterparts, tend to have their ties with reality seriously disturbed, as was clearly reflected in the diminished number of their popular responses.

Two other Rorschach variables considered to illuminate cognitive function are form (F) and animal (A) percentages. As a group, the deaf seem to have high scores on both these factors, suggesting a lack of richness in imagery and weak responsiveness to the variety of stimuli inherent in the ink blots. Combined with the previously mentioned indifference to precision, detail, and nuance, and with the emphasis on the most obvious aspects of reality, a picture emerges of cognitive functioning that closely resembles the "natural constriction" concept of Klopfer, et al. (121). Clinically, there is a trend toward concreteness and lack of facility with the abstract. To some extent, this kind of thought orientation probably reflects the early communication handicap, the effects of which go beyond the "simple" inability to reproduce spoken language. Early total deafness deprives the child of language as a symbolic as well as auditory experience, and it is primarily through the symbolic function of language that abstract ideas are represented.

One of the most complex of Rorschach determinants is M (human movement). In view of the objectively static quality of the ink blots, M is thought to represent an enlivening of the stimuli. It is assumed to be the most "projective" kind of response and, therefore, capable of illuminating some of the deeper personality features. Among them are such traits as general creativity, self-concept, empathic capacity, and the potential for organizing behavior in terms of long range goals (value system) rather than immediate needs.

The analysis of M may serve as a bridge between discussion of the cognitive and effective components of personality. All three groups were characterized by few M responses. Only five of the 31 had as many as three M and the average was 1.4. The schizophrenic series differed slightly in that it had the largest number of persons with no M, a finding consistent with the previously mentioned personality impoverishment associated with the illness.

The paucity of M responses might be taken to indicate a psychological deficit which is correlated with the frequently seen "acting out" behavior pattern in the clinic groups. This pattern would also be predicted by the ratio of human to animal movement (M:FM). In both the normal and the neurotic series, the predominant test results were similar to those found in the young child who tends to act on impulse and has little capacity for postponement of gratification. In the schizophrenic group, FM as well as M was reduced, again reflecting the gross personality deficit.

When experience balance (M:Sum C) is examined, the relative meagerness of inner resources associated with infrequent M may be interpreted as revealing an extratensive trend. Nevertheless this extratensive orientation is passive rather than active; it is one in which reality is pretty much accepted as found and where little effort is made to organize or restructure it according to personal needs.

### Emotional Factors

The extratensive component of experience is supposed to be reflected in the sum of the responses to chromatic blot areas (Sum C)—that part of the Rorschach test usually interpreted as indicating emotionality. As with M, but to a lesser degree, the most commonly seen pattern was that of limited chromatic responsiveness with more than one-half of the total group having a Sum C of less than three. Of those with Sum C of at least three, approximately one-half showed findings consistent with adaptive emotional response. The others had a pattern reflecting inadequate emotional control with a tendency to act out self-needs, and with too little attention to social demands. Since those with few color responses also had few M, they might not be expected to show adequate impulse control.

While such generally diminished sensitivity to both inner and outer stimuli may serve to reduce the frequency of emotional involvement, feeling response, when evoked, is likely to be crude and maladaptive. This phenomenon was observed clinically in some deaf persons who displayed what may be described as primitive personality characteristics. The highly egocentric affective behavior of the child is carried on into adolescence and young adulthood where it may be manifested in rage reactions with assaultive and destructive features.

This qualitative trend in the emotionality of the deaf might be expected to be mirrored in their response to the differentiated and undifferentiated shading areas. All three groups showed an underrepresentation of responses usually associated with sensitivity, introspection, and healthy acceptance of affectional need. Almost one-half of all cases had no shading responses whatever. Shading did occur with greatest frequency in the neurotic group where it might reflect anxiety over failure to achieve adequate gratification of dependency needs.

The test data, therefore, may be interpreted as consistent with the observations that the deaf are disinclined to self-exploration, generally not anxiety-prone, and deficient in impulse control. At the same time, the data give the impression of an overall lack of depth in emotional responsiveness.

### Reality Testing

Among Rorschach factors, the percentage of accurately perceived forms in non-M and C responses is viewed as an indicator of the integrity of the person's reality-testing capacity, as a major determinant of adjustive potential. From a diagnostic standpoint, the F+ % seemed to be as useful with the deaf as with the non-deaf. If an F+ % of 80 is the minimum for effective adaptive potential, the most deviant individuals were found in the schizophrenic category. Only two of the ten schizophrenics obtained an F+ % in excess of 80. One of them was an ambulatory paranoid, a most unusual finding in this nosological group. The other presented a clinically clear picture of an early hebephrenic reaction with the primary defect being in the emotional rather than intellectual sphere.

In the neurotic series, eight of the 11 persons had an F+ % of at least 80. The F+ scores of those that fell below 80 were not as deviant as those of the psychotic series, the lowest being 63. This value was found in the protocol of a woman who had an obsessional neurosis with cleaning and counting compulsions. She was one of the very few deaf persons who had a detail score slightly in excess of the expected frequency.

In the control group (deaf twins), the lowest of the deviant F+ scores was also 63 (observed in two of the three low F+ % protocols). Low F+ % in the non-psychotic deaf was associated with vague and uncritical thinking, although the content was free of bizarre and morbid characteristics.

In contrast to the content of the control group which tended to show many simple animal responses, the schizophrenics produced frequent references to blood, anatomical, and sexual content. Their records at the same time revealed gross thought disorder including blocking, illogical reasoning, and extreme variation in the quality of response.

### Diagnostic Considerations

The schizophrenic deaf patients studied, like their hearing counterparts (120), seemed to be characterized on Rorschach tests by generally reduced responsiveness (low R), difficulty in viewing situations like others (low P), outright reality distortion (low F+ %) and preoccupation with morbid and highly personalized content. In using such Rorschach test data as well as clinical interviews for differential diagnosis, it is important to avoid misinterpretation with respect to some signs of thought disorder usually considered indicative of schizophrenia. Deaf persons in general, by the nature of their defect, tend to think in vaguely wholistic and concrete terms. Hence, a thought disorder may be strikingly simulated in their written communications which often show a fragmented, confused, and primitive quality. Without knowledge of the specific language handicap of the deaf, these written communications might suggest the kind of thought pathology seen in chronic schizophrenia.

It must be clear that adequate diagnostic evaluation of the deaf requires familiarity with manual language, which for many deaf persons is the normal mode of communication. A good understanding of manual language offers the most direct access to the thought content of these deaf patients. By reducing the non-oral patient's need for expressing himself in the written modality where his handicap may have produced its gravest effect, manual language enhances rapport and facilitates a free flow of ideas.

# Chapter 13

## PSYCHOTHERAPY FOR THE DEAF

JOHN D. RAINER, KENNETH Z. ALTSHULER,
and FRANZ J. KALLMANN

Although the deaf population of the world may be estimated at three million (249), organized psychiatric information on emotionally disturbed persons with early total deafness is meager. To be sure, psychologists have contributed to our understanding of certain alterations of intellectual function associated with this perceptual defect, and personal accounts have provided insight into the subjective experiences of those who share a soundless world (16, 21, 96, 97, 204).

Psychodynamic theories involving the ear and the conceptualization of hearing loss have been discussed by some investigators. Others have offered theoretical formulations on the significance of hearing in conscience formation and perception of space and motion (105, 109, 122, 123, 234). A few workers have written on characterologic reactions and psychopathological responses to deafness (149, 209).

When it comes to therapy, however, the subject is usually dismissed with a brief reference or two. Emphasis is placed on preventive measures or direct counseling, conveying a general sense of pessimism about psychiatric efforts made in the face of the limitations imposed by deafness (147, 155, 251). Indeed, there exists no scientific body of normative data as a baseline for psychiatric treatment of the deaf.

Until recently, very few psychotherapists were trained in the diagnosis and treatment of emotional disorders among the deaf, and no attempt was made to synthesize on a statewide basis information regarding the specific adjustment problems of this severely handicapped group. This lack was acutely felt, not only by mental hospital and clinic personnel, but also by workers in rehabilitation centers and social agencies under pressure by numerous requests for psychiatric treatment and vocational rehabilitation of the deaf. To fill that gap in the State of New York, this pilot project was organized here.

During the project's period of operation covered by this report (1955-1960) we dealt with the psychiatric problems of approximately 500

Portions of this chapter originally formed the subject of a lecture held at the 5th International Congress of Psychotherapy, Vienna, 1961. They are reproduced, by permission of the authors and the publisher, from *Advances in Psychosomatic Medicine, Vol. III*, B. Stokvis (ed.), Basel/New York, S. Karger, 1963.

totally deaf people. Over 250 of them were in mental hospitals or had to be hospitalized, while 217 comprised the clinic population.

### In-Patient Treatment

In the case of the hospitalized deaf, 52.2 per cent of whom were schizophrenic (Chapter 14), all the usual methods of somatic treatment were employed—drugs and various shock therapies. Psychiatric treatment in this respect did not differ from that used with the hearing. However, the lack of adequate facilities prevented a more systematic attempt to combine these methods with psychotherapy. No arrangements could be made to deal with deaf hospital patients as a special group by bringing them together rather than having them scattered over many hospitals and various services within each hospital. Psychotherapy also suffered from the fact that no specialized personnel was available. Until attempts are made to remedy this situation, the rehabilitation of disturbed deaf patients will not be comparable to that achieved in the hearing.

### Out-Patient Treatment

Generally speaking, the 217 patients dealt with in this group fell into the same diagnostic categories as a similar group of hearing clinic patients —covering the whole range of psychoneuroses, sexual maladjustment, and psychoses. Using as a guide various overlapping schemes to classify methods of psychotherapy (162, 177, 248) (Figure 1), we can examine the indications for and applications of these techniques, as well as their limitations, illustrated by a number of clinical examples.

Psychotherapy has been called "the use of human influence for the treatment of behavior disorders." It is widely instituted to alleviate an individual's emotional suffering associated with his inappropriate or mis-

### FIGURE 1
#### Types of psychotherapy

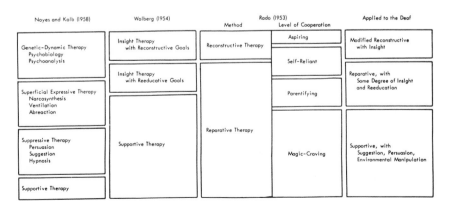

guided behavior. This disturbed behavior also causes pain to the people around him. It is only logical that the goals of the therapy should vary with the degree of pathology, the patient's maturation potential, and his ability to cooperate in understanding and modifying his behavior in treatment sessions as well as in his daily life. Often overlooked is the fact that treatment goals also vary with the chances society affords the patient for life adjustment and the opportunity given him in psychotherapy for meaningful communication.

In the case of the deaf, all these factors play a role in complicating the task of effective psychotherapy. Severe pathology, psychotic or psychopathic in nature, may not be evident to the psychiatrist who is unfamiliar with the methods of differential diagnosis in the deaf. Also, the conceptual immaturity of many deaf patients may affect motivation for treatment and entail modification of treatment plans based on insight and self-reliance. Moreover, fruition of a well-conceived program may be nipped in the bud by the sheer lack of opportunities for social and vocational self-realization. Finally, the most obvious and persistent hindrance to effective diagnosis and psychotherapy lies in the difficulty of communication between psychotherapist and patient.

It is mainly with their eyes that the deaf receive information. Having heard no sounds from birth or early childhood, they have not been able to establish patterns of language. Some have learned to read lips and use their voices, and have maintained or improved this ability by constant practice. Many more, who are unable to rely on this method, can communicate effectively with one another by means of signs and finger spelling. The international language of signs, developed in France by de l'Epee in the 18th Century, has become a vivid means of expression, but it is limited in its ability to indicate inflections and abstract ideas.

While the use of finger spelling permits the deaf to draw on ordinary words in the spoken language, there is often a deficit in their comprehensive ability. Some deaf who are proficient neither at oral nor manual means of communication form an extremely isolated group. In conducting psychotherapeutic interviews with the deaf, it is essential to understand their spoken language and to use and read manual communication. In addition, it is equally important to be familiar with the educational, recreational, social and vocational milieu in which they live.

Regarding the criteria for selecting the method and goals of psychotherapy, it may be said that in the last analysis they depend on the level of the patient's desire and ability to cooperate (177). At the *aspiring* level, the patient wishes and is able to achieve marked self-advancement, utilizing all his potential resources for adaptive growth. At the *self-reliant* level, he is expected to learn how to help himself in the everyday matters of life. In either case, the patient's motivation for treatment is governed by common sense, and his behavior is that of an adult. By contrast, a helpless patient who reveals excessive emotional dependence on the therapist, longing for parental help or therapeutic miracles, relates like a child at the *parentifying* and *magic-craving* levels. He does not seek real learning or maturation, and is often incapable of achieving it.

The best kind of treatment and life behavior that can be achieved by a patient depends primarily on his personality structure, as constitutionally and developmentally determined (sometimes referred to as ego strength), and the efficiency of his mechanisms for controlling fear and rage (including conscience). Only those who can operate on an adult basis are eligible for insight therapy with reconstructive goals. With the deaf, even more than with the hearing, such eligibility is also predicated on intelligence, training, life opportunities, and especially the ability of the individual to communicate.

### Modified Reconstructive Therapy with Insight

In our clinic population only two patients were found suitable for insight therapy with reconstructive goals, although the psychoanalytic method did have to be modified. While the objective of the treatment did not reach the aspiring level, the goal was relief of symptoms and self-reliance. The technique used in these two cases was that of intensive psychotherapy. Strict psychoanalytic methods—treatment for at least three sessions weekly over a period of one, two or three years with the use of free association and interpretation of unconscious and transference data—were found to be impracticable. Factors other than the patient's need to sit facing the analyst, instead of lying on a couch, made such methods unusable.

Where psychoanalytic technique was tried, the patients' motivation and social flexibility, frustration tolerance, and abstraction ability necessary for the acceptance of generalized interpretations appeared to be insufficient to warrant continuing the method. At the same time, the analyst was handicapped by his own preoccupation with the problem of communication. Therefore he found it difficult to be sufficiently attentive or receptive to the "converging contextual aspect" of the patient's productions over a sustained period. The two cases treated by modified insight therapy were the following:

*Case 1:* A.B., a congenitally deaf female, was treated for 60 sessions over a two-year period. At the time of her first visit she was 24 years old, married to a deaf man, and the mother of three children. Her marital adjustment was so precarious that both partners had decided on a separation. She disclaimed any love for her husband, who presumably showed her no affection and "only wanted sex." On the whole, she described him as uncultured, inconsiderate, and selfish. Having decided that he was not her "type," she had fallen in love with another man whom she regarded as more refined and intelligent. For the sake of her children, however, she refused to have extramarital relations with him.

Generally, in working with marital problems, psychotherapists encounter many difficulties in cutting through the web of self-justification and over-reaction to partial realities, and reaching the nexus of motivational conflict. With this deaf couple, apart from the usual interlocking psychopathology, the treatment procedure was further hampered by obstacles in communication and lack of adjustive norms for comparison. It took two full months of joint counseling sessions, interviews by different psychiatrists and extensive batteries of psychological tests, to arrive at what appeared to be the core problem.

By comparing interview behavior with reported conflicts at home, it became apparent that the wife's behavior was the more neurotic of the two. She found fault with her husband no matter what he did. For example, if he kissed her affectionately, she turned away from him lest it end up in sex relations which were "all he really wants." If he did not kiss her, she considered him cold and unaffectionate. The husband, a passive and yet impulsive man, described himself as despicable and ungenerous because he was given to temper tantrums rather than talking things out. However, he worked on two jobs in order to support his family to whom he seemed truly devoted. He also reported recurrent stomach pains with increasing tension.

Since the wife seemed intelligent and sufficiently interested in knowing more about herself, arrangements were made for insight therapy twice a week. This method was chosen despite indications that her motivation was weak and stemmed mainly from the aura associated with "psychoanalysis."

It soon became evident that the proposed procedure had been the right choice. The wife's first dream in her third session of individual treatment was consistent with the diagnosis of hysterical character disorder. She dreamed that "Many animals who were one-half bird and one-half worm came into my apartment. It was revolting and horrible, and I tried to smash them by stamping."

Her drawing of these animals, especially when viewed upside down, was clearly phallic (Figure 2). Associations to this dream consisted of resentments

### FIGURE 2
Drawing made by deaf female patient to illustrate dream (Case 1)

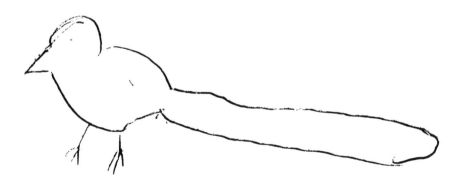

toward her husband for his many faults, and included a disclosure that she now agreed occasionally to sexual relations with him, but absolutely refused to kiss him. For interpretative purposes it may be noted that the manual sign for "kiss" is very like the one meaning "bird." Hence her sexual horror, its displacement upward, and the defensive aggressive reaction were succinctly illustrated in this dream and its associations.

Such observations revealed that the sign language itself provides associational threads to which the therapist must be alert. A play on words such as "bird" and "kiss" may serve as the clue to displaced behavior. More subtly, the literal representation of an object in a dream may be used to convey a feeling (expansiveness or constriction) attached to the gestural sign for that object.

In this case, as the therapy proceeded, interpretations gradually shifted the emphasis for the husband's failings to the patient's own problems. There ensued a period of increasing sexual anxiety with several revealing dreams, among which was the following: "My father's face was close up, he grabbed a pillow and ejaculated. It was terrible. There was a feeling I wanted sex and I felt horrible."

Effective interpretation of these dreams was hindered by problems in abstraction. The patient was unable to grasp the idea that past childhood feelings and fears in regard to significant adults may be revived in current relationships. As this phase drew on, the patient's anxiety and resistance mounted and her motivation began to fail. Giving various excuses, she insisted on cutting the sessions down to once a week and later every other week.

With the treatment curtailed over the next few months, the patient did not again approach the core conflict so closely. However, in the course of therapy she did accept her own responsibility in the marital discord and engaged less and less in uncontrolled acting out of her impulses. As a result, the marriage became more stable, although it was by no means free of neurotic dissension. One incidental feature of the change was a noticeable decrease in the husband's gastric symptoms following the relief of marital pressures.

*Case 2:* R.S., a 40-year-old male, became deaf at the age of three and was married to a deaf woman. He was troubled by marital disharmony as well as obesity, which in his mind was allied with the fear of being effeminate. According to his history, he had chronic rage directed at a colleague of his, coupled with a fear of homosexual attraction toward this man.

The patient brought to the treatment sessions at our clinic a high degree of motivation, good communication ability, both manual and oral, and a keen ability to form psychological connections and develop associative pathways in his biographical, current and dream material. His life situation was reasonably favorable and included a good income as a white-collar worker. After a brief period of therapy, he understood some of the guiding threads in his psychological development and modified some of the social anxiety which had interfered with his work and organizational life.

The patient was the oldest of three children and actually was able to recall the illness that led to his deafness. Interestingly, he associated it with his earliest memory of his mother. Other early memories, such as those of having been humiliated at school, traumatic mealtime experiences as a child, food deprivation, accusations of stealing food, led to an overvaluation of oral ingestion and were found to be associated with his obesity and body image distortions. Also, he was a compulsive and omnivorous reader, especially when emotionally upset. In one of his dreams, the sentences he was reading turned into hamburgers which he began to eat.

The patient's homosexual fears were traceable in his therapeutic sessions to homosexual play, at first forced on him at school and then resorted to for closeness and companionship. Also, his admiration and envy for more successful men, prototypes of his father, were expressed as a power struggle, symbolized in homosexual form. In another dream, his rival was seen making a sexual approach toward him. Interpretation of this power struggle helped to decrease his homosexual fear, although he still doubted his masculinity. Sexual confusion was evident in his drawings (Figures 3 and 4). Apparently, disappointment by and hatred toward his mother did affect his choice of mate and contributed to the marital discord. Despite high capability, the patient's dependency needs remained unsatisfied.

The good results that were obtained in this case served to illustrate the effectiveness of a brief course of psychotherapy. In this treatment procedure, the psychiatrist could utilize his psychodynamic information, his knowledge of the particular environment of the deaf, and his ability in communication to guide a responsive deaf patient to a beneficial relationship and useful insight.

### Reparative Therapy with Some Degree of Insight and Reeducation

In the deaf even more than in the hearing, we observed behavior disorders which for one reason or another do not lend themselves to depth psychotherapy. Here abbreviated therapeutic measures may bring about a satisfactory resolution. Aimed at repairing uncontrolled behavior distortion, these efforts rely primarily on the innate capacity for health. However, they must be assisted by the diminution of emergency responses, removal of road blocks, and relief of pressures.

This kind of therapy may be especially useful in transient stress situations, or when limited modification of behavior in specific areas is called for. Based on a knowledge of psychodynamics, the available methods include management and gratification of dependent needs, providing omnipotent "magical" support, manipulating the environment, and furnishing an objective review of stress situations. They are to be combined with education and guidance, emotional decompression and ventilation, and modification of the patient's goals and self-demands (83). The following cases illustrate various aspects of this approach:

Case 3: L.K., a 19-year-old congenitally deaf male, was referred by a rehabilitation agency while being trained as a printer. Always thin and sickly, he had a lifelong history of poor eating, anxiety, and vague gastrointestinal dysfunction in the face of stress. These symptoms, coupled with his anxious parents' excessively protective attempts to make his life easy, had led to repeated retreats from performance demands in several schools for the deaf. He had no friends and for the most part stayed home or tagged after his younger sister's set.

Tests by the rehabilitation service had led to his being placed in a printing school where he seemed to be getting along well until graduation approached and commercial employment became imminent. At this point, the old symptoms

## FIGURE 3
### Male figure drawing (Case 2)

returned, accompanied by ticlike head and shoulder shrugs and difficulty in sleeping.

Our interviews revealed a tense, asthenic young man of high-average intelligence, well able to express his anxiety over the responsibilities of employment and manhood. Since he was afraid that his slow work would cause him to fail, he anticipated with alarm any future employer's dissatisfaction. Although repeating to himself his mother's reassurances, he was fearful of the possibility that his parents might die and he would be left alone. This reaction led to a desire to retreat from the situation.

The patient's condition was diagnosed as a personality disorder in the inadequate or passive-dependent range. He seemed to have a good capacity for emotional response, limited mainly by a dependency motivation. The decision was

## FIGURE 4
### Female figure drawing (Case 2)

made, therefore, to utilize this tendency therapeutically. The patient was placed on meprobamate, and was given to understand that his fears were quite justifiable, even those about his parents' dying. After a few visits he was strongly assured that we would help him over this crisis and would recommend a sympathetic placement where undue demands would not be made. The interviews were relatively short and direct.

When our recommendations were made to the patient's rehabilitation counselor, emphasis was put on speedy placement so the boy would have a continued opportunity to practice his skills. The counselor, in turn, enlisted the cooperation of placement agencies. The result of this team approach, in which the patient's desire for magical help was utilized, reinforced by pharmacologic treatment, was a rapid dissipation of symptoms and abatement of the crisis.

*Case 4:* I.A., a charming 16-year-old girl, congenitally deaf, was brought to the clinic by her parents with a presumably severe school phobia. However, several interviews and psychological testing revealed a rather typical adolescent problem. The patient's warmth and hoydenish quality had provoked a good deal of teasing attention from boys, a situation which was resented by her girl friends. They became unfriendly and called her bad names, whereupon she responded in kind, occasionally with overt aggression, and with increasing evidence of anxiety.

In addition to this psychosexual problem, her projective tests disclosed another feature typical of many deaf persons. Rather than react to whole percepts, she would pick out details. When the entirety was pointed out to her, she was quick to perceive it. But on her own, however, she had not been able to gather parts into a useful cognitive whole. As this deficiency appeared to be a clue to her recent interpersonal problems, she was counseled accordingly in weekly sessions for a period of several months. The emphasis was on partial insight, support, emotional ventilation and education. The results were satisfactory, although the patient still continued at the time of this report to come for occasional refresher sessions.

### Supportive Therapy with Suggestion, Persuasion, Environmental Manipulation

The limited-goal type of treatment applied in Cases 3 and 4 proved to be useful for persons with mild responsive neurosis where depth therapy was not required. For those with neurotic or psychotic problems unsuitable for insightful efforts, and for persons of low mentality or completely dependent motivation, a more supportive regime had to be used. The use of drugs and community help, combining the efforts of psychiatrist, teachers, rehabilitation counselors and other social agencies, were often a necessary part of this type of therapy.

### Group Therapy

Aside from the methods of individual psychotherapy which have been discussed, *group therapy* should be given a special place in the treatment of the deaf. Treatment in groups would be particularly appropriate for deaf patients in psychiatric hospitals where the isolation of the deaf only adds to their psychopathology. Although the opportunity to interact and communicate in a group would be of special value here, it could not be used because of the unavailability of special wards and services for the deaf. Steps were recently taken to remedy this situation and to facilitate the application of such therapy.

In fact, the reorganization of mental health services for the deaf is a prerequisite for the secure handling of all their psychiatric needs. Clinics, day hospitals and special wards should be combined with facilities for counseling family members. The special needs of the deaf, determined by their social position, their psychological development and their communication limitations, require not only trained and experienced therapists, but a well-coordinated administrative setting.

A second application of group therapy is in the field of family, sex and marriage education for deaf adolescents and their parents. The mustiness of ignorance about the biological and social facts of life, including genetics, cannot be routed by mechanical teaching, but only by the fresh air of a truly psychotherapeutic atmosphere.

## Conclusions

Provisions for psychiatric treatment are strongly recommended for all states with a heavy concentration of persons with early total deafness. This is a widely neglected area of psychotherapy; it combines the challenge of a unique problem in communication and understanding with the remarkable opportunity to let a significantly large, deserving, and resourceful group share in those benefits which can be derived from psychotherapy.

PART THREE

PSYCHIATRIC CONSIDERATIONS: CLINICAL
INPATIENT PROGRAM

# Chapter 14

## DISTRIBUTION AND DIAGNOSIS OF PATIENTS IN NEW YORK STATE MENTAL HOSPITALS

### Kenneth Z. Altshuler and John D. Rainer

Generally speaking, the study of mental illness in a deaf population is of value from several standpoints. In observing the major categories of illness in this special group, it is possible to compare their incidence, symptoms, course, severity, and amenability to treatment with similar aspects of disease in the hearing. If any of these features vary consistently between the two groups, it may indicate an effect of deafness which cuts across diagnostic boundaries. At the same time, the influence of ego strength and flexibility, distortions in communication and the like upon trends of illness may be assessed by evaluating a population in which these parameters are modified by a common perceptual defect. While these definitive goals are not yet attained, the data collected in our study serve to correlate certain facts, suggest tentative answers, and point the way for further study.

The material on mental illness in the deaf was obtained through the following: (1) a continuous survey of deaf patients in New York State mental institutions; (2) evaluation and treatment of neurotic and psychotic individuals in our outpatient clinic for the deaf; and (3) comprehensive interviews of the families of certain deaf patients.

At the start it might be well to consider the basic question of whether the major psychoses diagnosed in the deaf represent the same clinical entities as in the hearing. Since the group of schizophrenics is by far the most common of the psychotic disorders, diagnostic problems in this category may be taken to represent difficulties arising in the evaluation of deaf patients generally.

The diagnosis of schizophrenia depends upon recognition of particular disturbances in thought processes and concept formation and in affective depth, response, and quality. The thoughts of a patient with schizophrenia do not follow a rational or logical sequence, but appear disconnected, rambling, and unrelated. Also characteristic is a frame of reference stretched to such a point that distant irrelevant ideas based only on similarity of sound or the meaning of an occasional word may be associated to the thought at hand and expressed without restraint.

In schizophrenics, the emotional tone tends to be either shallow or inappropriate to the ideas verbalized. Patients with this illness are inclined to retreat from reality into delusions, hallucinations and illusions, although the presence of these accessory symptoms is not pathognomonic. Naturally, the most severe cases are easily recognized, but noting more obscure manifestations in less disorganized patients may require many hours of intensive study.

In the deaf, psychiatric diagnosis is necessarily prolonged. The manual language used by many deaf persons is often only an approximation to the spoken word, with meanings open to subjective interpretation. Poor grammatical structure, exaggerated in manual communication, may mask or mimic a subtle disorder of thought. Idiomatic differences between spoken language and signing, and a tendency to respond in concrete terms, so common among the deaf, further complicate the task. Thus a patient may respond in the present tense to a question about the past. If asked, "How did you happen to come here?" he might answer, "By subway."

If the patient has some ability to speak and read lips, his general language structure may be better, and disordered thoughts more easily discernible. The written word sometimes helps to reveal a loosened connection of ideas and associations, but one must still consider variations in grammatical and language facility. Of course, failure to acquire proper tools for smooth expression, whether oral or manual, on the part of a deaf person with normal intelligence who has attended schools for a period of years, may in itself suggest schizophrenia.

In communicating nuances and emotional context, facial expressions and bodily gestures play a greater role in manual language than in normal speech. With this type of affective accentuation, the emotional expressivity of the deaf schizophrenic takes on an air of vitality and depth. Then, too, because of the intimate relation between ideational content and its gestural communication, dissociation of idea and affect, or incongruity between one and the other, is rare in all but the most poorly integrated patients. Prolonged observation is usually required to uncover such clues as slight but persistent inappropriateness of mood, defects of attention span, hints of autistic thinking, and the like.

Diagnostic obstacles of this kind, which are common in dealing with deaf people, can be overcome by specialized clinical training, a knowledge of the deaf and of their language, and a willingness to spend time and patience. During the course of our study, certain characteristic manifestations of schizophrenia in the deaf became apparent. The following cases present typical examples:

*Case 1:* A slowly progressive course with recurrent acute episodes was observed in J.R., a 38-year-old night watchman, deaf either since birth or his first year of life. He had been hospitalized several times, usually because of what was described as episodes of "impulsive, aggressive, bizarre behavior." The aggressive outbursts either followed some minor frustration or were entirely unprovoked. When interviewed in sign language, he grimaced excitedly but answered no questions, repeating through signs only those words that were used in the question. Subsequent attempts at communication elicited a manual word salad with an occasional delusional fragment.

*Case 2:* An acute exacerbation of a progressive but previously unrecognized process was seen in M.B., an 18-year-old congenitally deaf female high school student. After several years of much scholastic achievement but little social success, she required hospitalization following a two-week episode of acute disturbance, She postured, verbalized nonsense, was often incontinent and smeared her feces. When interviewed, she shuffled manneristically and merely repeated in signs the questions she was asked.

*Case 3:* An example of a paranoid development in a case previously marked only by such behavioral difficulties as temper tantrums and disobedience was J.T., a 16-year-old congenitally deaf student of a residential school. He was hospitalized after a prolonged borderline adjustment, with repeated episodes of sudden aggressive outbursts towards his mother, grandmother, and others. For several months he behaved well in the ward, and no gross evidence of thinking disorder was apparent. He formed a warm bond of friendship with one of the female attendants. Then one day, suddenly hallucinating, he reported seeing a man who conveyed to him in signs the words "sex! dirty! evil!" At the same time, he claimed to have "heard and felt" the man say these words. Later that day, he struck a male occupational therapist because he felt impelled by the force of his hallucinated experience to do so. At every interview, when asked to explain his explosive behavior, he persisted in relating two rather irrelevant incidents of previous years.

*Case 4:* D.A., a congenitally deaf man, unemployed at the age of 27, had a history of chronic maladjustment at a number of schools for the deaf. Of more than average intelligence, he had nevertheless been unable to make a satisfactory vocational or social adjustment. His relationships with people were complicated by frequent temper outbursts and hostile assaults. At each therapeutic session, he retold an incident in which his father, two years previously, had thrown away his favorite Tyrolean hat. It was the thought of this incident that gave rise to his frequent explosive rages at home. No clinical evidence could be obtained for hallucinatory, delusional, or catatonic phenomena.

The most striking symptom in the first two cases may be described as an echolalic echopraxia. Here the patient repeats in a stereotyped way in sign language the questions that he is asked. This condition is more likely to be present in severely disturbed cases. A repetitive preoccupation with events long past, as illustrated in the two other cases, is often seen early in the course of illness in less disorganized patients.

Regardless of classification, the *clinical picture* for most hospitalized deaf patients seemed to be dominated by behavior disturbance. Most commonly described as "impulsive, aggressive, bizarre behavior," such manifestations had to be diagnosed with caution. In the schizophrenic deaf, the disturbed actions furnish clues to the disordered affect and thought. These actions must be distinguished in respect to type of impulsivity and quality of bizarre motivation from similar behavior occurring on the basis of underlying mental defect, or the clouded sensorium of a chronic brain syndrome, or even simple misunderstanding.

That the *chief presenting symptoms* among the deaf are so often those associated with disordered behavior may reflect their immaturity and poorly developed control machinery (superego). This hypothesis would be consonant with the idea that audition plays an important role in the development of conscience. At the same time, it is possible that behavioral problems are predominant because the deaf are oriented toward action rather than thought. As noted earlier, for many deaf persons lifelong patterns of self-expression depend primarily on motor activity. Thus emotions of fear and rage are perhaps more likely to be played out in the field of gross behavior than to be manifested in the form of disorganized thought processes or verbal affective display.

Of course, in many cases it may be primarily *the unruly behavior* which leads to hospitalization in the first place. In a silent group within a hearing society many equally ill persons could pass unnoticed if their problems were confined to disturbances of thought. This point is to be considered in evaluating comparative expectancy rates for schizophrenia, since the calculations are based on hospital census figures.

One of the most challenging problems arising in a study of schizophrenia in persons with early total deafness concerns the occurrence of *auditory hallucinations*. Several patients in our series claimed to have had such experiences. Evaluating their validity called for elucidating the nature of the hallucinations.

Physiologic correlates noted in certain types of visual hallucinations have not been found in auditory forms. In the absence of such measurements the problem of subjectivity is not resolved. As long as organic activities presumed to underly these mechanisms are not in evidence, the experiences remain defined in terms of mental mechanisms (projection and wish fulfillment). Even if one accepts this explanation of auditory hallucinations in general, there remains the doubt whether an individual can really wish for something about which he has no knowledge from previous experience.

On close questioning of patients alleged to have had auditory hallucinations, the given phenomena appeared actually to be mediated through the vibratory and proprioceptive senses which were unimpaired by the hearing loss. The content of most of these experiences were reducible to such sounds as engines humming, or people scurrying about overhead. In others, words or messages were somehow "felt" within, as in the third case illustration. Elsewhere we presented the drawings of a schizophrenic patient, deaf since the age of 13 months, wherein he depicted his ability to hear the voice of God (11). In his pictures the voice was carried through wires attached all over the body, again raising doubts as to its auditory character.

With regard to the *choice of treatment method,* an eclectic approach had to be taken. There is reason to believe that a number of patients responded in varying degrees to the pharmacologic and physical modalities of treatment, combined with supportive psychotherapy. Of course, questions of spontaneous versus therapy-induced remissions, and the goal of long-term results are apt to be as elusive here as they are in the hearing. The effectiveness and limitations of any depth form of psychotherapy remained under continuing study, especially in behavior disorders in the neurotic range (Chapter 13).

It is among the psychotic group that major communication problems exist. Often, physician and patient are unable to understand each other, not only because of obstructions in the physical means of exchanging ideas, but because of limitations in abstract thinking imposed on the psychotic deaf by their perceptual defect, and their illness. Frequent corollaries are a complete lack of awareness that an internal problem exists, and a consequent absence of motivation for seeking treatment.

On the basis of our extensive observations on psychotic deaf individuals, we have come to the conclusion that schizophrenia is fundamentally the same clinical entity in the deaf as in the hearing. Similarly, no major differences have been observed between deaf and hearing patients in regard to features essential to the diagnosis of other forms of psychosis. In manic-depressive disease, involutional psychosis, psychosis with mental deficiency, and the group of organic brain syndromes, the basic diagnostic signs may be correctly diagnosed in deaf patients, provided the tendency to action disturbances, modifications in abstraction, and other obscuring aspects of language and grammatical problems are taken into consideration. A knowledge of manual language has been found to be invaluable for clearly eliciting the clinical features that require assessment.

With these factors in mind, we may now turn to compare the diagnostic distribution of psychotic disturbances in deaf and hearing persons. For this analysis, we used the records of 230 psychotic individuals, comprising the entire deaf population of New York State mental hospitals in 1958. The total count was obtained by visiting each of these institutions and canvassing individual wards. This procedure was repeated at least once a year during the course of the project, partly to maintain an accurate census. During these visits all patients were interviewed by our specially trained staff members to verify diagnoses and gather additional data. As the most prevalent form of disorder, schizophrenia will be the main focus of concern.

From Table 1 it can be seen that the 120 schizophrenic cases constituted 52.2 per cent of all deaf patients, a close approximation to the 56.5 per cent of non-deaf patients with the same diagnosis. An earlier comparison based on hospital diagnosis alone had indicated a greater disparity, i.e., 47.5 per cent as against 57.2 per cent. The discrepancy was apparently caused by the large number classified as "Psychosis with Mental Deficiency." This category comprised more than one-quarter of all deaf patients who had been given a hospital diagnosis at that time.

Our first impression was that the given category represented a "wastebasket" classification for deaf persons with poor communication skills who at some time showed signs of emotional disturbance. This impression was confirmed by our own diagnostic study. Careful evaluation through all

**TABLE 1**

Distribution of mental disorders among New York State mental hospital patients

| Type of disorder | Deaf patients | | | Hearing patients* | | | Per cent of hospital population | |
|---|---|---|---|---|---|---|---|---|
| | Total | Male | Female | Total | Male | Female | Deaf | Hearing |
| Total | 230 | 116 | 114 | 92,409 | 42,166 | 50,243 | 100.0 | 100.0 |
| Schizophrenia | 120 | 64 | 56 | 52,225 | 23,749 | 28,476 | 52.2 | 56.5 |
| Psychosis with mental deficiency | 42 | 23 | 19 | 3,401 | 1,618 | 1,783 | 18.2 | 3.7 |
| Senile and arteriosclerotic psychoses | 17 | 5 | 12 | 14,975 | 5,951 | 9,024 | 7.4 | 16.2 |
| Cycloid and involutional psychoses | 12 | 0 | 12 | 7,401 | 1,939 | 5,462 | 5.2 | 8.0 |
| Organic psychoses with retinitis pigmentosa other | 11 16 | 7 9 | 4 7 | 11,047 | 7,162 | 3,885 | 4.8 7.0 | 12.0 |
| Other behavioral disorders | 10 | 7 | 3 | 3,170 | 1,650 | 1,520 | 4.3 | 3.4 |
| Undiagnosed | 2 | 1 | 1 | 190 | 97 | 93 | .9 | .2 |

*State of New York, Department of Mental Hygiene, Annual Report, 1957

avenues of communication disclosed a breadth of general knowledge and conceptual ability, which in several instances made the diagnosis of subnormal intelligence untenable. In a number of these cases, the thought and affective derangements typical of schizophrenia were also revealed. Nevertheless, 18.2 per cent of the hospitalized deaf retained the diagnosis of psychosis with mental deficiency in contrast to 3.7 per cent in the hearing group.

This remaining group had to be considered in conjunction with the figures on the relative prevalence of organic psychoses, to which mental deficiency may be related. If an illness, encephalitis for example, leaves extensive immediate organic damage, a patient would probably be classified as a case of organic psychosis, and in severe cases associated deafness might never be noticed. Should the illness result primarily in a mental defect and the individual later develop disordered behavior, his diagnosis would be psychosis with mental deficiency. About one-half of all deafness is also acquired through such illnesses, and deafness is often not the only residual defect. Thus, in recovered cases, a greater proportion of deaf persons would be likely to come under the heading of psychosis with mental deficiency.

This impression is borne out upon closer scrutiny of the organic group. About 4000 patients, or approximately one-third of the hearing population so classified, were actually psychoses based on alcoholism, while among the hospitalized deaf there were no patients in this category. Without the alcoholic segment, the 8 per cent of hospitalized hearing closely approximates the 7 per cent of deaf patients who had uncomplicated organic psychoses.

An additional 4.8 per cent of deaf patients had a particular form of retinitis pigmentosa. This syndrome, recently investigated by Hallgren (91), consists of retinitis pigmentosa combined with congenital deafness, and in about one-quarter of cases includes intellectual subnormalcy. In Hallgren's series psychotic behavior was a not uncommon accompaniment, sometimes resembling schizophrenia and at other times more similar to psychosis with mental deficiency. In our series, three patients with retinitis pigmentosa and deafness showed a clinical picture resembling schizophrenia, while four were more typical of psychosis with mental deficiency. The syndrome is assumed to be transmitted by a single autosomal recessive gene. However, the psychotic symptomatology remains difficult to interpret and is possibly influenced by lengthy deprivation of both auditory and visual stimulation.

In summary, if the alcoholic psychoses among the hearing are set aside, there is an excess in the number of deaf patients that have a special form of organic psychosis and of psychosis with mental deficiency. The difference is based on the combined effects of genetic and acquired conditions in producing both the deafness and the other impairments.

The relative absence of severe *endogenous depressions* among the deaf should also be noted, although their number was too small to warrant any statistical inference. Only one deaf patient in the cycloid and involutional group (Table 1) showed primarily the clinical picture of depression. Considering the psychodynamic relationship between depression and alcohol or narcotic addiction, this observation may turn out to have special significance.

Among the schizophrenic patients no evidence was found for a preponderance of *paranoid* symptoms. Of those in the hospitals, 50 per cent were diagnosed as predominantly paranoid, a rate not significantly higher than in hearing schizophrenics. As a matter of fact, persons who were born deaf or deafened early in life are inclined to be overly trusting, in contrast to people deafened later in life, many of whom do show a tendency to suspiciousness.

In 1958, the average age at first admission of deaf schizophrenics on the hospital rolls was found to be 30.5 years. In 1954, the average age of first admission non-deaf schizophrenics was 32.4, and in 1957, 33.1 years. However, since the deaf series was composed for the most part of patients whose illnesses entailed prolonged institutionalization, rather than a group of patients admitted for the first time during any one year, these figures are not directly comparable.

Regarding the *expectancy rate for schizophrenia* in our census of 10,355 deaf New York State residents over age 15, an estimate of 2.5 per cent was obtained. If valid, this figure, derived from a study of hospitalized patients, would represent an increase over the one per cent rate for the hearing population. Calculations for both hearing and non-hearing groups were subject to correction first for age by the abridged Weinberg method (114, 239). Also, one extramural schizophrenic was added for every two who were institutionalized, a procedure in agreement with that for the general population (82).

However, the figure of 2.5 per cent for the risk of schizophrenia in the deaf is based on the assumption that the procedures of ascertainment for deaf and hearing schizophrenics were comparable. Differences in diagnostic standards, and ratio of hospitalized to non-hospitalized cases might very well alter the picture. Even using refined diagnostic techniques and not relying on hospital records, bases for discrepancy may lie in other directions. Comparable census figures for deaf and hearing patients (Table 2) show a significantly greater proportion of deaf schizophrenics hospitalized for more than five years or even longer than 20 years. Since no differences have been established in such matters as age of onset or severity of illness, we might attribute this finding to social factors that are unrelated to the psychiatric condition. Apart from clinical evaluation, sheltered. convalescent placement of destitute patients with limited ability to communicate remains a difficult task.

On the whole, hospitalized schizophrenics were found to represent 1.16 per cent of the total deaf population of New York State, as compared to 0.43 per cent in the hearing. However, with the number of undischarged

**TABLE 2**
Distribution of schizophrenic hospital patients in New York State
according to length of hospitalization

| Hospitalized schizophrenics in New York State | | Per cent of schizophrenics hospitalized | | |
|---|---|---|---|---|
| Hearing status | Total | Less than 5 years | 5 years and over | 20 years and over |
| Hearing* | 52,225 | 24.2 | 75.8 | 35.4 |
| Deaf | 120 | 10.8 | 89.2 | 47.5 |

*State of New York, Department of Mental Hygiene, Annual Report, 1957.

deaf patients as considerable as it is, the assumption of one extramural patient for every two in a hospital may not be valid for data on the deaf.

Certainly, any comparison of schizophrenia rates for deaf and hearing populations has to take into account the effect of certain genetic constellations. With heredity playing an important role in deafness, it is not surprising that the parental consanguinity rate in deaf families has been found to vary between 6 and 10 per cent (138). In our own survey, the observed consanguinity rate approximated 8 per cent for the parents of all deaf persons in New York State (Chapter 2). Cousin marriages in the general population are probably fewer than one per cent (74).

An increased frequency of parental consanguinity could influence schizophrenia rates for the deaf only if vulnerability to a schizophrenic process were more likely to be found under conditions favoring the manifestation of recessive traits. In line with the statistical considerations of Dahlberg (48), the increase actually found in consanguinity would not be expected to significantly alter the actual schizophrenia risk in this special group.

For these various reasons, the calculated overall schizophrenia expectancy rate of 2.5 per cent among the deaf can only be a rough approximation and allows no conclusion regarding causal relations between early total deafness and a change one way or the other in the expectancy rate of schizophrenia. A special study of the families of deaf schizophrenic index cases was instituted in an effort to clarify the possible relationship. The results and implications of this study are described in Chapter 15.

# Chapter 15

## DEAFNESS AND SCHIZOPHRENIA: A FAMILY STUDY

Kenneth Z. Altshuler and M. Bruce Sarlin

In order to assess more fully the relation between early total deafness and schizophrenia, a diagnostic study was undertaken of the families of all hospitalized deaf schizophrenics. Among the data sought were the effect of deafness upon the frequency of schizophrenia in the parents and siblings of the patients, and the likelihood that deafness and schizophrenia would occur together more or less often than expected by chance. The study was designed to be helpful in estimating the need for psychiatric services for the deaf. At the same time it promised to be of basic importance in understanding the psychopathology of the schizophrenic deaf, including the interaction of biological and cultural influences.

The psychological implications of early total deafness deserve careful scrutiny. Disordered communication and disruption of the early child-parent relationship epitomize the conditions under which the young deaf person develops. Years of special schooling are necessary to provide other tools of communication to make up for the lack of hearing. In many instances, this training cannot be effective unless it takes place in residential schools and begins at a very early age, entailing long periods of separation from the parental home.

Another disturbing factor is that parents are rarely encouraged to learn the manual (sign) language. Instead, verbalization is practiced to induce the child to speak, thus adding an element to the power struggle between child and parent. The result is a mutually frustrating, bewildering and tension-producing situation in which both sides seek to convey and gratify personal needs. Where parents are unable to control feelings of guilt, resentment, or disappointment over the child's defect, emotional communication is further distorted.

Speech development in normal children, according to Spitz (210), acts as "organizer of the psyche" and is necessary for both personality expansion and the formation of "relationships in the human pattern." Hampered by his handicap, the deaf child remains relatively fixed and isolated so that im-

---

Portions of this chapter are reproduced, by permission of the authors and the publisher, from *Expanding Goals of Genetics in Psychiatry*, F. J. Kallmann (ed.), New York, Grune & Stratton, 1962.

balanced development results. While his physical maturation may proceed normally, the emotional and intellectual aspects of his growth lag behind, limiting the expression and codification of evolving age-specific interests.

Many psychological studies of the deaf have shown such pronounced residual limitations in abstract conceptual ability that it is not certain that this developmental imbalance can ever be fully righted (16, 135). Rorschach tests confirm that many deaf persons are distinguished by ego rigidity and deficient emotional adaptability, descriptions usually applying to personalities that tend to be vulnerable to breaks in adaptation (132).

In short, the net effect of early hearing loss and its sequelae is extremely stressful, and is likely to disrupt and distort normal personality development. Nevertheless, the consequences of this disordering stress cannot glibly be equated with a schizophrenia-like process.

The clinical features of a real schizophrenia psychosis in the deaf were described in the previous chapter. Despite various modifications in symptomatology, the basic personality disorder was shown to be clearly discernible. The 2.5 per cent schizophrenia rate for the deaf computed from hospitalized cases at that time was not altogether acceptable because of several considerations, especially the prolonged hospital stay found for deaf patients. By the same token, the rate cannot be considered an accurate index of a change in schizophrenia risk based on the stresses just reviewed, e.g., disrupted personal relationships, disordered communication, or lack of harmony between the elements of psychological development and biologic maturation. Special care is required in appraising this problem through hospitalized cases alone, and the need for some other technique of investigation is evident.

Through the years, studies have been made of the risk for various psychiatric disorders in relatives of affected patients (index cases) in virtually all kinship categories (5). Despite differences in diagnostic standards, statistical procedures, availability of relatives and special demographic conditions, there has been a remarkable unanimity of findings. The results of these well-controlled studies are summarized in Table 1 which shows the consistently observed graded increase in schizophrenia rates with the increase in degree of genetic similarity to a schizophrenic index case. Representing an American (New York State) population which was ascertained and diagnosed according to conservative contemporary standards, Kallmann's 1946 study (111) warrants special note.*

* Despite the choice of twin rather than single-born index cases, the schizophrenia rates obtained for siblings and parents approximated those reported by others. Since Kallmann's study was similar to the current one in many aspects, i.e., New York State population, comparable diagnostic standards, and personal investigation, it would seem to offer the best base for comparison. Nonetheless, the longitudinal nature of his investigation (five years) and the selection of twin index cases are variables which serve to emphasize the lack of perfectly comparable data between investigations. In the absence of such data, large deviations in the whole range of findings are needed for observed differences to be considered meaningful.

## TABLE 1
Frequency of schizophrenia in the general population and in relatives of schizophrenics

| Source | Frequency of schizophrenia in general population | Frequency of schizophrenia in the relatives of one schizophrenic | | | | | |
|---|---|---|---|---|---|---|---|
| | | Step-sibs | Half-sibs | Full sibs | Dizygotic cotwins | Monozygotic cotwins | Parents |
| Various investigations (1916 to 1953) | 0.3-2.4 | – | 7.6 | 4.5-12.0 | 12.5-14.9 | 68.3-81.7 | 7.1-12.0 |
| Kallmann 1946 (twin index cases) | 0.85 | 1.8 | 7.0 | 14.3 | 14.7 | 85.8 | 9.2 |

If the stressful effect of deafness alone were to increase the manifestation of schizophrenia appreciably without any gene-borne vulnerability, the schizophrenia risk for hearing siblings and parents of deaf index cases should fall below the rates found for relatives of hearing schizophrenic probands. That is, persons with deafness would be more likely to develop schizophrenia, regardless of genetic predisposition. Hence, relatives of deaf schizophrenics, with neither the perceptual defect nor the genetic potential for schizophrenia, should be roughly similar to the general population. The morbidity risk among them should then approximate one per cent, rather than be increased because of genetic vulnerability as postulated in other family studies. Also, there should be a marked difference between hearing and deaf relatives of deaf index cases, since in the presence of similar genetic endowments, deafness as such should cause a significant increase in the frequency of schizophrenia. By studying the families of deaf schizophrenics along these lines we can assess the influence of stresses exerted by total hearing loss on the risk of schizophrenia.

In the course of our continuing survey of deaf persons admitted to mental hospitals, a total of 286 patients had been seen during a six-year period. Of these, 138 met our stringent diagnostic criteria for both deafness and schizophrenia. Deafness was defined as a "stress-producing hearing loss at an early age, making effective auditory contact with the world impossible and necessitating special educative efforts" (112). The diagnosis of schizophrenia was established in each case by a committee of three clinical psychiatrists trained in working with the deaf. No psychotic case was accepted without unanimity of opinion, nor was any undue pressure exerted to achieve uniformity of classification.

The diagnostic criteria employed were on the conservative side, and similar to those used in previous investigations. Essentially, these criteria emphasized a clearly discernible personality change; repudiation of reality relationships; disintegration of personality; impaired concept formation or loosened conceptual frame of associations; and blunting, apathy or other incongruities between thought and feeling. Disordered behavior and impaired judgement were always present, but delusions, hallucinations or deteriorating tendencies, while commonly found, were not required for the diagnosis.

In classifying the siblings and parents of deaf index cases, no relative, regardless of history, was called schizophrenic unless there were adequate hospital records or extensive personal interviews to substantiate the diagnosis. Shiftless individuals with suspicious histories remained unclassified or were placed in the category of "probable schizophrenia." On the other hand, fairly healthy life performance reports by other relatives, even where possibly biased, led to classifying a missing hearing person as nonschizophrenic. Since the communication problem of the hearing-impaired may mask an underlying personality disorder, no deaf person was given any mental status classification whatsoever unless historical records were supplemented by personal psychiatric interview. By thus keeping to a minimum the ascertainment of schizophrenia cases among hearing relatives, and increasing the proportion of schizophrenics found among the hearing-impaired, any difference between the two groups, hearing and deaf, would be a maximum.

The general data on the *siblings* of our sample of deaf schizophrenics are tabulated in Tables 2 and 3. Of the total of 349 siblings, 18 died before they

### TABLE 2
#### Age distribution of the siblings of deaf schizophrenics

| Age | Living | | Deceased | | Total |
|---|---|---|---|---|---|
| | Male | Female | Male | Female | |
| 0 – 14 | 0 | 0 | 12 | 6 | 18 |
| 15 – 24 | 0 | 7 | 6 | 3 | 16 |
| 25 – 34 | 14 | 18 | 2 | 2 | 36 |
| 35 – 44 | 38 | 43 | 3 | 1 | 85 |
| 45 – 54 | 52 | 37 | 6 | 2 | 97 |
| 55 – 64 | 30 | 26 | 6 | 1 | 63 |
| 65 and over | 7 | 11 | 8 | 8 | 34 |
| Total | 141 | 142 | 43 | 23 | 349 |

### TABLE 3
#### Hearing status of the siblings of deaf schizophrenics

| Age | Deaf | Hard of hearing | Hearing | Undetermined | Total |
|---|---|---|---|---|---|
| 0 – 14 | 1 | 0 | 11 | 6 | 18 |
| 15 – 24 | 1 | 1 | 14 | 0 | 16 |
| 25 – 34 | 0 | 1 | 35 | 0 | 36 |
| 35 – 44 | 11 | 0 | 74 | 0 | 85 |
| 45 – 54 | 5 | 3 | 89 | 0 | 97 |
| 55 – 64 | 2 | 1 | 60 | 0 | 63 |
| 65 and over | 2 | 1 | 31 | 0 | 34 |
| Total | 22 | 7 | 314 | 6 | 349 |

entered the age of risk for schizophrenia, which was assumed to extend from the ages of 15 to 45 years. The other 48 deceased relatives survived all or part of this period and were recorded as of the age at death.

No significant early impairment of hearing was present in 314 siblings, although a few did develop some degree of hearing loss late in life. Six others died in infancy with hearing status undetermined. Of the remaining

29 siblings, 22 (including one who had died at the age of three years) met our criteria for deafness. The other seven were classified as hard of hearing. Except for degree of deafness or age of onset, their developmental histories were substantially the same as those of the deaf.

Comparable information about the *parents* of 138 index cases is presented in Tables 4 and 5. All but 21 of them lived through the age of risk for schizophrenia. In 38 couples, the only information obtained was the fact that they had died. With more than 70 per cent of the parents deceased, hearing status could be determined only in 200 of them, including four cases of deafness and one of marked hearing impairment. Since the predominant mode of transmission in hereditary deafness is generally assumed to be recessive, the limited number of deaf parents in this sample comes as no surprise.

Psychiatric classification as to the presence or absence of schizophrenia was possible in 310 of the 331 siblings known to have survived at least part of the age of risk (Table 6). The remaining 21 cases consisted of 19

**TABLE 4**

Age distribution of the parents of deaf schizophrenics

| Age | Living | | Deceased | | Total |
|-----|--------|--------|----------|--------|-------|
|     | Male | Female | Male | Female | |
| 15 – 24 | 0 | 0 | 0 | 1 | 1 |
| 25 – 34 | 0 | 0 | 3 | 1 | 4 |
| 35 – 44 | 1 | 1 | 8 | 6 | 16 |
| 45 – 54 | 5 | 8 | 14 | 9 | 36 |
| 55 – 64 | 3 | 10 | 17 | 19 | 49 |
| 65 and over | 28 | 25 | 59 | 58 | 170 |
| Total | 37 | 44 | 101 | 94 | 276 |

hearing and two deaf siblings who could not be satisfactorily diagnosed. Eighteen siblings died before age 15.

An unequivocal diagnosis of schizophrenia was made in 28 siblings, while another six were classified as probably schizophrenic because of our inability to confirm the classification through hospital records or personal interview. Typical of the latter group was an extremely suspicious woman who for several years had remained in self-imposed house confinement. She entered only very briefly into bizarre bits of conversation with our visiting team, all the while refusing to unbolt her door.

If only fully verified cases are considered, the age-corrected schizophrenia risk figure for all siblings is 11.6 per cent (Weinberg method: 114, 239). It increases to 14.1 per cent if the six doubtful cases are included (Table 8). These and subsequent computations relate the number of schizophrenics to

## TABLE 5
### Hearing status of the parents of deaf schizophrenics

| Age | Deaf | Hard of hearing | Hearing | Undetermined | Total |
|---|---|---|---|---|---|
| 15 – 24 | 0 | 0 | 1 | 0 | 1 |
| 25 – 34 | 0 | 0 | 4 | 0 | 4 |
| 35 – 44 | 0 | 0 | 16 | 0 | 16 |
| 45 – 54 | 0 | 0 | 28 | 8 | 36 |
| 55 – 64 | 0 | 1 | 37 | 11 | 49 |
| 65 and over | 4 | 0 | 109 | 57 | 170 |
| Total | 4 | 1 | 195 | 76 | 276 |

## TABLE 6
### Psychiatric classification of those 331 siblings of deaf schizophrenics who lived beyond the age of 14 years

| Age | Schizophrenia | | | | Without schizophrenia | | Undetermined | | Total |
|---|---|---|---|---|---|---|---|---|---|
| | Definite* | | Probable | | Male | Female | Male | Female | |
| | Male | Female | Male | Female | | | | | |
| 15 – 24 | 1 | 0 | 0 | 0 | 5 | 9 | 0 | 1 | 16 |
| 25 – 34 | 3 | 3 | 0 | 1 | 13 | 16 | 0 | 0 | 36 |
| 35 – 44 | 4 | 5 | 1 | 1 | 35 | 38 | 1 | 0 | 85 |
| 45 – 54 | 4 | 2 | 2 | 1 | 48 | 34 | 4 | 2 | 97 |
| 55 – 64 | 1 | 5 | 0 | 0 | 31 | 16 | 4 | 6 | 63 |
| 65 and over | 0 | 0 | 0 | 0 | 14 | 17 | 1 | 2 | 34 |
| Total | 13 | 15 | 3 | 3 | 146 | 130 | 10 | 11 | 331 |

*Includes 15 cases who were not hospitalized.

an age-corrected frame of reference based on all psychiatrically classified cases. In the comparisons to follow, only the minimum rate will be used.

The most interesting finding is the absence of a statistically significant difference between the schizophrenia risks for hearing and deaf siblings. With 25 cases of schizophrenia among the 284 hearing siblings their corrected expectancy rate is 11.2 per cent. The corresponding rate for the 26 siblings with impaired hearing who were available for classification is 15.8 per cent. This is reduced to 14.3 per cent if the three cases of schizophrenia are related to all 28 hearing-impaired siblings, including those two who were reported to have been emotionally well-adjusted but could not be

**TABLE 7**

Psychiatric classification of the parents of deaf schizophrenics

| Age | Schizophrenia | | | | Without schizophrenia | | Undetermined | | Total |
|---|---|---|---|---|---|---|---|---|---|
| | Definite* | | Probable | | Male | Female | Male | Female | |
| | Male | Female | Male | Female | | | | | |
| 15 – 24 | 0 | 0 | 0 | 0 | 0 | 1 | 0 | 0 | 1 |
| 25 – 34 | 0 | 0 | 0 | 0 | 2 | 1 | 1 | 0 | 4 |
| 35 – 44 | 1 | 1 | 0 | 0 | 7 | 6 | 1 | 0 | 16 |
| 45 – 54 | 1 | 1 | 2 | 0 | 11 | 12 | 5 | 4 | 36 |
| 55 – 64 | 2 | 2 | 1 | 0 | 12 | 21 | 5 | 6 | 49 |
| 65 and over | 3 | 2 | 5 | 3 | 45 | 47 | 34 | 31 | 170 |
| Total | 7 | 6 | 8 | 3 | 77 | 88 | 46 | 41 | 276 |

*Includes 4 cases who were not hospitalized.

**TABLE 8**

Schizophrenia risk in the siblings and parents of deaf schizophrenics

| Relatives of deaf schizophrenics | Number of siblings | | | Corrected frame of reference* | Crude risk (%) | Corrected risk (%) |
|---|---|---|---|---|---|---|
| | Surviving age 15 | Psychiatrically classified | Definitely schizophrenic | | | |
| Hearing sibs | 303 | 284 | 25 | 223 | 8.8 | 11.2 |
| Deaf sibs** | 28 | 26 | 3 | 19 | 11.5 | 15.8 |
| Total | 331 | 310 | 28 | 242 | 9.0 | 11.6*** |
| Parents of deaf index cases | 276 | 189 | 13 | 179 | 6.9 | 7.3 |

* The sum of all cases over 45 and one-half the cases between 15 and 45, for whom information was available.
** Includes seven cases with marked hearing loss.
*** 14.1% if probable cases are included.

interviewed. If the seven hard of hearing siblings are omitted, this figure is raised to 23 per cent, but with a small sample such as this, even this difference is not statistically significant.

Of similar importance is the finding that all groups of siblings, the hearing as well as the deaf and the combined total, have significantly greater risks for schizophrenia than the general population (1%-2%). Compared with the general population, the risks for these groups are roughly of the same order of magnitude as those computed in other family studies. In particular, they closely approximate the rate of 14.3 per cent reported by Kallmann in 1946 for the siblings of schizophrenic index cases without a hearing loss (111).

As previously mentioned, our rates were obtained under conditions which tended to maximize the difference between the rates for hearing and deaf siblings. If the number of schizophrenics is related to the *total* number of siblings in each group, whether psychiatrically classified or not, the divergence between rates for hearing and deaf siblings still does not reach the level of statistical significance (10.4% for hearing and 14.3% for deaf siblings).

In any case, we cannot say that there are statistically significant differences in schizophrenia risk between deaf and hearing siblings of deaf schizophrenics. On the whole, all groups of siblings of our deaf index cases show a definite increase in morbidity risk over the general population similar to the one that has been so consistently reported in earlier studies. Although the findings do not preclude the possibility of some role played by stressful factors in the simultaneous occurrence of deafness and schizophrenia, the weight of evidence indicates that early total deafness, with all its deprivations and distortions in the normal development patterns, has little bearing on the statistically demonstrable risk of schizophrenia.

Although less precise because of the large number of deceased, our data on the parents of deaf schizophrenics point in the same direction (Tables 7 and 8). In many instances, classifications had to be based on descriptions provided by their children, and thus may have been subject to victimization or eulogy.

In a total of 189 members of the parental generation, the information obtained was considered enough to warrant classification. For this group, 13 persons, none of whom was deaf, were diagnosed as schizophrenic through psychiatric interview or hospital records, yielding a minimum schizophrenia rate of 7.3 per cent for the parents of deaf schizophrenics. This figure is only slightly below the rate observed by other investigators in parents of schizophrenics without perceptual defect (approximately 9%). Again, if incompletely studied parents are counted as normal, the schizophrenia risk varies from 5.1 to 9.5 per cent, depending on whether "probable" cases of schizophrenia are included or excluded.

The *results* of this investigation may be summarized as follows:

1. Early total deafness imposes unusually stressful and disruptive conditions on childhood development and later life. These stresses include disturbed and distorted communication, developmental imbalances, and marked disorder of parent-child relationships.

2. The deaf of New York State show a slightly increased schizophrenia rate (2.5%) over that of the general population (1%-2%). How-

ever, this rate is based on a sample of hospitalized cases, with standard extrapolation for those living on the outside. Therefore it is subject to error, chiefly due to the prolonged length of time spent by deaf patients in mental hospitals. A more accurate schizophrenia rate for the deaf would be virtually unobtainable.

3. The siblings of deaf schizophrenics show a schizophrenia rate (12%-14%) significantly higher than the general population and similar to that observed for the siblings of hearing schizophrenics. The rates are not significantly different whether the given siblings are deaf or hearing. Similar findings obtain for the parents.

4. It would appear from these data that the severe and varied stresses associated with early total deafness do little to increase the chance of developing clinical symptoms of schizophrenia.

5. As a corollary to these findings, it remains essential to distinguish the personality problems associated with deafness from those seen in schizophrenia and to make the latter diagnosis only when clinically warranted.

# PART FOUR

# CONCLUSIONS AND RECOMMENDATIONS

# Chapter 16

## PREVENTIVE MENTAL HEALTH PLANNING

### JOHN D. RAINER AND FRANZ J. KALLMANN

For most deaf persons, the important recommendations in the field of mental health planning lie in the preventive area. Conditions leading to frustration, poor adjustment, and sexual and other forms of delinquency arise within the matrix of the family and the early residential setting of the school. Deaf adolescents grow up and go on to parenthood, often without adequate knowledge and guidance.

The most fruitful approach to prevention of maladjustment is to center attention on preparation for family living, since it is in this context that most unhappiness and behavior disorder manifest themselves. Certainly education and vocational training are also important, but to be effective they require an emotionally stable student. While the individual with a sound foundation for healthy living in school and home has the best chance to achieve vocational and personal fulfillment, the result of neglect and ignorance is often discord, failure and disturbed behavior. As will be shown, these unhappy consequences may involve sexual delinquency or deviation as well as all degrees of interpersonal and vocational maladjustment.

Although facilities for psychiatric treatment are badly needed, even more urgent are mental hygiene programs such as sex education and preparation for marriage for young deaf persons in high school or college. These will benefit not only those deaf persons but their families-to-be. No group is more entitled to counseling in marriage, parenthood and genetics than the deaf. But since counseling in these highly important areas is itself a form of psychotherapy (115), it can best be given by persons trained in psychiatric methods used with the deaf, as well as in the biology of deafness.

Certain problems of sex adjustment in the deaf, especially those encountered in residential school settings, were investigated during the course of the project. However, this concern with sex adjustment, sex education and family planning should not be taken to mean that sexual delinquency patterns were unusually prevalent in this group. Actually, the reluctance of a morally stringent society to deal with sexual maladjustment as a psychological and developmental, rather than a disciplinary matter, continues to be so strong, even in the most progressive circles, that it interferes with the accrual of data on variations in sex behavior.

With so little known about the extent and background of sexual deviations in the hearing population, including residential schools for children, is it any wonder that the available information about their deaf counterparts should be even more limited? The main sources of information about sex problems in the Eastern schools for the deaf were the teachers and house-parents connected with these schools. In the course of the project, there was ample opportunity to find out that sexual delinquency and immaturity, lack of preparation for a successful marriage and stable family life, and the more extreme forms of deviant sex behavior are no less common among the deaf than in any other group of people.

If we are motivated by a sincere desire to promote prevention and cure of these delinquency patterns, it is certain that all problems of this kind must be looked at in the light of normal sexual development. Disturbances in sexual maturation and adjustment represent deviations from a normal pattern that is determined not only by man's biological nature but also by the family, school, and psychological atmosphere in which he develops.

The most complete study, at least statistically, of sexual behavior in the two sexes was made by Kinsey and his associates (117). Their aim was to determine some generally valid facts, without going more deeply into the reasons. In the adult male they reported that four per cent of the population studied were exclusively homosexual, while one-third of all males indicated some homosexual experience during their life. Of the males who were still unmarried at the age of 35, about one-half provided evidence of a homo-sexual pattern with some degree of consistency. However, these figures and any statistics that might be obtained by similar surveys among the deaf would mean little and would be of limited practical use if they were not based on a firm knowledge of normal sex development and the various forms of homosexual behavior.

Interest in sex and love do not develop suddenly in a person's life and spring out of nowhere. Affectionate feelings by children and towards them begin on the first day of life. Love, warmth, tenderness and a feeling of pleasure in the attention of others and in one's own sense of bodily well-being start in the cradle. It would be a mistake to underrate the lasting effect of these intra-family relationships and the degree to which they exist in the experience of the baby and young child. It may be a moot question whether deafness in a child deprives him of some close contact with his parents, or whether in some instances it increases the parental concern and affection for the child. Undoubtedly, however, a healthy love of parents toward a child is important in setting the stage for his future interpersonal relationships.

It is understandable that a proper appreciation and respect for one's own bodily sensations starting early in childhood should be likewise important. Pleasure in sucking, pleasure in eating, in being bathed, in warmth and in coolness, in touching and in the vague but pleasant sensations connected with the genitals—all these are part and parcel of the infant's and child's developing pleasure potential and his ability to remain sentient and re-sponsive to the world at large.

Small boys and girls of preschool age—three, four and particularly five or six year olds—begin to stretch out and extend their curiosity toward others in their environment. They become interested in the physical makeup of other children, their brothers, their sisters, their classmates and various people about them. This newfound preoccupation with the body, which cannot actually be called sexual curiosity at this stage, is something little children of this age are eager to satisfy. This natural curiosity, which is a prerequisite for the development of a wholesome attitude toward the human body, one's own as well as that of others, is best fulfilled by the presence of other children in the home, especially of both sexes.

Modern nursery schools favor unrestricted intermingling of the sexes at the age of four to six, with boys and girls living in the same dormitory, eating at the same table, using the same bathroom, and the like. A similar arrangement would seem advisable for residential schools caring for children of comparable age to compensate for their lack of family life. Needless to say, this inquisitive interest in the physical characteristics of other children, whether of the same or opposite sex, does not represent sexual behavior in the adult sense of the word.

One of the strongest factors in shaping a healthy attitude toward sexual and social development is the example set by the parents. It is from them that children learn to live together in an atmosphere of mutual affection and respect. At a very early age they begin to identify with the parents, the boy with his father, the girl with her mother. In a well-adjusted home children continue to imitate parental ways and attitudes through the pre-adolescent period when making new friends and competing with their peers in work and at play. Cushioned against undue fears by the reassuring family atmosphere the child learns to distinguish between what is normal and pleasurable and what is strange and "dirty."

At this age most children prefer friends of their own sex, but it is well known that early experiences with a childhood sweetheart form a bridge between childish affections of the past and the more mature love of the future. Before adolescents learn to act like young men and young ladies, interest in sex manifests itself in shocking each other with certain words, passing around certain poems and pictures, teasing girls, always seeking to learn more about each other. These curiosities must be directed into healthy channels. The pre-adolescent child has a need for constructive sex teaching, for the outward expression of general biological urges, for absorbing and stimulating recreation—something to do together with other boys and girls.

In adolescence the advent of puberty leads to an increased interest in sex, making the need for intelligent guidance and instruction particularly urgent. During this period of life, many attitudes are developed that are essential for future marital happiness. By now the child is supposed to have learned to socialize with other youngsters, boys and girls alike. If his early sex curiosity has been normally satisfied in a good school or home environment, neither unduly suppressed nor overstimulated, he will have no trouble going through the period of adolescent interests and preparing himself for coping with future matters of mate selection and sexual relationship. By this time socializing has progressed to the point where boys and girls become interested in going to parties, having dates, being with each other while engaging in recreational or educational activities.

If the adolescent's maturational development is normal and prudently fostered by helpful members of the older generation, the persistence of homosexual and other deviant tendencies is expected to be infrequent. Early sex curiosities, pre-adolescent explorations and mutual contacts will be channeled into new directions, and increasing social and cultural demands will combine with academic and artistic achievements to promote normal companionship between the sexes.

The homosexual behavior that persists has been described by Kinsey according to six grades of consistency, from the exclusively homosexual to the exclusively heterosexual. In developmental terms, we have seen that children in the adolescent and pre-adolescent age ranges find it natural to be interested in a wide variety of things that excite their curiosity. Mutual exploration in itself does not constitute homosexual behavior, especially when it takes place between children of the same age.

When it comes to the causes of overt homosexuality, defined as the continuing practice of actual sexual contacts between persons of the same sex in late adolescence and adulthood, there is evidence of some constitutional components, as there is in many other specific patterns of personality integration. These predisposing factors tend to limit the number of people who might develop into actual homosexuals under the particular pressures placed upon them. The influences favoring the formation of a permanent homosexual pattern may be restrictive, inhibitory, conducive or permissive in nature.

A fear of sex may easily grow into a fear of any and all sexual contact with women, thus leaving a boy with the alternative of what appears to him a safer though more clandestine form of expression. In many instances this fear of sex is engendered before the boy-dates-girl age by admonitions and punishments, singling out normal self-exploratory and other inquisitive experiences before adolescence. Later causative factors are prohibitions against normal, healthy contacts with members of the opposite sex, and deficits in the degree of identification with members of the same sex, such as fathers, teachers, house-fathers, coaches and other men who are masculine friendly figures and examples of good husbands and fathers.

On the whole, the factors counteracting the formation of a deviant sexual pattern are the examples set by a healthy and well-adjusted father and mother or their substitutes and the moral values derived from a sensible and mature approach to problems of family life and socialization. Conversely, the factors fostering a deviant sexual pattern are those associated with restriction, ignorance, punitive attitudes and prolonged contact with people who have faulty sexual orientation.

With respect to deaf children, the question is whether the development of homosexual tendencies is facilitated by the effect of early total deafness. It may be argued that deaf children are even more dependent on closeness to each other than hearing youngsters, because they lack one essential means of mutual expression. What may otherwise be expressed by the warmth and intimacy of a kind voice requires facial expressions, gestures, or the gentle touch and caress of a parent or teacher. It is conceivable that this need for physical closeness may be so pronounced in their direct contacts with one another that it could easily be misinterpreted as an unhealthy form of expression or a deviant pattern of sex behavior.

Regarding residential schools or specialized schools in general, the obvious weak spots that may be conducive to the development of a homosexual behavior pattern may be summarized as follows:

1. A restrictive attitude toward sexual interest, instead of a normal amount of sex education extending to all areas of the child's world—his reading, his studies, his recreation and creative endeavors.

2. The relative absence of home life, and the difficulties inherent in the parent-child relationship even when the deaf child goes home to either hearing parents or deaf ones.

It may be mentioned in this connection that homosexual tendencies are the main problem in about ten per cent of the cases in the clinic, while the vast majority of the others present disturbances in their relations with other people, with members of the opposite sex, or with their partners in marriage. In cases where boys had some sex play with other boys in school, a punitive or derisive attitude on the part of the school authorities usually failed to help the individuals involved. Often an already fearful and fragile personality was forced into a lifelong pattern of maladaptation. Some of these youngsters made unhappy and loveless marriages. Others were prevented from fulfilling a promising career by the emotional turmoil ever-present in such forms of sexual maladaptation.

Some young persons drifted about after expulsion from school, their families perhaps well-meaning but of little help, while others entered into the homosexual underworld which is the product of bigotry and ignorance. These men became one of the hundred or so deaf homosexuals who go through the magistrates court every year in New York City alone. This special society with its carefully disguised groups, clubs and organizations that are so difficult to detect even among the hearing apparently includes many deaf persons, representing the removal of a number of otherwise worthwhile individuals from the benefits of a healthy life in a normal society.

What can be done to cope with this situation? On the basis of a biologically and psychologically sound approach to sex development, sex instruction, and sex preparation for marriage, certain recommendations can be made. The first requirement is an attitude that is free of groundless fears, prohibitions and inhibitions. It is important to realize that the socialization and education of future men and women cannot be accomplished overnight, and certainly not by legislating out of existence any contact between them. The branding of sex curiosity and social and affectionate ties between young people as "dirty" is but one indication of the harmful negative attitude which must be avoided. It is regrettable that in some young deaf persons who use the sign language the concept of sex and the sign for "dirty" are closely and inseparably associated.

As has been noted, the family is usually the chief educator in the inculcation of normal and decent behavior. Many pupils in residential schools lack an opportunity to be with their families. Some may go home on holidays and weekends or even daily if they live close by. Such arrangements for residential school students are all to the good, but they require the education and full cooperation of the parents. True, this task falls on the already overburdened shoulders of the educators, psychologists and social workers connected with the schools. Yet in any case part of the sex education program of the schools should involve regular contact with parents, hearing and deaf ones alike.

Furthermore, in all schools, especially residential ones, a thorough program of sex education given by competent persons and adjusted to the age and developmental stage of the pupils is a necessity. At present there is an unfortunate vacuum in this area, partly due to the fact that instructors themselves have not been properly prepared and trained. It is clear that the training of instructors, parents and personnel has to be left to unbiased, scientifically mature and qualified personnel.

Certainly coeducation in residential schools for the deaf is most desirable. Boys and girls who are kept apart during the formative years of childhood and adolescence cannot be expected to enter into normal marriage attachments. They would do far better to start out by eating together, going to class and attending school functions together and then, in adolescence or early adulthood, attending courses in marriage and parenthood. In this way boys and girls could gravitate toward a serious and at the same time pleasurable conception of their growing minds and bodies in relation to one another.

Deaf adolescents should be given a chance to meet deaf and hearing students of the same age at various social functions—dances, parties, sports events. Questions of whom to marry, whether a deaf or hearing person, whether to have children at once or later, how to deal with the psychological and domestic aspects of marriage—these can only be taken up if the groundwork has been laid in earlier years. Such instruction, far from precipitating the students into premature sexual activity, will rather encourage them to place their growing sexual feelings into proper context and teach them how to form friendships and eventually intimate relationships of a permanent nature.

To reiterate, growing boys and girls, by their very nature, have a strong awareness of sex. Proper handling of this awareness will direct it into healthy channels, while punitive or ostrichlike attitudes will only force it into murky detours. Sexual delinquency, like any other kind, cannot be wiped out completely, but there is no doubt that an enlightened and humane attitude will go a long way toward diminishing it.

Another recommendation is based on the fact that in a certain number of cases homosexual behavior is part of a general mental or emotional disturbance not easily diagnosed and not even noticeable to a non-psychiatrist. Therefore, it is suggested that every child that presents some question of deviant sexual practice have the benefit of a complete psychiatric workup, and every adolescent in such circumstances be brought under the wing of the psychiatrist and not the disciplinarian or the courts. In other words, a boy or girl found engaging in deviant sexual practices should not be dismissed summarily, but should be considered as a person whose entire adaptation requires scrutiny. Specialized psychiatric treatment facilities, properly integrated sex education throughout the school years, and individualized help for those with special problems would seem to be the most constructive program for dealing with sexual deviations.

In addition to sexual difficulties, there are many other results of broken homes which create an urgent need for premarital counseling and family planning for the deaf and for relatives of the deaf. The decision to marry or not, the choice of a mate and plans regarding family size are matters of enormous consequence. For those seeking it, competent guidance should be available. Moreover, in any program of action, each step must be suited to the particular needs and resources of the given person.

Perhaps some illustrations chosen from the hundreds of case histories in the project's files will be enlightening. In one case, the only hearing member of a deaf family wanted to marry but felt obliged to do so only within her tightly inbred religious community. Five years later, having nevertheless married an outsider, she and her husband returned for parenthood counseling, asking advice regarding the risk of deafness if they had a child. Statistics were not very helpful, but the woman's background, her fears and social conflicts had to be considered along with the genetic probabilities. In view of the fact that her dread of deafness outweighed every other consideration, she was encouraged to follow her plan to adopt a child rather than bear one.

In a number of other cases well-intentioned but inaccurate advice given to hearing parents of a congenitally deaf child led to their having a second deaf son or daughter and made it difficult for them to provide the special care and guidance necessary for either one.

When it comes to deaf parents, their often-voiced conviction that all their children needed to be assured of a normal start in life was to be hearing is not borne out by the many instances of great domestic upheaval encountered. Often, these family tragedies might have been prevented by a more realistic guidance program.

### Illustrative Case Studies

*Case 1:* The parents of this 16-year-old congenitally deaf only child were divorced when the patient was an infant. Subsequently, the mother entered into two other marriages, which were later dissolved. The mother worked at various jobs in order to support her child, since the father's financial contribution to the family was small. While the father showed little interest in seeing his daughter, a strong attachment developed between the child and her mother. The patient, a very graceful personable girl, showed a good adjustment to group activities. She is a slow learner in the dull-normal range of intelligence. At her mother's request she was referred by the New York State Division of Vocational Rehabilitation for psychological evaluation.

The problem presented by the patient was that she became uncomfortable at home. She "wanted one father" rather than the boy friends who visited her mother. Meanwhile, she became attached to a 19-year-old boy without realizing that he was a member of a group of juvenile offenders and was on probation. Following an accident in front of the school in which she and her boy friend were involved she was expelled. The problem was considered one of situational maladjustment, an adjustment reaction of adolescence, and placement in an upstate school for the deaf was recommended.

*Case 2:* A 16-year-old congenitally deaf male was referred by a social agency to our clinic for psychiatric evaluation, after having been charged with homosexual activity. The mother, 36 years old, was married at 15 to a 21-year-old truck driver. They had two children, the patient and a daughter, 3 years older. The marriage ended in divorce and the children were forcibly taken away by the father. He remarried and the children were treated harshly by him and the stepmother. The patient voluntarily returned to his mother at the age of 13, as had his sister the year before. Both children felt threatened with placement in a foster home.

The mental examination of the patient did not reveal actual psychosis or mental retardation. With the Wechsler-Bellevue test the full scale I.Q. was 87, the verbal I.Q. 61, and the performance 118. The diagnostic impression was one of severe maladjustment to the surrounding hearing world. Placement in a residential school for the deaf was recommended, with psychological supervision.

*Case 3:* A 24-year-old female, congenitally deaf, whose parents were Irish immigrants. The father was 20 years his wife's senior. He was the owner of a bar-restaurant and had retired prior to the marriage in a very comfortable financial situation. Between 1928 and 1935 six children were born, the patient being the youngest. During those years the deterioration of the financial situation of the parents was such that the mother returned with her children to Ireland to stay with her relatives. While there she was hospitalized in a mental hospital for five years. Subsequently she and the children rejoined her husband in the United States. Meanwhile, the father, a heavy drinker, had experienced continual difficulties in obtaining work. He died of cancer at the age of 72. Three years later the mother was placed for a short time in a mental hospital. The patient's siblings, one brother and four sisters, graduated from high school and made good life adjustments. During the later years of the father's illness and after his death, the oldest son assumed the responsibility for the family.

The patient, the only deaf member of the family, entered a residential school for the deaf in Ireland at the age of 6, remaining there five years. At the age of 11, she was admitted to a school for the deaf in New York City where she continued as a resident for almost seven years. She made a good adjustment in school with relation to her schoolmates and showed average ability in academic work. She was referred to our clinic because of her preoccupation with her parents' illnesses and the fears that she might suffer from the same things. The patient expressed feelings of loneliness, since she was unable to find satisfaction in associating with other deaf people. She prefers the company of hearing men. Since the age of 21 she has had a number of "affairs" with different men, most of them married. It was only recently that one of her older sisters started to guide her in sex education.

*Case 4:* A 22-year-old congenitally deaf female was referred to us by the State Division of Vocational Rehabilitation for psychiatric evaluation. Her mother, 58 years old, was 17 when she married. She had ten children, the last one at the age of 37. At that time a psychological evaluation ascertained that she was mentally retarded and she was placed in an institution for mental defectives where she remained four years. The father was 56 years old and has always been considered to be mentally unfit. He had an uncontrollable temper, insulting and beating his wife and children. At the age of 35 he had been placed in a mental institution where he remained ever since. Three of the patient's siblings are in the dull-normal range of intellectual ability. There are no other known cases of deafness in the family.

The patient was placed in a foster home at the age of 18 months, and in a residential school for the deaf at the age of six years. When she was 20 years old, she was expelled for having temper tantrums and fighting with her schoolmates. Most recently, she lived in the home of one of her brothers.

Psychological evaluation showed an average intellectual ability, although she was not up to her potential verbally. She had an I.Q. of 100 on the Wechsler-Bellevue performance scale. The clinical examination revealed no evidence of organicity or psychosis. There was no thinking disorder or inappropriateness of affect. The patient's emotional outbursts at home seemed to be in reaction to an oppressive and restrictive family situation, living as she did in a small village with her oldest brother and his family. There she was subjected to a servant-like existence not warranted by her intelligence or ability to relate to people.

It was recommended that she receive further language training and vocational preparation consistent with her mental and physical capabilities. For the time being, she was to be placed with a deaf family in a large city where opportunities could be offered her for social and vocational advancement.

*Case 5:* A 14-year-old deaf female was referred to our outpatient clinic for psychiatric evaluation and counseling. The father, then 54, had separated from his previous wife and was living in a common law relationship with the patient's mother. He died in 1957. The mother, 50 years old and mentally defective, had been hospitalized in a mental institution for several years. A psychological evaluation when she was 42 years old indicated a middle-grade mental deficiency with an I.Q. of 57. Both mother and father were heavy drinkers.

The patient had two brothers and two half-sisters, born from her father's previous marriage. At the age of two and a half years she was sent to a home for dependent and neglected children where she stayed until she was four years old. Then she was placed with a foster family, a middle-aged couple with three children, and made a good adjustment. At the age of 10, at the school for the deaf, the patient's behavior started to deteriorate. She became hyperactive, aggressive and destructive, but the foster parents resisted any plans for psychiatric evaluation. Severe illness of the foster mother followed by her hospitalization brought the opportunity for the patient, now 11 years old, to be hospitalized for the purpose of diagnosis. No serious psychiatric disturbances were observed. The child was placed consecutively in two residential schools for the deaf, where her behavior grew even worse, with manifestations of sex deviation, and suicidal tendencies.

The patient was found to be deaf as a result of a pneumococcus meningitis. Her intellectual ability was in the average range. The diagnostic impression was that of an emotionally unstable personality, an impulsive adolescent, but not psychotic. Her adjustment difficulties in the last few years seemed to be related to the temporary disorganization of the foster home following the foster mother's acute illness and operation. It was recommended that she be returned to the care of the foster parents to whom she showed much attachment, and placed in a day school for the deaf, where her aggressive behavior should be treated as a psychological rather than a disciplinary problem.

*Case 6:* A 14-year-old male, congenitally deaf, was referred by the guidance counselor of his school for psychiatric observation. The father, 39 years old, had a criminal record and his whereabouts were unknown. The mother, 37 years old, had sole responsibility for the family. She was unemployed and received support from the City Department of Welfare. The patient had four siblings, 17, 15, 12 and 11 years of age, the last three being deaf.

The patient in the classroom had shown disturbed behavior, fighting with classmates and teachers. Following such incidents, the patient ran away from school several times. Psychological examination showed an I.Q. of 74 on the performance scale, placing him in the dull-normal range of intellectual ability. An earlier psychological examination had shown a lower I.Q. with a retarded intellectual functioning, reflecting his limited economic and educational opportunities as well as his limited communication ability and emotional problems. The projective tests revealed a picture of a schizophrenic process, consistent with a clinical impression of a withdrawn and unemotional adolescent.

Psychiatric supervision was recommended, within an institutional setting if further observation showed deterioration.

*Case 7:* A 36-year-old female, congenitally deaf and referred by a rehabilitation agency for psychiatric evaluation in connection with a child neglect petition filed against her by the school district attendance teacher.

The patient was married at 17 and bore two children, a girl and a boy. The marital relationship was difficult. Subsequently, the patient gave birth to a second son out of a casual liaison with another man. She then forced her legal husband to leave the home and began a common law relationship with a third man. This union produced a son and daughter. This man was physically abusive to the children to such an extent that the Children's Court forced him to leave the home. Neither the first husband nor the other two men contributed to the support of the children. The family received assistance from the Department of Public Welfare.

The presenting problem was the patient's negligence towards her children. A poor housekeeper, she kept her apartment sparsely furnished, disarranged and dirty. She did not enforce the children's school attendance and all were habitual truants. Several of the children presented behavior problems when at school, and the oldest son was on probation for juvenile delinquency. The patient was able to communicate mainly with her oldest daughter, the only member of the family with a knowledge of sign language. Social agencies made several attempts to help the patient improve the conditions for her children, but she did not show too much interest in cooperating and finally withdrew completely.

Our psychiatric examination indicated that the patient was not psychotic. However, she was emotionally unstable, having to cope with a severe handicap that made her interpersonal relationships difficult. It was suggested by the court that she be permitted to have custody of her children only if given intensive supervision.

*Case 8:* A 34-year-old female, congenitally deaf, was referred by a social agency for psychiatric evaluation and counseling regarding her difficulty in managing her children. The patient's husband, 47 years old, became deaf during infancy. He worked in a warehouse, but his income was inadequate to support the family. The couple had two children, a girl 10 and a boy 4, the latter born with clubfeet.

The patient's problems in managing her children began with the birth of her son and her bewilderment over his congenital malformation. At this time she began to complain of anorexia and insomnia. She tried to sleep during the day, but this left the boy without care. Further, the patient became easily irritated by both children, beating them frequently. Unable to hear them when they were in trouble, she felt inadequate in her maternal role. The psychiatric examination showed an anxiety state, adult situational reaction, which improved with combined psychotherapy and pharmacological treatment.

The first six cases were those of deaf adolescents or young adults, products of broken homes who reacted with emotional disturbance or delinquency. The last two illustrated extreme cases in which emotionally unstable and dependent deaf women, one with no husband, one with a hard working deaf spouse, found it very difficult to raise a family although the children were hearing.

All these cases, representative of many more in the clinic files, showed the combined deleterious effects of disrupted home environment and deafness. In such families, it is clear that better guidance, given early enough, might have been the ounce of prevention, certainly preferable to the lengthy readjustment which is as close to a cure as is possible in these unhappy families.

# Chapter 17

## CLINICAL MANAGEMENT OF DEAF PSYCHIATRIC PATIENTS

### John D. Rainer

Although prevention of disordered behavior through proper family guidance and school mental hygiene programs is more important in the long run, the problem of the diagnosis and clinical management of the deaf psychiatric patient remains a serious one. Early recognition of mental illness and prompt treatment may forestall more irreversible illness or unfortunate consequences to family or society.

To illustrate the need for early psychiatric appraisal, a number of case histories from the clinic files are briefly outlined:

*Case 1:* A 26-year-old male, congenitally deaf, was referred by the director of an upstate mental hospital for evaluation of mental status. Patient had been remanded for observation after he had killed his two children. At the age of seven, when he was evaluated at a local mental hygiene clinic, he was diagnosed as a primary behavior disorder. Psychiatric examination by our staff revealed an immature man, ill-fitted for the responsibilities of marriage and a family. Apparently, he had worked under increasing tension with the overvalued idea that his wife and children constituted heavy personal responsibilities. In an acute anxiety attack, feeling certain he would die, he impulsively killed the two children to rid himself of the burden. *Diagnosis:* Emotionally unstable personality, with schizophrenia to be ruled out by further observation. *Disposition:* Although prolonged psychiatric observation was recommended, he was sentenced to prison by the court.

*Case 2:* A 21-year-old female, deaf since age 14 months, was referred from Gallaudet College. She had been expelled from school after discovery of a homosexual relationship; later she became a prostitute since it was a way to get money without long hours of work. There was no previous psychiatric treatment. *Diagnosis:* Passive dependent personality with homosexuality. *Treatment and Course:* In individual psychotherapy she came to value herself more highly. She gave up prostitution and an attachment to a married man which had been associated with it, and turned to dates with deaf men in an effort to form a real relationship. She settled on one man but married him precipitously, thus short-circuiting efforts first to explore the relationship further. He turned out to be an extremely short-tempered man who impulsively raged and beat her up, according to her "for no reason." After interrupting one pregnancy conceived on a whirlwind trip around the country with him, she became pregnant again, returned to New York and again requested treatment. In counseling sessions some of her provocativeness was demonstrable and her husband was placed on

228

tranquilizing medication in an effort to reduce his tendency to temper tantrums. There appeared to be a prospect of holding the marriage together and maintaining her adjustment at the higher level achieved.

*Case 3:* A 20-year-old congenitally deaf male was referred by his priest at the family's request. The patient was noted to have the ideas that he was changing into a girl, that his father and mother would die, and that the spirit of Jesus was speaking to him while his own eyes were changing color. There was no previous psychiatric treatment. *Diagnosis:* Acute schizophrenic reaction, paranoid. *Treatment and Course:* Patient was hospitalized for nine months and received individual psychotherapy and insulin coma treatment, followed by tranquilizing medication. A satisfactory remission was achieved and he was discharged when a cooperating agency was able to place him vocationally in a photography firm. After six months there was a mild exacerbation leading to a change in jobs but requiring no hospitalization.

*Case 4:* A 62-year-old male, deaf since age five, was referred by a general hospital for evaluation and therapy. Four years before he had felt the people at the printing shop where he worked were against him. He had quit the job and slashed his wrists. He then received nine electro-convulsive treatments at the referring hospital. Following his return to work, the ideas persisted and became more intense. When seen, he was afraid of being jailed and even feared to leave the safety of his home. At the same time he would occasionally pound his head, feeling he was a terrible person. He refused to return to the referring hospital because of his fear of shock treatment. *Diagnosis:* Involutional psychosis, paranoid type. *Treatment and Course:* Individual psychotherapy and medication over a period of five months led to a remission in all symptoms, increasing pleasant socialization, a gain in weight and realistic plans to retire to residence in a warmer climate. A Christmas card received four months after his last visit indicated realization of these plans and continued remission.

In the first of these cases, it was clear that early recognition of psychiatric disturbance was not followed by an adequate treatment program; nothing further was done until tragedy occurred. The young lady described next might have avoided a psychologically destructive course of behavior if she had received psychiatric treatment in school. In the last two cases, despite severe psychopathology, social remission was achieved after early recognition and intensive treatment.

Histories such as these and others cited in this report document strikingly the need for easily accessible services for early psychiatric diagnosis and treatment of the deaf.

Early in the project's history it became clear that expansion of outpatient diagnostic and treatment services had to go hand in hand with the establishment of special hospital wards. The survey of over 250 deaf patients in state hospitals for the mentally ill left no doubt as to the need for drastic reorganization of psychiatric services directed at rehabilitating a large proportion of hospitalized deaf persons. Rather than let them lie fallow and inaccessible to therapy in chronic wards, it seemed far more advisable to set aside specialized wards for deaf people in a few mental hospitals where they could profit from the care of specially trained personnel.

The existence of many cases with a long history of mental illness before admission in itself indicated the need for some coordinated system facilitating early diagnosis and immediate treatment for psychiatric disorders in the deaf. In line with observations made, it was recommended that special services for mental health work with the deaf be established in at least every major population area. These facilities might be located at one of the larger state hospitals where those deaf patients requiring hospitalization would receive the particular care they needed.

Instead of being dispersed in many hospitals, these patients would greatly profit from being together in special units set aside for them. Following discharge, they could be assigned to a separate division of a convalescent clinic for aftercare. Such clinics could also provide the families of deaf patients with whatever guidance and supportive measures were needed. Furthermore, with a nucleus of doctors and other workers with knowledge of the deaf, the clinics would be available for ambulatory treatment of emotionally disturbed deaf people.

After two and a half years of work in the project, its advisory council composed a resolution to be distributed to agencies concerned with the health and family problems of the deaf in the State of New York. This statement read as follows:

"It is the consensus of the members of the Advisory Council that there is an urgent need for more adequate and more integrated mental health services for the deaf in the districts covered by this pilot project. The need extends to psychiatric services for both sexes (children and adults) on an inpatient and outpatient level (metropolitan and upstate districts) as well as to a properly coordinated vital statistics system for the deaf (preferably coordinated by an interdepartmental agency with the authority to unify the principles of reporting and recording).

"Prerequisites for this program are: (a) the availability of specialized professional personnel; (b) progressive attitudes toward the special adjustment problems of this subpopulation; and (c) the realization on the part of all agencies and organizations dealing with these particular problems, that the deaf are entitled to the same quality and amount of mental health services as are available for the hearing.

"It is unrealistic and contrary to the best interests of the deaf to perpetuate the tendency to minimize the need for an active mental health program for this group."

This resolution was presented on June 14, 1958 to a large group of deaf leaders gathered at the Psychiatric Institute in a special conference of New York State organizations for the deaf (185). Within the following year, letters of endorsement were received from every major club and organization of the deaf in New York State.

The Empire State Association of the Deaf, at its 1958 Convention, passed the following resolution:

"Whereas the mental health needs of the deaf of New York are as great as those of people with normal hearing; and whereas the great values of mental health counseling, which benefit hearing people so much, have not been available to the mentally ill deaf because of the inability of mental health workers to communicate with sick deaf people; and whereas this serious barrier to equal mental health services for deaf people has been breached successfully with excitingly effective results and promise in diagnosis and therapy by the New York State Psychiatric Institute under the direction of Dr. Franz J. Kallmann whose special staff has become skilled in communicating with the deaf and has acquired understanding of their special adjustment problems through a Federal research and demonstration grant; therefore, be it resolved that the above described work of the Mental Health Center for the Deaf is hereby vigorously endorsed by the Empire State Association of the Deaf; and be it further resolved that it is the urgent wish of the Empire State Association of the Deaf that the work of Dr. Kallmann's Center be extended over all of New York under the regular State mental health program so that all deaf people in need of mental health care will receive the quality of service to which they as citizens and taxpayers are entitled; and be it further resolved that the State Mental Health Commission be apprised of the wish of New York deaf people for a State-supported statewide clinical program through a copy of these resolutions and such subsequent follow-up as may be indicated."

A mental health committee was formed within this Association, headed by Mr. Max Friedman.

With the need established, the pilot project in operation and the interest and backing of the deaf secured, the recommendation embodied in these resolutions appeared ready for universal acceptance and implementation. The combination of inpatient and outpatient facilities for psychiatric treatment, together with centers for counseling and preventive mental health, training and research, was deemed the most effective approach to a constructive mental health program for the deaf.

# Chapter 18

## RECOMMENDATIONS FOR FUTURE RESEARCH

### John D. Rainer

At the conclusion of this report, which is essentially a record of the background and findings of a seven-year program of research, clinical work, and training, it may be useful to set down briefly some recommendations for continuing investigation in the field of deafness, particularly in its psychiatric aspects. These suggestions could open with no better injunction than to search for the knowledge so sorely needed to prevent in the first place deafness itself, and, secondly, maladjustment among the deaf and their families.

While advances in maternal care during pregnancy and treatment of infectious disease in infancy have gone a long way toward reducing the incidence of certain kinds of early deafness, the mode of inheritance and the developmental dynamics of the genetic forms are only beginning to receive clarification. The twin and family studies reported in Chapter 3 have furnished important leads to the study of these problems, including the question of variable penetrance. It is urgent that these leads be pursued diligently so that the chromosome-determined biochemical (enzyme) deficiency can finally be detected.

Once this goal has been reached, it will not be too much to hope that proper replacement or protective therapy may be instituted during the crucial developmental months, or throughout life, to avoid or ameliorate the hearing loss. As stated in a recent editorial, ". . . the inborn errors of metabolism, far from inciting an attitude of therapeutic nihilism, lend themselves peculiarly well to therapeutic ingenuity" (63). If it should ever happen that studying a pair of twins with, for instance, one deaf and the other hearing or having only a slight hearing loss, provides the key to preventing or reducing the expression of gene-borne deafness, such a discovery would be of paramount value in the preventive realm.

Meanwhile, there are other measures on the preventive level for lessening the burden of potential unhappiness and social and personal deprivation due to deafness. Research workers would do well to double their efforts to discover the optimum life choices open to deaf adolescents, so that they and their deaf or hearing parents may receive the best guidance when they seek advice regarding education, vocation, marriage and parenthood.

Turning to the clinical area, where proper diagnosis and treatment of

232

emotional upset and mental illness are so necessary, continued research is called for on the basic neurophysiological and psychological correlates of deafness. A number of questions remain unanswered on such complex matters as the relation of deafness to the thought process, to abstract reasoning and communication; the connection between auditory sensory deprivation and personality development, and between deafness and psychopathology. Is it true, for instance, that impulse disorders are common among the deaf, while depressive and obsessional patterns are rare? Are auditory hallucinations possible in a congenitally deaf person?

The psychologist has yet to perfect intelligence and projective tests for the deaf and to devise a measure for the most prevalent characteristic of this group, immaturity.

Further research in methods of psychiatric treatment—particularly pharmacological and group therapy—is possible now that special wards are being established where larger numbers of hospitalized deaf patients can be assembled. An essential research task is evaluation of the results of treatment. Adequate baseline data on the number of deaf persons treated in and out of hospitals, length of treatment, and outcome are prerequisites for appraising changes in census figures and admission rates under new treatment methods and facilities.

A long-term study of such changes would require a permanently active research organization working with a clinical team, and the maintenance of careful ascertainment, reporting and recording systems. What effect the availability of adequate outpatient clinics would have on hospital admission rates, what impact on the problems in the schools, and the potential interaction with vocational rehabilitation procedures are but part of the whole research challenge in this field.

Whether the road be cellular or biochemical, preventive or clinical, psychological or social, all highways leading to more useful knowledge regarding family and mental health problems in the deaf population need to be paved with carefully laid research plans, self-critical treatment service, and the indispensable training of new personnel.

# Chapter 19

## MAIN FINDINGS AND SOME PROJECTIONS

FRANZ J. KALLMANN

This pilot study of the family and mental health problems of a deaf community such as that of New York State served to illustrate the multiple investigative, training and counseling functions of an interdisciplinary research organization specializing in the field of psychiatric genetics.

Originally conceived as a fact-finding inquiry into the size, adjustive norms, vocational propensities and reproductive trends of an ostensibly well sheltered population group, the project began in something of a clinical and statistical vacuum (see Introduction). Step by step, it proceeded to the documentation of a minimum action program for an aggregate of clearly frustrated but nonvociferous people who in an enlightened society would seem to need family guidance services with as much justification as any of their hearing counterparts.

Obviously, one cannot guide troubled families without knowing something about them, nor is much accomplishable in the management of their problems by sweeping them under the carpet. By the same token, if those textbook inferences were correct in crediting a deaf community with freedom from schizophrenia, suicide and delinquency or with comparable magic qualities, one might seriously consider remodeling our existing mental health services for the hearing along similar lines.

In our search for a realistic but dynamically integrated mental health program for deaf family units, we realized very soon that *capricious community attitudes* toward human disability tend to be epitomized by a flagrant lack of understanding of what early total deafness means in maturational terms. For obvious reasons, excessive defensiveness of the man in the street toward this crippling disability is bound to have an ostracizing effect. Indeed, such compensatory tendencies may be so pronounced as to come close to being a throwback to those ancient times when social concepts of deafness were apt to be "cloaked in ignorance and superstition" (see Historical Review). A peculiar reflection of this anachronism may be seen in the stereotyped apologies offered for subtly distorted notions about the psychological impact of deafness. People are inclined to exclaim, "I always thought I'd rather be deaf than blind!"—as if such a preference could magically transform deafness into a more desirable defect.

At the *professional* level, *chronic misconceptions* regarding family and mental health problems of the deaf seem at least partly explained by the fact that most specialists look at deafness in the frame of their particular disciplines. To the otologist, deafness is primarily a case of an- or dysacusis that calls for audiometric measurement and special speech therapy. To the psychologist and guidance counselor, deafness is an audio-communicative deficiency which by blotting out the ability to hear conversation, blocks the learning of verbal language and thereby interferes with the formation of early parent-child relations. For educators of the deaf, the favorite preoccupation has been to demonstrate the usefulness of one system of language instruction and vocational training over another, but there is little disagreement among them when it comes to placing guidance in sex education and family planning beyond the scope of school responsibility. To the clinical psychiatrist, deaf adolescents and adults represent one more minority group whose members are difficult to reach, are given to paranoid reaction formation, and lack adequate treatment facilities to about the same extent as their hearing counterparts. If the psychiatrist happens to be in an administrative position, he may add regretfully that statistical data on the mental health needs of widely scattered deaf families are not well enough documented to permit comprehensive programs for specialized treatment and counseling services.

Against this backdrop of professional fragmentation and public indifference, we decided in 1955 to organize a regional pilot study of the deaf population of New York State (see Introduction). According to the best estimate, there were approximately 150,000 totally deaf persons in the United States, including over 27,000 students of 415 residential schools, special day classes and some speech clinics. In the absence of adequate census data, however, the exact number, social stratification and geographic distribution of deaf persons in the adult age ranges were strictly a matter of conjecture. Just as little was known about the size and composition of deaf populations in mental hospitals or correctional institutions.

In order to insure comprehensiveness with respect to the adjustive norms of a deaf community, our study was designed to cover *three general areas*: research, psychiatric guidance, and a training program for specialized guidance workers that would include regular classes in sign language. The three programs proceeded simultaneously so that the work could be coordinated as it progressed. One cannot be constructive in guiding poorly adjusted members of a deaf group, unless one knows the various life performance levels of those who appear relatively well-adjusted.

In the search for factual information about the variable *emotional stresses of deafness,* it seemed advisable to keep in mind that deaf people, although no longer regarded as unteachable, may not be adequately prepared for coping with the intensified pressures of modern society. Social isolation may be enforced as much from without as from within, and emotional deprivation may be perpetuated by the illusion that the soundlessness of a silent world is equivalent to the tranquility of a sheltered life which eliminates the need for psychiatric guidance.

Within the limits of this concluding chapter, only a brief résumé of our demographic research data, psychological test results, twin study findings and psychiatric observations can be presented. Whenever detailed statistical substantiation is needed, the reader is referred to the many tabulated data included in each chapter.

## 1. Size of Deaf Population and Some Definitions

As to the diagnostic criteria that were used in classifying the literate deaf in our two samples—about 12,000 single-born deaf above the age of 12 and over 100 pairs of deaf twins of all ages—it may be emphasized that *deafness* was defined as a stress-producing hearing loss, from birth or early childhood, rendering a person incapable of effecting substantial auditory contact with the environment (see Introduction).

*Literacy* was measured by the capacity for entering into meaningful communication with the investigator, either verbally (spoken, written, or fingerspelled language) or by means of the sign language. A prerequisite for each member of our research staff was the ability to conduct an interview by *manual communication*.

The deaf persons that were ascertained who met these criteria formed the *frame* or list of subjects used in the investigative areas of the project. This list was carefully prepared over a two-year period with the help of a large number of agencies and organizations for the deaf as well as by extensive personal visits to all sizable communities. The methodological aspects of this task, particularly the *sampling procedure,* were described in Chapter 1.

## 2. Genetic and General Demographic Data

*Demographically,* it may be noted that the *total sex ratio* of the deaf population of New York State (15 years and older) was estimated at 113 males to 100 females (Chapter 2). While social factors may have been responsible for some underascertainment of females, the observed *excess of males* may also indicate a sex-specific increase in the male's vulnerability to deafness-producing agents or may partly reflect the operation of a sex-linked genetic factor in some families.

Another distinguishing feature of the population was a considerable increase in the *parental cousin-marriage rate*. This rate was found to be increased to at least 8.7 per cent in one large segment of the total population (Chapter 2) and proved to be as high as 12.15 per cent in the group with very early onset of the hearing loss (before the age of 4 years) and no tangible exogenous cause (Chapter 3).

Tabulation of *marriage data* revealed a rate of 60.3 per cent ever married for males, and 68.9 per cent for females. These rates are still slightly below those in a comparable general population, particularly for males, but they are much higher than they were reported to be 40 years ago. Apparently, the improved marriage opportunities of the present deaf generation are paralleled by a higher degree of marital instability. The current *divorce rate* of deaf females exceeds those of hearing females and deaf males.

While the percentage of deaf women ever married increased from 30.7 in 1900 to 68.9 in 1960, the *marital fertility* rate of deaf mothers decreased, though relatively little compared with that for hearing mothers. Since 1920, the given fertility rates have declined from 260 to 229 children in deaf mothers, and from 330 to 235 children in hearing ones. The highest observed marital fertility rates for deaf mothers were found in Roman Catholic women (239 per 100 mothers) and in the non-hospitalized New York City population (232 per 100 mothers).

Among the factors *perpetuating* the size of a contemporary deaf population (present population frequency of early total deafness in New York State: 0.06%) are the *relatively high marriage and fertility rates,* a possible *compensatory* trend toward larger family size in families with at least one deaf child, and the *assortative mating pattern* that continues to be typical of deaf communities. In our sample, only five per cent of women born deaf and less than ten per cent of those that became deaf at an early age were found to be married to hearing men. The vast majority are likely to have husbands who have been deaf since birth or early childhood. It is not surprising, therefore, that almost 30 per cent of the marriages where both partners were born deaf, and from 14 to 21 per cent of those where only one partner was born deaf, resulted in deaf children, usually more than one.

According to the *overall reproductivity data* for our deaf population, it may be stated that nearly ten per cent of all children born to deaf subjects are themselves deaf. On the other hand, less than ten per cent of all deaf members of a large deaf community such as that of New York State may be expected to have one or two deaf parents. Not even in such a conspicuous family constellation, however, does the possession of two deaf parents tend to keep their deaf children from marrying and in turn contributing to the recurrence of deafness in the next generation.

The need for special family counseling services for the deaf was further illustrated by the appalling *lack of knowledge* that seems to exist in this group regarding the *workings of heredity.* In personal interviews with a representative sample of deaf subjects and their families (Chapter 5), 86 per cent of those questioned as to the preferred hearing status of prospective mates expressed a preference for a *deaf spouse,* although only 6.5 per cent of deaf persons with a desire for marriage wanted to have *deaf children.* Equally ominous was the observation that 74 per cent of persons with adequately defined congenital deafness appeared unconcerned about their mate's type of deafness.

With respect to the *genetic aspects* of early total deafness (Chapter 3), it was established by a population survey (sampled by mail questionnaire) that about one-half of the present deaf population of New York State represent *sporadic* cases. Hence, they seemed to be due to exogenous causes, complicated modes of inheritance, or new genetic mutations. With clearly inherited *dominant* genes accounting only for about ten per cent of all deafness, the remaining cases fell mainly into the autosomal *recessive* category.

While *parental cousin-marriage* rates revealed an incidence of 12 per cent in that group of persons in which the hearing loss occurred before the age of four years and without obvious exogenous causation (70%), the *population frequency* of this form of deafness was found to be .06 per cent. Apart from providing strong evidence for the usual *recessiveness* of the genetic factor in operation, these data indicated the existence of *many different genes,* each producing early total deafness when homozygous (two members of the same pair of genes). Depending on the assumptions made, the number of recessive genes in the gene-pool of the population would seem to range upward from a minimal value of 45.

As to the distribution of hearing defects in families affected by the *dominant* type of gene, our carefully analyzed data (Professor Howard Levene) showed an average penetrance rate of only 50 per cent, as against the nearly complete penetrance figure computed by Chung's team from an earlier study of deafness in Northern Ireland conducted by Stevenson and Cheeseman (Chapter 3). The *incomplete penetrance* of the dominantly inherited form of deafness in the New York State population extended to *unilateral* expression as was confirmed by audiometric twin data. Another important finding which emerged from our *twin-family study* (37 pairs) was the demonstration in one-egg pairs of a definite hearing loss in one-half of the partners of deaf twins classified in clinical terms as deaf from exogenous causes. It may be concluded, therefore, that genotype and extrinsic agents *interact* in producing certain cases of early total deafness.

Finally, the observation of a number of twin families, in which deafness was found to be associated with *pigmentary and other non-auditory anomalies,* would seem to indicate that special syndromes of this kind tend to occur in a significant fraction of early deafness cases.

### 3. Variable Adjustment Patterns in a Deaf Community

In order to obtain an estimate of the *retarding effect* of deafness on *intellectual performance,* a special study was undertaken (Chapter 4) in which twins with early hearing loss in at least one member of a pair were tested audiometrically as well as psychometrically (Arthur Point Scale, Wechsler-Bellevue Intelligence Scale, Form 1). In this series of 16 one-egg and 17 two-egg pairs, of whom 12 were completely concordant, 8 partially concordant and 13 discordant as to early total deafness (yielding definite discordance rates of 12.5 per cent in one-egg and 64.7 per cent in two-egg twins), comparison of the measurable intelligence quotients led our psychologically well-trained investigators to the conclusion that the *average intelligence reduction* ascribable to the hearing loss approximates 20 points on language-dependent tests. The *technical difficulties* encountered in the test-ing of deaf subjects were expertly reviewed in Chapter 11.

As to the *general educational status* of our total deaf community, it was established through personal interviews with a sample of deaf adults (Chapter 7) that although the deaf seem to have shared in the universal trend toward better education, over 16 per cent of them reported that they had left school without graduating (before the age of 16). However, almost all members of the deaf population of New York State had some formal schooling, and 3.7 per cent had more than a high school education. Inter-estingly, girls were found to be more likely than boys to *graduate* from a grade school and to be rated as *bright*. It may also be noted that the propor-tion of those who reported that they had liked their school as well as their teachers amounted to 76 per cent.

In various other respects and particularly in that area of the educational process which may be referred to as *preparation for life,* our findings seemed far less satisfactory. For instance, less than 20 per cent of the women questioned had the experience of dating outside of group situations during their school years, and over one-half had had no experiences which could be described as dates. Moreover, while actual sexual experiences were denied by the entire female group interviewed, homosexual rather than heter-osexual activity was reported as the more common form of sex behavior by those males who admitted some sexual experience while at school (nearly 20 per cent of the respondents). At the same time, marital adjustment was found to be directly related to length of courtship, with over 90 per cent of those with the longest courtships reporting good adjustment to family life.

In the *vocational* field, a substantial number of deaf persons, many with high potentials, claimed to have entered the competitive job market with ill-defined goals and with the feeling of being poorly prepared. In fact, 30 per cent of those interviewed either had no plans at all or had no specific work plans after leaving school.

Of the *deaf labor force* of New York State, the vast majority of those employed (87.5%) were found to perform some kind of manual labor (30.4% in the unskilled category) and a considerable proportion (68%) expressed the belief that there was some discrimination against the deaf. Practically all the men had full-time jobs, and over 93 per cent had held the same job for more than three years. Only two per cent of all deaf workers had accidents on their jobs, attributable to deafness.

With respect to *socialization* patterns (Chapter 6), almost one-half of deaf adults (45%) reported that they had both hearing and deaf friends. An even greater proportion (69%) claimed to have voted within the last three years, and only 24 per cent stated that they had never voted. Regular attendance at either hearing or deaf churches was affirmed by more than one-third (39%), with some degree of religious activity reported by 84 per cent of the total population.

Analysis of *intra-family relationships* within the deaf community revealed that speech was reported more often to be the preferred communication method among deaf persons whose families were all hearing than among those with other deaf members. In families with both deaf and hearing children, deaf parents were found to have more problems of control and obedience with hearing children than with deaf ones. Apparently, the deaf approach their deaf children with less uncertainty, making fewer demands of them, and having a more realistic understanding of their potentials and limitations. Toward hearing children their attitudes are shakier, perhaps bogged down by greater expectations and an overvaluation of the absence of impaired hearing.

On the whole, it was indicated by our *population data* (Chapter 6) that persons with total deafness can establish adequate socialization patterns and are able to make good use of general community services. However, qualitative and quantitative differences in community attitudes do exist and have to be taken into consideration if antisocial behavior is to be forestalled.

Since *outstanding vocational achievement* in the presence of early total deafness is rather infrequent, a special study of deaf persons with exceptional success in life, according to criteria established by an expert committee, was undertaken to determine some of the correlates of such achievement (Chapter 8). In the series of 27 deaf persons so designated, the preponderance of males (23:4) was striking. Among the careers open to the gifted student with a complete hearing loss were the arts, architecture, engineering, chemistry, dentistry and accounting. However, to overcome the markedly detrimental effects of this disability, far greater effort, endowment and opportunity seemed to be required than for hearing persons. Other important findings were that over 90 per cent of deaf achievers received supplemental educational aid during their school years, and that the majority of the parents were in the middle or upper income bracket. Over 80 per cent of the fathers were either business executives or professionals.

### 4. Forms of Severe Maladjustment

At the lower end of the distribution of deafness-specific adjustment patterns, special attention was paid to the frequency and causation of *such severe forms of maladjustment* as mental retardation, psychoses, delinquency, suicide, sexual deviations, alcoholism, and drug addiction. With respect to *marriages* in this group, information was also obtained on the frequency of broken homes due to desertion, divorce, or hospitalization of a parent (Chapter 16).

As to the types of *delinquency* and *crime* observed (Chapter 9), it may be noted that the offenses committed by the deaf virtually covered the entire spectrum found in a hearing population, ranging from vagrancy to first degree murder. While the largest number of cases was in the area of sexual offenses, there were also numerous instances of assault, disorderly conduct, and burglary, in addition to several murderers, forgers, narcotics peddlers and shoplifters. The majority of offenders in this series came from homes with two hearing parents (60%), and an even larger proportion were un-married at the time of their arrest, with a mean age of about 24 years. Like hearing offenders, many of the deaf law breakers were from lower socio-economic levels and were listed as unemployed when apprehended. Psycho-logical tests classified these delinquents as even more impulsive, immature and irresponsible than their hearing counterparts. Patterns of gross im-maturity were also discernible in the acts of violence committed by deaf offenders. While there was no evidence that deaf persons were unable to plan criminal acts, it was generally our impression that they were often the dupes of hearing individuals who involved them in premeditated offenses.

In appraising the particular preventive problems posed by deaf violators of the law, our investigators found an almost universal lack of special treat-ment facilities with qualified personnel. They noted especially that residen-tial schools were totally unequipped to work with real problem children. It appeared that a well-organized effort to help rather than expel delinquent children would prove to be a potent preventive measure for combatting adult crime.

### 5. Schizophrenia in the Deaf

In the group of *psychotic* deaf persons, a little more than one-half of hos-pitalized patients (52.2%) were diagnosed as *schizophrenic*, a close approx-imation to the proportion of non-deaf patients (56.5%). No evidence was found in these schizophrenics for a preponderance of paranoid symptoms. At the same time, severe depressions and alcoholic psychoses seemed under-represented. Hospitalized schizophrenics were estimated at 1.2 per cent of the total deaf population of New York State, while the overall schizophrenic risk was 2.5 per cent (Chapter 14).

A special study of deaf families with one or more schizophrenic members furnished no indications that the severe and varied stresses associated with a total hearing loss are likely to *increase the chance* of developing clinical symptoms of schizophrenia (Chapter 15). While the sibs of deaf schizo-phrenics yielded a schizophrenia rate (12.14%) significantly higher than the general population, and similar to that found among the brothers and sisters of hearing schizophrenics, the risk figures did not differ according to whether the given sibs were deaf or hearing. Similar findings were ob-tained for the parents of deaf schizophrenics.

In the *clinical management* of schizophrenic hospital patients (Chapter 14), no basis was found for the assumption that this type of psychosis does not represent the same clinical entity in the deaf as in the hearing. Hence, all the usual methods of somatic treatment were employed, including drugs and the various shock therapies. However, systematic attempts to combine these methods with psychotherapy were precluded by the lack of adequate facilities (Chapter 13). Moreover, the existence of many cases with a long history of mental illness *before* admission pointed to the need for some coordinated system facilitating early diagnosis and immediate treatment for psychiatric disorders in the deaf. In this group, too, prevention of irreversible mental illness through early recognition and prompt treatment should be regarded as an essential psychiatric objective that might forestall many unfortunate consequences to family as well as society.

At present, we know of no other state hospital system which aims at bringing deaf patients together, thus making it possible to deal with them as a special group. Usually, these patients are scattered over many hospitals and over numerous services within the same hospital, often lying fallow and inaccessible to therapy in chronic wards. One may say, therefore, that until appropriate steps are taken to remedy this situation, the results of psychiatric efforts toward rehabilitating disturbed deaf hospital patients will not be comparable to those achieved in the hearing (Chapter 17).

Instead of being dispersed in many hospitals, deaf patients would greatly profit from being together in *special treatment units* (Chapter 17) set aside for them in a centrally located hospital. Following discharge, they could be assigned to a separate division of a convalescent clinic for aftercare. Such clinics would also provide the families of deaf patients with whatever guidance and supportive measures were needed. Another advantage of a centralized inpatient service would be that with a nucleus of doctors and other psychiatric personnel with knowledge of the deaf, the clinics would be available for ambulatory treatment of emotionally disturbed deaf people. Actually, a well-integrated combination of inpatient and outpatient facilities for psychiatric treatment, together with centers for family counseling, research and training, would seem to be the most effective approach to a constructive mental health program for the deaf.

### 6. Psychiatric Services for the Deaf in a Clinic Setting

Because of limited funds and a persisting shortage of trained personnel, our *outpatient clinic* for the deaf (Chapter 10) functioned officially on no more than a two-day-per-week schedule. During the few years of its operation as a pilot project, 217 persons applied for help and over one per cent of the total deaf community of the state were actually treated within this brief trial period. The patients came from private physicians, schools, clubs, religious organizations and especially from rehabilitation agencies, and they fell virtually into every known psychiatric category, with some defying classification by any ordinary criteria. The most common reasons for referral were acute psychiatric illness, homosexuality, poor work adjustment, social conflicts, and family problems.

Since there are at least as many different types of emotional disturbance and mental disorder in non-hearing persons as there are in hearing ones, we found out fairly soon that the usual *diagnostic dilemmas* of psychiatric classification are compounded in the deaf. With incompleteness of background information and perplexing obstacles in communication making every psychiatric diagnosis in this group an extremely complex affair, all conceivable efforts should be made to refer deaf people with symptoms of maladjustment to the most competent diagnostic outfit available. Educators and counselors may be highly skilled in their own fields, but they cannot be expected to have the specialized knowledge required, for instance, for an early diagnosis of schizophrenia.

Fluency in *manual language,* the normal mode of communication for many deaf persons, is just as essential in the diagnostic evaluation of emotionally disturbed patients in this group as is familiarity with their particular *personality characteristics* (Chapter 12). Since the deaf tend to think in vaguely wholistic and concrete terms and their written communications often show a fragmented, confused and primitive quality, the writings of deaf patients may strikingly simulate a severe thought disorder. Hence, it is only the manual language which by enhancing rapport and facilitating a free flow of ideas, offers a direct access to the thought content of these patients.

As to *counseling services* for families with early total deafness (Chapter 13), it may be noted that counselors should be prepared for an extraordinary amount of misinformation and superstition in their work. Our study uncovered many tragic situations that a genetically trained counselor might have easily prevented. On the other hand, we were able in numerous instances to reassure severely perturbed people that their fears in connection with marriage or parenthood had been groundless. Generally speaking, the importance of considering each family on its own merits cannot be over-emphasized when it comes to specific questions having to do with family planning.

Concerning the modes of *psychotherapy* which may prove to be useful in the setting of an outpatient clinic, it may be stressed that the criteria for selecting the most suitable method and goals depend on the level of the patient's desire and ability to cooperate. At the aspiring level, the patient wishes and is able to achieve self-advancement through utilization of all his potential resources for adaptive growth. At the self-reliant level, he is expected to learn how to help himself in the everyday matters of life and to behave like an adult with common sense. By contrast, a helpless patient who reveals excessive emotional dependence on the therapist, longing for parental help or therapeutic miracles, relates like a child at the parentifying and magic-craving levels. He does not seek real learning or maturation, and is often incapable of achieving it.

In our clinic group, only two patients were considered suitable for insight therapy with reconstructive goals. Even in these two cases, however, the technique used was that of *intensive psychotherapy* rather than a strictly psychoanalytic method. The latter procedure was found to be impracticable in the deaf, since factors other than the patient's need to sit facing the analyst, instead of lying on a couch, seemed to preclude this form of therapy. In most instances where the psychoanalytic technique was tried, continuation was contraindicated by inadequacies in the patient's motivation and social flexibility, his frustration tolerance, or in his abstraction capacity, the prerequisite for the acceptance of generalized interpretations. Under the given circumstances our guiding principle was to *vary treatment goals* not only with the degree of pathology and the patient's maturation potential, but also with his social opportunities for life adjustment and the possibilities of meaningful communication.

The *supportive or limited-goal type* of psychotherapy was used especially in transient stress situations and in patients of relatively low mentality or overly dependent motivation. Aimed at repairing uncontrolled behavior distortion and based on a knowledge of psychodynamics, such abbreviated therapeutic measures may bring about a satisfactory solution, if they are combined with a removal of road blocks and a relief of pressure. Calling for a limited alteration of behavior in specific areas and a diminution of emergency responses, the available methods include management and gratification of dependent needs, furnishing an objective view of stress situations, emotional decompression and ventilation, and modification of the patient's goals and self-demands through guidance and education. Community help, cooperation of rehabilitation and other social agencies and the use of drugs are essential parts of this type of individual psychotherapy (Chapter 13).

In addition, *group therapy methods* should be given a special place in the treatment of the deaf. Treatment in groups would be particularly appropriate for deaf patients in mental hospitals where isolation often adds to their psychopathology. Of course, the availability of special wards, trained personnel and a well-coordinated administrative setting would be necessary for the development of this form of psychiatric service for the deaf.

Another application of group therapy is in the field of family, sex and marriage education for deaf adolescents and their parents. The mustiness of ignorance about the biological and social facts of life, including genetics, cannot be routed by mechanical teaching, but only by the fresh air of a truly psychotherapeutic atmosphere.

### 7. Preventive Mental Health Program for the Deaf

Although facilities for psychiatric treatment are badly needed, the most urgent recommendations for the average deaf person lie in the area of *preventive mental health planning* (Chapter 16). Conditions leading to frustration, poor adjustment, and sexual and other forms of delinquency arise within the matrix of the family and the early residential setting of the school. Many deaf adolescents grow up and go on to parenthood without any sex education or guidance for marriage.

A straight approach to prevention of maladjustment would be to center attention on preparation for *family living,* since it is in this context that most unhappiness and behavior disorder tend to manifest themselves. No one denies that education and vocational training are important, but they require an emotionally stable student to be effective. While the individual with a sound foundation for healthy living in school and home has the best chance to achieve vocational and personal fulfillment, ignorance and neglect invariably breed discord, failure and disturbed behavior. These unfortunate developments may extend to sexual delinquency or sexual deviation as well as to many other disturbances in interpersonal relationships.

As to problems of *sex adjustment* in the deaf, especially those encountered in residential school settings, our study confirmed that the reluctance of a morally stringent society to deal with sexual maladjustment as a psychological and developmental, rather than a disciplinary matter, continues to be so strong, even in the most progressive circles, that it interferes with the accrual of data on sex behavior deviations. With so little being known about the background and extent of sexual deviations in the hearing population, including residential schools, it is not surprising that the available information about their deaf counterparts should be even more limited. However, we were able to determine, with the aid of teachers and houseparents in our Eastern schools for the deaf, that sexual delinquency and immaturity, lack of preparation for a successful marriage and a stable family life, and the more extreme forms of deviant sex behavior are by no means less common among the deaf than in any other group of people. In our series of clinic patients, homosexual tendencies were found to be the main problem in more than ten per cent of the cases.

In those numerous instances where boys had some sex play with other boys in school, we usually observed that a punitive or derisive attitude on the part of the school authorities had failed to help the individuals involved. It frequently happened that an already fearful and fragile personality was forced into a lifelong pattern of maladaptation. Some of these youngsters made unhappy and loveless marriages. Others were prevented from fulfilling a promising career by the emotional turmoil ever present in such forms of sexual maladjustment.

Some boys drifted about after expulsion from school, their families perhaps well meaning but of little help, while others entered into the homosexual underworld which is the product of bigotry and ignorance. These men became one of the 100 or so deaf homosexuals who go through the Magistrates Court every year in New York City alone. This special society with its carefully disguised clubs and other organizations, that are so difficult to detect even among the hearing, includes many deaf persons, thus removing a number of otherwise worthwhile individuals from the benefits of a healthy life in a normal society.

If we sincerely desire to promote prevention and cure of these delinquency patterns, we shall have to learn to look at them as *deviations* from a normal maturational process that is determined not only by man's biological nature, but also by the family, school, and psychological atmosphere in which he develops. Although there is definite evidence for some constitutional components in the etiology of adult homosexual behavior, it is also a truism that interest in sex and love does not develop suddenly in a person's life, springing out of nowhere. Modern nursery schools favor unrestricted intermingling of the sexes at the age of four to six, with boys and girls living in the same dormitory, eating at the same table, using the same bathroom, and the like. A similar arrangement would seem advisable for residential schools caring for children of comparable age to compensate for their lack of family life.

In a well-adjusted home, children learn to live together in an atmosphere of mutual affection and respect. They continue to identify with their parents through the pre-adolescent period while making new friends and competing with their peers in work and at play. In adolescence, the advent of puberty leads to an increased interest in sex, making the need for intelligent guidance and instruction particularly urgent. At this time, the child is supposed to have learned to socialize with other youngsters, boys and girls alike. If his early sex curiosity has been normally satisfied in a good school or home environment, neither unduly suppressed nor overstimulated, he will have no trouble in completing his maturational development. The persistence of homosexual and other deviant tendencies is expected to be infrequent in adolescents, whose maturation has been prudently fostered and whose earlier sex curiosities have been properly channeled.

In line with these general principles, the obvious *weak spots,* that may be conducive to the development of a homosexual behavior pattern in residential schools for the deaf, may be summarized as follows:

(a) A restrictive attitude toward sexual interest, instead of a normal amount of sex education extending to all areas of the child's world—his reading, his studies, his recreation and his creative endeavors.

(b) The relative absence of home life, and the difficulties inherent in parent-child relations even when the deaf child goes home to either hearing parents or deaf ones.

### 8. Psychiatric Recommendations

Psychiatrically, it is fully justified to conclude that *coeducation* in residential schools for the deaf is just as essential as a thorough program of *sex education* given by competent persons and adjusted to the age and developmental stage of the pupils. At present, there is an unfortunate vacuum in this area—at least in some countries—, partly due to the fact that instructors themselves have not been adequately prepared and trained. Obviously, however, the training of instructors, parents and personnel should be left to unbiased, scientifically mature and professionally qualified specialists.

Another recommendation is based on the fact that homosexual behavior may sometimes be part of a general mental or emotional disturbance not easily diagnosed and perhaps not even noticeable to a non-psychiatrist. It may be suggested, therefore, that every child presenting some question of deviant sexual practice have the benefit of a *complete psychiatric workup,* and that every adolescent in such circumstances be brought under the wing of the psychiatrist and not the disciplinarian or the courts. In other words, a boy or girl found engaging in deviant sexual practices should not be dismissed summarily, but should be considered as a person whose entire adaptation requires scrutiny. Specialized psychiatric treatment facilities, properly integrated sex education throughout the school years, and individualized guidance for those with special adjustment problems would seem to be the most constructive program for dealing with sexual deviations as well as with other forms of disordered behavior in the deaf.

As to the clinical and investigative objectives of *future psychiatric programs* for deaf communities (Chapters 17, 18), it can be said without reservation that our interdisciplinary team has been in full accord. The consensus is that whether the road be cellular or biochemical, preventive or clinical, psychological or social, all highways leading to more useful knowledge regarding family and mental health problems in the deaf need to be paved with carefully laid research plans, self-critical service, and the indispensable training of new personnel.

### 9. Specialized Psychiatric Inpatient Services

With these objectives in mind, some concrete recommendations were made to the authorities concerned (New York State Department of Mental Hygiene and Office of Vocational Rehabilitation, United States Department of Health, Education, and Welfare), before the first stage of our pilot project, covered by this report, was concluded at the end of 1962. Foremost among these recommendations was the plan to establish centralized psychiatric facilities for the local deaf community at a suitable and well located hospital in the State of New York.

At the time when this volume had to go into press, it could be announced with considerable pleasure and pride on our part that the scheme of a *clinical demonstration project* for the evaluation of "comprehensive mental health services for the deaf" had been approved as of January 1, 1963. With the aid of a new grant from the Vocational Rehabilitation Administration (Commissioner: Miss Mary E. Switzer), the implementation of the scheme is now well under way, with clinical inpatient and aftercare facilities to be established at Rockland State Hospital (Director: Alfred M. Stanley, M.D.) and with the other psychiatric activities (diagnostic, consultative and supervisory services as well as training and evaluation) remaining at the currently used premises of the New York State Psychiatric Institute (Director: Lawrence C. Kolb, M.D.).

The selection of Rockland State Hospital for providing *inpatient services* for the downstate districts with a population of 13,000,000 people, including more than 13,000 deaf persons in all age groups, was made by the Commissioner of Mental Hygiene (Paul H. Hoch, M.D.) on the basis of the hospital's central location and easy accessibility (near the New York Thruway). Also, excellent clinical and research facilities as well as fully integrated community mental health services are available at or near Orangeburg in Rockland County. The hospital itself is located 20 miles from New

York City on the west side of the Hudson River and has direct bus service to that part of the city where the Psychiatric Institute is situated.

These inpatient facilities will be in operation shortly, and certainly at the time when this report is published. Planned as a *model unit* and staffed exclusively with *specially trained personnel,* they will function in close cooperation with outpatient and aftercare clinics, with group therapy services, with specialized training and research centers, and with educational community programs. We confidently expect that such a *specialized psychiatric combination unit* will prove to be not only the most appropriate, but also the most economical way of dealing with the particular emotional, rehabilitative and family problems of the deaf in densely populated areas.

It is also our hope that the effectiveness of such centralized mental health services for the deaf can soon be documented in further progress reports and will gradually become a yardstick for a sound, harmonious and productive union between the two major disciplines engaged in this program, *clinical psychiatry* and *mental health genetics.*

# BIBLIOGRAPHY

1. Alanen, Y. D.: *The Mothers of Schizophrenic Patients.* Copenhagen: Munksgaard, 1958.
2. Albrecht, W.: Über die Vererbung der konstitutionell sporadischen Taubstummheit der heridatären Labyrinthschwerhörigkeit und der Otosclerose. *Arch. Ohren Nasen Kehlkopfheilk. 110:* 15, 1923.
3. _____: Die Bedeutung der Konstitution bei den Erkrankungen des Ohres und der Luftwege. *Ztschr. Laryng. Rhinol. Otol. Grenzgeb. 14:* 1, 1926.
4. Alström, C. H.: A study of inheritance of human intelligence. *Acta Psychiat. Neurol. Scand. 36:* 175, 1961.
5. Altshuler, K. Z.: Genetic elements in schizophrenia: A review. *Eugen. Quart. 4:* 92, 1957.
6. _____: Developments in providing mental hygiene services for the deaf. In: *New Trends in Rehabilitation.* Washington: Office Voc. Rehab., 1959.
7. _____: Psychiatric considerations in the adult deaf. *Am. Ann. Deaf, 107:* 560, 1962.
8. _____: Psychiatric considerations in the school age deaf. *Am. Ann. Deaf, 107:* 553, 1962.
9. _____ and Baroff, G. S.: Mental health problems and needs of the deaf. *Psychiat. Quart. Suppl., 36:* 44, 1962.
10. _____ and Rainer, J. D.: Institute on personal, social and vocational adjustment to total deafness: Psychiatric aspects. *Am. Ann. Deaf 103:* 317, 1958.
11. _____: Patterns and course of schizophrenia in the deaf. *J. Nerv. Ment. Dis. 127:* 77, 1958.
12. _____ and Sarlin, M. B.: Deafness and schizophrenia. In: *Expanding Goals of Genetics in Psychiatry* (F. J. Kallmann, ed.). New York: Grune & Stratton, 1962.
13. Arsenian, S. (ed.): *Rudolf Pintner.* Washington: Gallaudet College Press, 1951.
14. Arthur, G.: *A Point Scale of Performance Tests.* New York: Commonwealth Fund, 1930.
15. Aurell, E.: A new era in the history of the education of the deaf. *Am. Ann. Deaf 79:* 223, 1934.
16. Barker, R. G. et al.: *Adjustment to Physical Handicap and Illness: A Survey of the Social Psychology of Physique and Disability.* New York: Soc. Sci. Res. Council, 1953.
17. Baroff, G. S.: A psychomotor, psychometric and projective study of mentally defective twins. Unpublished doctoral dissertation. New York: New York Univ., 1955.
18. _____ and Altshuler, K. Z.: A mental health program for the deaf. Presented at 8th World Congr. Internat. Soc. Welfare Cripples, New York, 1960.

19. Barron, F.: The need for order and for disorder as motives in creative activity. In: *The Second (1957) Conference on the Identification of Creative Scientific Talent* (C. W. Taylor, ed.). Salt Lake City: Univ. Utah Press, 1958.

20. Bateson, G. et al.: Toward a theory of schizophrenia. *Behav. Sci. 1:* 251, 1956.

21. Berlinsky, S.: Measurement of the intelligence and personality of the deaf. *J. Speech Hear. Disord. 17:* 39, 1952.

22. Best, H.: *Deafness and the Deaf in the United States.* New York: Macmillan, 1943.

23. Bigman, S. K.: Occupations of the deaf. *Rehab. Rec. 1:* 23, 1960.

24. _____ and Lunde, A. S.: *Occupational Conditions Among the Deaf.* Washington: Gallaudet College, 1959.

25. Bishop, H. M.: Performance scale tests applied to deaf and hard of hearing children. *Volta Rev. 38:* 447, 1936.

26. Braceland, F. J.: The role of the psychiatrist in rehabilitation. *J.A.M.A. 165:* 211, 1957.

27. Bradway, K. P.: The social competence of deaf children. *Am. Ann. Deaf 82:* 122, 1937.

28. Brodhage, G. and Wendt, G. G.: Die Verwendung qualitativer Fingerleistenmerkmale im Vaterschaftsgutachten. *Ztschr. menschl. Vereb. Konst. 30:* 212 and 221, 1951.

29. Brunschwig, L.: *A Study of Some Personality Aspects of Deaf Children.* Contributions to Education, No. 687. New York: Teachers Coll., Columbia Univ., 1936.

30. Bunch, C. C.: Age variations in auditory acuity. *Arch. Otolaryng. 9:* 625, 1929.

31. Burchard, E. and Myklebust, H. R.: A comparison of congenital and adventitious deafness with respect to its effect on intelligence, personality and social maturity. *Am. Ann. Deaf 87:* 140, 241 and 341, 1942.

32. Burgess, E.: Personality factors of over- and under-achievers in engineering. *J. Educ. Psychol. 47:* 89, 1956.

33. Castle, C. S.: A statistical study of eminent women. *Columbia Univ. Contrib. Philos. Psychol. 22:* 1, 1913.

34. Cattell, J. McK.: A statistical study of eminent men. *Pop. Sci. Monthly 62:* 359, 1903.

35. _____: A further statistical study of American men of science II. *Science 32:* 672, 1910.

36. _____: Families of American men of science. *Pop. Sci. Monthly 86:* 504, 1915.

37. Chung, C. S. et al.: A note on deaf-mutism. *Ann. Hum. Genet. 23:* 357, 1959.

38. Ciocco, A.: Audiometric studies on school children. V. Changes in air conduction acuity after an interval of five years, with particular reference to the effect of age and sex. *Ann. Otol. Rhinol. Laryng. 47:* 926, 1938.

39. _____ and Palmer, C. E.: The hearing of school children: A statistical study of audiometric and clinic records. *Monogr. Soc. Res. Child Devel. 6:* 29, 1941.

40. _____ et al.: Studies on pupils of the Pennsylvania School for the Deaf: 2. Resemblances in the auditory acuity of siblings. *Hum. Biol. 11:* 259, 1939.

41. Clarke, E. L.: American men of letters, their nature and nurture. *Columbia Univ. Studies Hist. Econ. Pub. Law. 72:* 1, 1916.

42. Clarke, F. D.: A question in psychology. *Proc. Conv. Am. Instr. Deaf 14:* 35, 1895.

43. Clarke, K. E.: *American Psychologists: A Survey of a Growing Profession.* Washington: Am. Psychol. Assoc., 1957.

44. Close, R.: Heredity and productivity in families of institutionalized deaf. *Eugen. Quart. 8:* 34, 1961.

45. Cochran, W. G.: *Sampling Techniques.* New York: John Wiley and Sons, 1953.

46. Cox, R. P. and MacLeod, C.: Relation between genetic abnormalities in man and susceptibility to infectious disease. In: *Methodology in Human Genetics* (W. J. Burdette, ed.). San Francisco: Holden-Day, 1962.

47. Crammatte, A. B. and Friedman, M.: What of the Products? *Am. Ann. Deaf 86:* 407, 1941.

48. Dahlberg, G.: *Mathematical Methods for Population Genetics.* Basel: S. Karger, 1948.

49. Davis, H. and Fowler, E. P., Jr.: Hearing and deafness. In: *Hearing and Deafness* (H. Davis and S. R. Silverman, eds.). New York: Holt, Rinehart and Winston, 1960.

50. Day, H. E. et al.: *A Survey of American Schools for the Deaf.* Washington: Nat. Res. Council, 1928.

51. Deming, W. E.: On simplification of sampling design through replication with equal probabilities and without stages. *J. Am. Statis. Assoc. 51:* 24, 1956.

52. _____: Discussion. *Eugen. Quart. 6:* 127, 1959.

53. _____: *Sample Design in Business Research.* New York: John Wiley and Sons, 1961.

54. Deraemaker, R.: Recessive congenital deafness in a North Belgian province. *Acta Genet. 10:* 295, 1960.

55. de Reynier, J. P.: La surdi-mutité en Suisse en 1953. *Biblioth. Oto-Rino-Laryng. 5:* 1, 1959.

56. Doctor, P. V.: Summary of schools and classes for the deaf in the United States. *Am. Ann. Deaf 106:* 162, 1961.

57. Doll, E. A.: *Vineland Social Maturity Scale: Manual of Directions.* New York: Educ. Test Bureau, 1947.

58. Douglass, F. M. et al.: *A Differential Study of Communication Disorders.* New York: St. Joseph's School for the Deaf, 1961.

59. Doyle, J. and McConnell, F.: Relationship between causes of hearing loss in children and audiogram patterns. *J. Except. Child. 21:* 63 and 69, 1954.

60. Drever, J. and Collins, M.: *Performance Tests of Intelligence*. Edinburgh: Oliver and Boyd, 1928.

61. Duis, B. I. and Eickhoff, H.: Eineiige Zwillinge mit dominanter Innenohrschwerhörigkeit. *A. Ge. Me. Ge. 3:* 210, 1954.

62. Editorial: Jaundice and deafness. *Brit. Med. J. 2:* 162, 1961.

63. _____: Treatment in inherited disease. *New Eng. J. Med. 266:* 100, 1962.

64. Elstad, L. M.: The deaf. In: *Special Education for the Exceptional, Vol. II* (M. E. Frampton and E. D. Gall, eds.). Boston: Porter Sargent, 1955.

65. Farnsworth, R. R.: The limitations of Cattell's space method of studying eminence. *J. Psychol. 44:* 169, 1957.

66. Fay, E. A.: *Marriages of the Deaf in America*. Washington: Volta Bureau, 1898.

67. Feingold, L.: A psychometric study of senescent twins. Unpublished doctoral dissertation. New York: Columbia Univ., 1950.

68. Finney, D. J.: The truncated binomial distribution. *Ann. Eugen. 14:* 319, 1949.

69. Fisch, E. L.: *Fisch on New York Evidence*. Pomona, N.Y.: Lond, 1959.

70. Fisch, L.: The etiology of congenital deafness and audiometric patterns. *J. Laryng. Otol. 67:* 479, 1955.

71. _____ and Norman, A. P.: Hyperbilirubinaemia and perceptive deafness. *Brit. Med. J. 2:* 142, 1961.

72. Fowler, E. P.: Otosclerosis in identical twins. *J.A.M.A. 154:* 304, 1954.

73. Fowler, E. P., Jr. and Kastein, S.: Hypoacusis, dyacusis and retardation. *Res. Publ. Assn. nerv. ment. Dis. 39:* 270, 1962.

74. Freire-Maia, N.: Inbreeding levels in different countries. *Eugen. Quart. 4:* 127, 1957.

75. Furusho, T.: A genetic study on the congenital deafness. *Jap. J. Hum. Genet. 2:* 35, 1957.

76. Fusfeld, I. S.: Six points of reading weaknesses as discovered through Gallaudet College entrance examinations. *Proc. Conv. Am. Instr. Deaf 37:* 94, 1955.

77. Galton, F.: *Hereditary Genius*. New York: Appleton, 1870.

78. Gedda, L. et al.: Les jumeaux sourds-muets: Analyse génétique et clinique de sept couples de jumeaux atteints de surdi-mutité. *J. Génét. Hum. 2:* 1, 1953.

79. Glorig, A., Jr.: *Noise and Your Ear*. New York: Grune & Stratton, 1958.

80. Glueck, S. and Glueck, E.: *Unraveling Juvenile Delinquency*. New York: Commonwealth Fund, 1950.

81. Goldberg, H. R.: Administering curriculum change. *Volta Rev. 62:* 378, 1960.

82. Goldhamer, H. and Marshall, A. W.: *Psychosis and Civilization*. Glencoe, Ill.: Free Press, 1953.

83. Goldman, G.: Reparative psychotherapy. In: *Changing Concepts of Psychoanalytic Medicine* (S. Rado and G. Daniels, eds.). New York: Grune & Stratton, 1956.

84. Goodenough, F. L. and Shirley, M.: A survey of intelligence of deaf children in Minnesota schools. *Am. Ann. Deaf 77:* 238, 1932.

85. Greenberger, D.: Doubtful cases. *Am. Ann. Deaf 34:* 93, 1889.
86. Grewel, F. and van den Horst, A. P. J.: Hereditary congenital deafness in uniovular twins. *A. Ge. Me. Ge. 8:* 99, 1959.
87. Guilford, J. P.: The relation of intellectual factors to creative thinking in science. In: *The 1955 University of Utah Research Conference on Identification of Creative Scientific Talent* (C. W. Taylor, ed.). Salt Lake City: Univ. Utah Press, 1956.
88. Habbe, S.: *Personality Adjustments of Adolescent Boys with Impaired Hearing.* Contributions to Education, No. 697, New York: Teachers Coll., Columbia Univ., 1936.
89. Haldane, J. B. S.: A method of investigating recessive characters in man. *J. Genet. 25:* 251, 1932.
90. _____: The estimation of the frequencies of recessive conditions in man. *Ann. Eugen. 8:* 255, 1938.
91. Hallgren, B.: *Retinitis Pigmentosa Combined with Congenital Deafness; with Vestibulo-cerebellar Ataxia and Mental Abnormality in a Proportion of Cases.* Copenhagen: Munksgaard, 1959.
92. Hammerschlag, V.: Über kombinierte Heredopathien und ihren mutmasslichen Erbgang. *Wien klin. Wschr. 45:* 772 and 808, 1932.
93. Hanhart, E.: Die "sporadische" Taubstummheit als Prototyp einer einfachrezessiven Mutation. *Ztschr. menschl. Vereb. Konst. 21:* 609, 1938.
94. Haraoka, K.: Relations between efforts for academic records and home environment. *Jap. J. Educ. Psychol. 4:* 159, 1957.
95. Hauser, P. M. and Duncan, O. D.: *The Study of Population.* Chicago: Univ. Chicago Press, 1959.
96. Heckman, H.: *My Life Transformed.* New York: Macmillan, 1928.
97. Heiner, M. H.: *Hearing is Believing.* Cleveland: World, 1949.
98. Hirsch, N. D. M.: *Genius and Creative Intelligence.* Cambridge, Mass.: Science-Art, 1931.
99. Hodgson, K. W.: *The Deaf and Their Problems.* New York: Philosophical Library, 1953.
100. Hopkins, J. et al.: Some non-intellectual correlates of success and failure among university students. *Brit. J. Educ. Psychol. 28:* 25, 1958.
101. Hopkins, L. A. and Guilder, R. P.: *Clarke School Studies Concerning the Heredity of Deafness.* Northampton, Mass.: Clarke School, 1949.
102. Hudson, A. F.: The union of kindergartners for the deaf. *Am. Ann. Deaf 38:* 277, 1893 and *39:* 25, 1894.
103. Husén, T.: Über die Begabung von Zwillingen. *Psychol. Beiträge. 1:* 137, 1954.
104. _____: *Psychological Twin Research.* Stockholm: Almquist and Wiksell, 1959.
105. Isakower, O.: On the exceptional position of the auditory sphere. *Internat. J. Psycho-anal. 20:* 340, 1939.
106. Ishikuni, N. et al.: Hosojima. *Am. J. Hum. Genet. 12:* 67, 1960.
107. Jarvik, L. F. et al.: Longitudinal study of intellectual changes in senescent twins. In: *Social and Psychological Aspects of Aging* (L. Tibbits and W. Donahue eds.). New York: Columbia Univ. Press, 1962.

108. Johansen, H.: Investigations on hearing reduction caused by advancing age. *Acta Otolaryng. 32:* 194, 1944.

109. Jones, E.: Madonna's conception through the ear. In: *Essays in Applied Psycho-analysis, Vol. 2.* London: Hogarth, 1951.

110. Kaelin, A.: Estimation statistique de la fréquence des tarés en génétique humaine. *J. Génét. Hum., 7:* 67 and 243, 1958.

111. Kallmann, F. J.: The genetic theory of schizophrenia. *Am. J. Psychiat. 103:* 309, 1946.

112. _____: Objectives of the mental health project for the deaf. *Proc. Conv. Am. Instr. Deaf 37:* 266, 1956.

113. _____: Psychiatric aspects of genetic counseling. *Am. J. Hum. Genet. 8:* 97, 1956.

114. _____ and Rainer, J. D.: Genetics and demography. In: *The Study of Population* (P. M. Hauser and O. D. Duncan, eds.). Chicago: Univ. Chicago Press, 1959.

115. _____: Psychotherapeutically oriented counseling techniques in the setting of a medical genetics department. In: *Topical Problems of Psychotherapy, Vol. 4* (B. Stokvis, ed.). Basel: S. Karger, 1963.

116. Keller, H.: *Helen Keller in Scotland.* London: Methuen, 1933.

117. Kinsey, A. C., et al.: *Sexual Behavior in the Human Male.* New York: Saunders, 1948.

118. Kirk, S. A.: Behavior problem tendencies in deaf and hard of hearing children. *Am. Ann. Deaf 83:* 131, 1938.

119. Klein, D.: Albinisme partiel (leucisme) avec surdi-mutité, blépharophimosis et dysplasie myo-osteo-articulaire. *Helvet. Paed. Acta 5:* 38, 1950.

120. Klopfer, B. and Kelley, D.: *The Rorschach Technique.* New York: World Book, 1942.

121. _____ et al.: *Development in the Rorschach Technique, Volume 1, Technique and Theory.* New York: World Book, 1954 .

122. Knapp, P. H.: Emotional aspects of hearing loss. *Psychosom. Med. 10:* 203, 1948.

123. _____: The ear, listening and hearing. *J. Am. Psychoanal. Assoc. 1:* 672, 1953.

124. Knapp, R. H. and Greenbaum, J. J.: *The Younger American Scholar, His Collegiate Origins.* Chicago: Univ. Chicago Press, 1953.

125. Kraatz, J. J.: Hereditary deaf-mutism: A study of the Mendelian factors in the inheritance of deaf-mutism. *J. Hered. 16:* 265, 1925.

126. Laird, C.: *The Miracle of Language.* Cleveland: World, 1953.

127. Lamy, M. et al.: Résultats d'une enquête génétique sur la surdi-mutité. *Sem. Hôp. 25:* 2351, 1949.

128. Landis, C. and Bolles, M. M.: *Textbook of Abnormal Psychology.* New York: Macmillan, 1950.

129. Lane, H. S. and Schneider, J. L.: A performance test for school age deaf children. *Am. Ann. Deaf 86:* 441, 1941.

130. Lejeune, J.: Sur une solution "a priori" de la méthode "a posteriori" de Haldane. *Biometrics 14:* 513, 1958.

131. Levine, E. S.: Mental health clinic in New York. *Silent Worker 9:* 7, 1956.

132. _____: *Youth in a Soundless World.* New York: New York Univ. Press, 1956.
133. _____: Psychological aspects and problems of early profound deafness. *Am. Ann. Deaf 103:* 324, 1958.
134. _____: Psychological assessment of the deaf. *Rehab. Rec. 6:* 33, 1960.
135. _____: *The Psychology of Deafness: Techniques of Appraisal for Rehabilitation.* New York: Columbia Univ. Press, 1960.
136. _____ and Safian, M. S.: Psychological evaluation in vocational adjustment. *Am. Ann. Deaf 103:* 348, 1958.
137. Li, C. C.: *Human Genetics.* New York: McGraw-Hill, 1961.
138. Lindenov, H.: *The Etiology of Deaf-Mutism with Special Reference to Heredity.* Copenhagen: Munksgaard, 1945.
139. Luchsinger, R. and Hanhart, E.: Über erhebliche Manifestationsschwankungen rezessiver Taubheit bei drei eineiigen Zwillingspaaren. *Arch. Julius Klaus Stift. 24:* 417, 1949.
140. Lyon, V. W.: Personality tests with the deaf. *Am. Ann. Deaf 79:* 1, 1934.
141. _____ et al.: Report of the 1931 survey of the Illinois School for the Deaf. *Am. Ann. Deaf 78:* 157, 1933.
142. MacFarlon, D.: Identical hearing in identical twins. *Laryngoscope 37:* 846, 1927.
143. MacKane, K. A.: *A Comparison of the Intelligence of Deaf and Hearing Children.* Contributions to Education, No. 585. New York: Teachers Coll. Columbia Univ., 1933.
144. MacMillan, D. P. and Bruner, F. G.: *Children Attending the Public Day Schools for the Deaf in Chicago.* Special Report, Dept. Child Study and Pedagogic Invest. Chicago: Chicago Public Schools, 1906.
145. Mann, M. J.: Relationships among certain variables associated with post-college success. *Educ. Psychol. Measmt. 19:* 351, 1959.
146. Matzker, J.: Concerning discordant congenital deafness in monozygotic twins. *Ztschr. Laryng. Rhinol. Otol. Grenzgeb. 34:* 117, 1955.
147. May, K. M.: The psychology of deafness. *Penn. Med. J. 40:* 177, 1930.
148. Meer, B. and Stein, M. I.: Measurement of intelligence and creativity. *J. Psychol. 39:* 117, 1955.
149. Menninger, K. A.: The mental effect of deafness. *Psychoanal. Rev. 11:* 144, 1924.
150. Morton, N. E.: Morbidity of children from consanguineous marriages. In: *Progress in Medical Genetics, Vol. 1* (A. G. Steinberg, ed.). New York, Grune & Stratton, 1961.
151. Mott, A. J.: A comparison of deaf and hearing children in their ninth year. *Am. Ann. Deaf 44:* 401, 1899 and *45:* 33 and 223, 1900.
152. Mourant, A. E.: *The Distribution of the Human Blood Groups.* Springfield, C. C. Thomas, 1954.
153. Murphy, B. W.: Genesis of schizoid personality: Study of two cases developing schizophrenia. *Psychiat. Quart. 26:* 450, 1952.
154. Myklebust, H. R.: The psychological effects of deafness. *Am. Ann. Deaf 105:* 372, 1960.

155. Nash, T.: Psychiatric treatment of the deaf as a rehabilitation source from the viewpoint of a counselor. In: *Rehabilitation of the Deaf and the Hard of Hearing.* Washington: Office Voc. Rehab., 1950.

156. National Institute for the Deaf: *The N.I.D. Comprehensive Survey* (mimeographed proposal). London, 1959.

157. Neel, J. V. and Schull, W. J.: *Human Heredity.* Chicago: Univ. Chicago Press, 1954.

158. Newman, H. H. et al.: *Twins: A Study of Heredity and Environment.* Chicago: Univ. Chicago Press, 1937.

159. New York City Magistrates' Court: *1959 Annual Report.* New York: New York City Magistrates' Court, 1960.

160. Nixon, W. L. B.: On the diagnosis of twin-pair ovularity and the use of dermatoglyphic data. In: *Novant'anni delle Leggi Mendeliane* (L. Gedda, ed.). Roma: Istituto Gregorio Mendel, 1956.

161. North Regional Association for the Deaf (Manchester, Eng.): Deaf in mental hospitals. *Silent Northerner* p. 2, July 1959.

162. Noyes, A. P. and Kolb, L. C.: *Modern Clinical Psychiatry.* Philadelphia: Saunders, 1958.

163. Ormerod F. C.: The pathology of congenital deafness. *J. Laryng. Otol. 74:* 919, 1960.

164. Parker, N.: Congenital deafness due to a sex-linked recessive gene. *Am. J. Hum. Genet. 10:* 196, 1958.

165. Payne, R. W.: Cognitive abnormalities. In: *Handbook of Abnormal Psychology* (H. J. Eysenck, ed.). New York: Basic Books, 1961.

166. Peet, I.: The psychical status and criminal responsibility of the totally uneducated deaf and dumb. *Am. Ann. Deaf 17:* 65, 1872.

167. Perry, J. W.: A Jungian formulation of schizophrenia. *Am. J. Psychother. 10:* 54, 1956.

168. Petersen, E. G.: Testing deaf children with the Kohs Block Designs. *Am. Ann. Deaf 81:* 242, 1936.

169. —————— and Williams, J. M.: Intelligence of deaf children as measured by drawings. *Am. Ann Deaf 75:* 273, 1930.

170. Pfändler, V. and Schnyder, E.: Recessive deaf-mutism in Werdenberg. *J. Genet. Hum. 9:* 158, 1960.

171. Pintner, R. and Paterson, D. G.: The Binet Scale and the deaf child. *J. Educ. Psychol. 6:* 201 1915.

172. —————— et al.: Personality tests of adult deaf. *J. Genet. Psychol. 51:* 305, 1937.

173. ——————: *The Psychology of the Physically Handicapped.* New York: Crofts, 1941.

174. Plant, J. S.: Mental hygiene aspects of problems of the deaf. *Proc. Conv. Am. Instr. Deaf 28:* 40, 1933.

175. Post, R. and Hopkins, L. A.: "Deaf-mutism" in two pairs of identical twins. *J. Hered. 47:* 88, 1956.

176. Race, H. V.: Mental health. *Proc. Conv. Am. Instr. Deaf 26:* 127, 1929.

177. Rado, S.: Recent advances in psychoanalytic therapy. *Proc. Assoc. Res. Nerv. Ment. Dis. 21:* 42, 1953.

178. Rainer, J. D.: Marriage patterns and family composition in early total deafness. In: *Proc. 2nd Internat. Conf. Hum. Genet.,* in press.

179. _____ and Firschein, I. L.: Mating and fertility patterns in families with early total deafness. *Eugen. Quart. 6:* 117, 1959.

180. _____ and Kallmann, F. J.: Behavior disorder patterns in a deaf population. *Pub. Health Rep. 72:* 585, 1957.

181. _____: A constructive psychiatric program for a deaf population. *Proc. Conv. Am. Instr. Deaf 38:* 212, 1958.

182. _____: Genetic and demographic aspects of disordered behavior patterns in a deaf population. In: *Epidemiology of Mental Disorder* (B. Pasamanick, ed.). Washington: Am. Assoc. Adv. Sci., 1959.

183. _____: Observations, facts and recommendations derived from a mental health project for the deaf. *Tr. Am. Aca. Opth. Otol. 63:* 179, 1959.

184. _____: Problems of sex adjustment and family planning in the deaf. Presented at Conf. Exec. Am. Schools Deaf, Colorado Springs, 1959.

185. _____ et al. (eds.): *Mental Health Planning for the Deaf.* New York State Psychiatric Institute, 1958.

186. _____: Psychotherapy for the deaf. In: *Advances in Psychosomatic Medicine,* Vol. 3 (B. Stokvis, ed.), Basel: S. Karger, 1963.

187. Raskin, E.: A comparison of scientific and literary ability: A biographical study of eminent scientists and men of letters of the nineteenth century. *J. Abn. Soc. Psychol. 31:* 20, 1936.

188. Reamer, J. C.: Mental and educational measurements of the deaf. *Psychol. Monogr. 29:* No. 132, 1921.

189. Rodin, F. H.: Identical hearing defect in identical twins. *Arch. Otolaryng. 17:* 179, 1933.

190. Roe, A.: A psychological study of eminent biologists. *Psychol. Monogr. 65:* 1, 1951.

191. _____: *The Making of a Scientist.* New York: Dodd, Mead, 1952.

192. Rogers M. and Quigley, S. P. (eds.): Research needs in the vocational rehabilitation of the deaf. *Am. Ann. Deaf 105:* 335, 1960.

193. Roy, H. L.: Counseling center for the deaf. *Rehab. Rec. 1:* 35, 1960.

194. Sank, D.: The genetic and adjustive aspects of early total deafness. In: *Expanding Goals of Genetics in Psychiatry* (F. J. Kallmann, ed.). New York: Grune & Stratton, 1962.

195. _____: *Genetic Aspects of Early Total Deafness (Supplement): Summarized Twin-Family Data.* (To obtain, order Document No. 7469 from the Chief, Photoduplication Service, Library of Congress, Washington 25, D.C., Auxiliary Publications project, remitting $4.50 for 35 mm microfilm or $13.75 for photocopies.)

196. _____ and Kallmann, F. J.: Genetic and eugenic aspects of early total deafness. *Eugen. Quart. 3:* 69, 1956.

197. Sarwer-Foner, G. J. et al.: A self-contained women's ward as a therapeutic community. In: *Research Conference on Therapeutic Community* (H. C. B. Denber et al., eds.). Springfield, Ill.: Thomas, 1959.

198. Sataloff, J. et al.: Sex-linked hereditary deafness. *Am. J. Hum. Genet. 7:* 201, 1955.
199. Schick, H. F.: The use of a standardized performance test for pre-school age children with a language handicap. In: *Proceedings at the International Congress on Education of the Deaf.* W. Trenton, N. J.: New Jersey School for the Deaf 1933.
200. Scholten, P.: The premarital examination. *J.A.M.A. 167:* 1171, 1958.
201. Schulz, B.: *Methodik der medizinischen Erbforschung.* Leipzig: Thieme, 1936.
202. Schunhoff, H. F.: *The Teaching of Speech and by Speech in Public Residential Schools for the Deaf in the United States, 1815-1955.* Romney, W. Va.: West Virginia School for the Deaf and Blind, 1957.
203. Secreton, J. P.: De la surdi-mutité récessive et de ses rapports avec les autres formes de surdi-mutité. *Arch. Julius Klaus Stift. 29:* 1, 1954.
204. Sifton, M.: Fulfillment. In: *Opportunity and the Deaf Child* (I. R. Ewing and A. W. G. Ewing, eds.). London: Univ. London Press, 1947.
205. Slatis, H. M.: Comments on the inheritance of deaf-mutism in Northern Ireland. *Ann. Hum. Genet. 22:* 153, 1958.
206. _____ et al.: Consanguineous marriages in the Chicago region. *Am. J. Hum. Genet. 10:* 446, 1958.
207. Smith, W. D. et al.: A new syndrome of multiple congenital anomalies caused by an extra autosome. *Am. J. Dis. Child. 100:* 492, 1960.
208. Smith, S. M. and Penrose, L. S.: Monozygotic and dizygotic twin diagnosis. *Ann. Hum. Genet. 19:* 273, 1955.
209. Solomon, J. C.: Psychiatric implications of deafness. *Ment. Hyg. 27:* 439, 1943.
210. Spitz, R. A.: *A Genetic Field Theory of Ego Formation.* New York: Internat. Univ. Press, 1959.
211. Springer, N. N.: A comparative study of the intelligence of a group of deaf and hearing children. *Am. Ann. Deaf 83:* 138, 1938.
212. _____: A comparative study of behavior traits of deaf and hearing children in New York City. *Am. Ann. Deaf 83:* 255, 1938.
213. _____: A comparative study of psychoneurotic responses of deaf and hearing subjects. *J. Educ. Psychol. 29:* 459, 1938.
214. _____ and Roslow, S.: A further study of the psychoneurotic responses of deaf and hearing children. *J. Educ. Psychol. 29:* 590, 1938.
215. Stanley, J. C.: The riddle of creativity. *Peabody J. Educ. 34:* 78, 1956.
216. Stateman, R.: *Mental Measurement of Preschool Children.* New York: World Book, 1931.
217. Stein, M. I.: Creativity and culture. *J. Psychol. 36:* 311, 1953.
218. _____ and Heinz, S. J.: *Creativity and the Individual.* New York, Free Press of Glencoe, 1960.
219. Stern, C.: *Principles of Human Genetics, 2nd Ed.* San Francisco: Freeman, 1960.
220. Stevenson, A. C. and Cheeseman, E. A.: Hereditary deaf-mutism with particular reference to Northern Ireland. *Ann. Hum. Genet. 20:* 177, 1956.

221. Streng, A. and Kirk, S. A.: The social competence of deaf and hard of hearing children in a public day-school. *Am. Ann. Deaf 83:* 244, 1938.
222. Szalita-Pemow, A.: Remarks on the pathogenesis and treatment of schizophrenia. *Psychiatry 14:* 295, 1951.
223. Taylor, H.: The mind of the child. *Am. Ann. Deaf 39:* 244, 1894.
224. _____: A spelling test. *Am. Ann. Deaf 42:* 364, 1897 and *43:* 41, 1898.
225. _____: A résumé of research. *Am. Ann. Deaf 81:* 315, 1936.
226. Therman, E. et al.: The D trisomy syndrome and XO gonadal dysgenesis in two twin sisters. *Am. J. Hum. Genet. 13:* 193, 1961.
227. Tietz, W.: Dominant albinism associated with deaf-mutism. Presented at annual meeting, Am. Soc. Hum. Genet., Memphis, 1960.
228. van Gilse, P. H. G. et al.: Heredity in diseases in the field of oto-rhino-laryngology. *Bibliographia Genetica, 13:* 301, 1942.
229. Vernon, J. et al.: Sensory deprivation and hallucinations. *Science 103:* 1808, 1961.
230. Vinson, M. R.: The pupils case-I. *Am. Ann. Deaf 87:* 114, 1942.
231. Visher, S. S.: *Scientists Starred 1903-1943 in "American Men of Science": A Study of Collegiate and Doctoral Training, Birthplace, Distribution, Backgrounds, and Developmental Influences.* Baltimore: Johns Hopkins Univ. Press, 1947.
232. Waardenburg, P. J.: A new syndrome combining developmental anomalies of the eyelids, eyebrows, and nose root with pigmentary defects of the iris and head, hair, and with congenital deafness. *Am. J. Hum. Genet. 3:* 195, 1951.
233. Walker, H. M. and Lev, J.: *Statistical Inference.* New York: Holt, 1953.
234. Wallenberg, M.: The relation of hearing to space and motion. *Psychiat. Quart. 17:* 633, 1943.
235. Washburne, C.: Mental hygiene. *Proc. Conv. Am. Instr. Deaf 29:* 265, 1925.
236. Wechsler, D.: *The Measurement of Adult Intelligence, 2nd Ed.* Baltimore: Williams and Wilkins, 1941.
237. _____: *Wechsler Intelligence Scale for Children: Manual.* New York: Psychological Corp., 1949.
238. Wedenberg, E.: Preliminary report. Hereditary background of auditory impairment. Laboratory detection of heterozygotes of deafness. A Békésy-audiometric examination of parents with children deaf from birth. *Acta Otolaryng. 49:* 451, 1958.
239. Weinberg, W.: Zur Probandenmethode und zu ihren Ersatz. *Ztschr. Neurol. 123:* 809, 1930.
240. Welles, H. H.: *The Measurement of Certain Aspects of Personality Among Hard of Hearing Adults.* Contributions to Education, No. 545, New York: Teachers Coll., Columbia Univ., 1932.
241. Wendt, G. G.: Der individuelle Musterwert der Fingerleisten und seine Vererbung. *A. Ge. Me. Ge. 4:* 330, 1955.
242. White, P. J.: Mental hygiene and the teacher, *Proc. Conv. Am. Instr. Deaf 32:* 183, 1941.

243. Wigmore, J. H.: *Wigmore On Evidence, 3rd Ed.* Boston: Little, Brown, 1940.
244. Wildervanck, L. S.: A deaf-mute and a "hearing-mute" uniovular twin. *A. Ge. Me. Ge. 3:* 34, 1954.
245. _____: Audiometric examination of parents of children deaf from birth: The influence of consanguineous marriages. *A.M.A. Arch. Otolaryng. 65:* 280, 1957.
246. _____: Heredity counseling as a preventative measure. In: *The Modern Educational Treatment of Deafness* (A. Ewing, ed.). Manchester, Eng.: Manchester Univ. Press, 1960.
247. Williams, B. R. and Chase, E.: Deafness: new approaches. *Rehab. Rec. 1:* 17, 1960.
248. Wolberg, L.: *Technique of Psychotherapy.* New York: Grune & Stratton, 1954.
249. World Health Organization: The prevalence of blindness and deaf-mutism in various countries. *Epidem. Vital Statist. Rep. 6:* 1, 1953.
250. Zazzo, R.: Situation géméllaire et dévelopment mental. *J. Psychol. Norm. Pathol. 45:* 208, 1952.
251. Zeckel, A.: Psychopathological aspects of deafness. *J. Nerv. Ment. Dis. 112:* 322, 1950.
252. _____ and van der Kolk, J. J.: A comparative intelligence test of groups of children born deaf and of good hearing by means of the Porteus Test. *Am. Ann. Deaf 84:* 114, 1939.
253. Zonderman, B.: The preschool nerve-deaf child (study of etiological factors). *Laryngoscope 69:* 54, 1959.

# Appendix I

## PERSONALITY TRAITS AND DEPRESSIVE SYMPTOMS IN THE DEAF*

### KENNETH Z. ALTSHULER

Certain unusual personality features of the deaf have been described by various investigators (1–5) in terms of social or general immaturity, ego rigidity, deficient emotional adaptability, and limitations in abstract conceptual thinking. To enhance our understanding of the adjustive and behavioral aspects of these traits, an attempt will be made in this report to define them clinically, to relate them to some characteristic modifications in psychotic illnesses in the deaf, and to discuss their implications from a physiodynamic as well as a psychodynamic point of view.

Information on more than 700 deaf persons, obtained as part of our Mental Health Project for the Deaf (1955–1962), is available for this evaluation. The data include the histories of some 200 deaf persons who have been seen in our special outpatient clinic; those of hospitalized deaf patients, numbering approximately 225 at any given time; and information obtained in interviews of the more than 300 normal deaf persons and their families who represent a random sample of our census of the deaf in New York State. All of the subjects were totally deaf, with the handicap defined as a "stress producing hearing loss at an early age, making effective auditory contact with the world impossible, and necessitating special educative efforts" (6). The majority of the hearing losses were either congenital or acquired through illness in the preverbal years of life.

### Personality Traits

Among the outstanding personality features of the deaf observed in the course of this project are: a lack of understanding of, and regard for, the feelings of others (empathy) coupled with inadequate insight into the impact of their own behavior and its consequences in relation to others. With a generally egocentric view of the world and with demands unfettered by excessive control machinery (conscience), the adaptive approach is characterized by gross coercive dependence. The preferred defensive re-

This report is the twenty-seventh in a series on the progress of the Mental Health Project for the Deaf, which is being conducted by the Department of Medical Genetics of the New York State Psychiatric Institute, Columbia University, aided by a grant from the Vocational Rehabilitation Administration of the U.S. Department of Health, Education, and Welfare.

* Reprinted from *Recent Advances in Biological Psychiatry,* Vol. VI, 1964, Edited by Joseph Wortis, Plenum Press, New York.

ˈactions to tension and anxiety are typified by a kind of primitive riddance through action (8). In the presence of more sophistication, such defensive reactions remain at the level of simple projection. Behaviorally, this mode of handling tension is reflected in considerable impulsivity and the absence of much thoughtful introspection (9).

The given traits, interrelated and overlapping as they are, may be brought into clearer focus by some illustrative case material.

*Case 1.* G.R. was a 28-year-old white, congenitally deaf male observed periodically over a 5-year span. He was first seen at the request of his hearing parents, because of increasing unmanageability at home. Described as demanding and abusive, he had at one time inadvertently broken his mother's finger. He had had a private tutor from 3 to 6 years of age and then had been sent away to school. There he seemed tense and more obstinate than others, reacting with angry refusal when prodded to learn, and vomiting daily for some time. Nevertheless, he made slow but satisfactory progress, and he left school at the age of 18. Subsequently working at a shipping clerk for his father, he did only what he pleased. When asked to do jobs that "bored" him, he became either anxious or angry, and often had temper tantrums (for example, one time kicking in a door). He frequently demanded a new home from his parents, similar to that of his brother who was a successful executive, and he urged that his father find a wife for him. When admonished about touching one of the girls in the warehouse, he impulsively broke a plate glass window and refused to work. When his mother professed ignorance in attempting to answer some of his questions, he became angry and accused her of lying to him.

On psychiatric interview, he conceded grudgingly that his behavior had been inappropriate. However, he blamed his parents, fellow workers, and others for bothering him. Psychometric evaluation revealed normal intelligence, and Rorschach testing "a lack of self-critical viewing . . . and hostile dependent demands with poor control." There was no evidence for a diagnosis of schizophrenia.

*Case 2.* R.C. was a 33-year-old white male, deaf since the age of 16 months and twice-married. He was referred by a judge because of poorly controlled and easily provoked temper outbursts at home, and received supportive treatment and regular medication over a period of one year. Being of high average intelligence, he had worked steadily at a trade, except for a temporary layoff after a violent episode. The most recent of his arrests occurred during the course of treatment when, at 10 o'clock at night, he decided the hour of his appointment the next day was too early. He asked his wife to arrange a change in time. When she refused because of the late hour, he flew into a rage, struck her, smashed the TV set, and insisted on something being done. Hence, she went to the police. On another occasion, his mother-in-law bought tickets for a dinner-dance that he and his wife wanted to attend. He drank so excessively that he vomited over himself, the table, and some of his neighbors. He could not understand why his wife was upset about the incident and finally blamed his mother-in-law for encouraging him to be a playboy by buying the tickets (and incidentally paying for the night's work he missed). When asked how he felt about his behavior, he shrugged and then—trying hard to follow what the therapist was driving at—replied, "I guess ashamed? Yes, that's it, ashamed!" Annoyed with his wife at other times for not following his request—actually a demand—to stop smoking, he would spitefully, but without guilt, steal one pack for each one he paid for when buying cigarettes for her.

*Case 3.* A.I. was a 16-year-old congenitally deaf female who sought psychiatric help because of increasing anxiety over attending school. She was charming, pert, and intelligent, but her earlier good marks had recently fallen off, and so had her relations with her girl friends. She was full of resentful feelings toward the many acquaintances who "pestered or ignored [her], and called [her] names" apparently without reason. In response to these presumed insults, she had become more and more tense and occasionally showed a tendency to violence.

Several interviews revealed a simple adolescent problem complicated only by the patient's difficulty in apprehending the salient features of the total situation, particularly the impact of her own behavior. Apparently, the patient's warmth, budding sexual development, and tomboy manner had elicited a good deal of teasing attention from boys. Her less successful girl friends became resentful and unfriendly, and with neither subtlety nor reservation, snubbed, jostled, and called her names. The difficulty in synthesizing whole percepts was also reflected in her Rorschach productions, where she either reacted to details or fused the whole in a blurred, incongruous fashion.

*Case 4.* D.I., a 30-year-old white male, was referred for the purpose of marriage counseling. He was a diligent worker with above-average intelligence, held two jobs at once, and had served as a leader in deaf clubs. However, he would frequently go out to play baseball when his wife was having dinner guests. He often returned late and disheveled, and showed anger and disbelief when she was displeased. By the same token, he could not see why she refused to go to bed with him no matter how angry she was.

At work he preferred to finish a job quickly, although he shared a compositor's board with a slower, hearing worker. One day when the latter disappeared briefly to sneak a smoke in the lavatory, the patient called out to him from the middle of the shop that he was a lazy bum and should return at once so they could get on. When the partner came back and angrily wanted to know what was going on, the patient knocked him out. His explanation was: "How could he question me! He was the one who slowed us down!" When he was questioned about the situation and asked to put himself in the other's place, he readily admitted with a look of sheepish recognition, "If things don't go my way, I get mad." The conviction that his wishes and actions should under no circumstances be interfered with manifested itself frequently, although it decreased with therapy.

These clinical summaries are not cited to imply that the deaf always remain so fixed at early levels of development that only the most primitive conflicts are evident. While this may be true in some cases, it is more likely that the traits described usually tend to become a built-in part of general character equipment or impediment. As such, they are utilized or accentuated for defensive purposes when deaf individuals are confronted by other emotional conflicts common to our culture. Tendencies of this kind as well as the limitations imposed on therapy by the difficulties in abstract conceptual ability are illustrated by the following case:

*Case 5.* A.B. was a 24-year-old white female and one of the few deaf patients with whom an analytically oriented, insightful form of treatment was attempted. She was of high intelligence and professed enthusiasm for treatment. Born as the congenitally deaf child of two deaf parents, she had had a seductive father who was later divorced by his strict and somewhat puritanical wife, presumably because of his penchant for other women. The typical oedipal problem which ensued led to a defensive hostility against men, clearly revealed in an early dream: "My apartment was invaded by animals which were plump birds in the body, but long thick worms in the neck and head. I was stamping on them to kill them." When anxiety was provoked by her husband's sexual attentiveness, she consistently shrugged him off with irritation and an impulsive angry outburst. Described as frigid and physically and verbally abusive, she seemed to have no awareness of his feelings for her, his limitations and problems, or the effect of her own behavior on him.

Over a period of 18 months at two sessions per week, she learned to recognize certain consequences of her actions and slowly made some efforts toward controlling them. When her anxiety mounted she dreamed: "My father's face was close up; he grabbed a pillow and ejaculated. It was terrible; there was a sexual feeling and I felt horrible." While her associations made the husband-father equation unmistakable, she failed to understand the analogy whereby past feelings and experiences persisted in the present, and was unable to stand apart from her concrete current experience to see the continuity of her life pattern. Hence, it was virtually impossible to interpret the subsequent resistance to her in any meaningful way. On various pretexts, she gradually reduced the frequency of her visits and finally gave up treatment altogether.

Except for the first case, these illustrations of typical character traits of the deaf have been drawn from the least disabled clinic cases. The characteristics described are even more openly displayed in more malignant forms of mental illness. Nevertheless, the impression gained in clinic interviews and the general population survey is that they are present among relatively well-adjusted deaf as well. Indeed, this impression has recently been confirmed by Myklebust (10).

Using the Minnesota Multiphasic Personality Inventory, he investigated college students, the cream of the deaf community. Even these selected students showed significantly lower than normal scores for empathy, ability to understand reality, and ability to develop normal feelings of what is expected of them. They were higher on the "Hypomanic" scale, measuring abnormal tendencies to activity without emotional control, and lower on measures of introverted thinking. It is true, of course, that these features alone are not unique to deafness and that all of them may be observed in hearing neurotics. However, their uniformity and general prevalence in the deaf population would seem to indicate that they are relevant to the conditions of development imposed by the handicap.

The sensory isolation created by deafness prevents the congenitally deaf child not only from receiving auditory stimulation, but also from learning to use meaningful sounds in communication without considerable delay and many years of special training. Both these blocks in communication have far-reaching effects.

The developmental importance of auditory stimulation and experience has often been emphasized. In Bowlby's opinion, for example, speech and hearing play an essential role in the development of the child's attachment to his mother (11). Without the contact afforded by the voice, this bond is distorted or attenuated. As a consequence, an emotional separation exists even before the actual separation entailed in seeking early and pro-longed speech training outside the home. The nurturing effect of sound in growth and in the generation of emotional response can already be seen at a few weeks of age when a baby may be quieted by the sound of his mother's voice; later—when the child's vacillation between growth and attachment is at its peak—separation can be tolerated if he is reassured by the sound of an unseen mother in the next room (12, 13). Apparently, sound is a necessary part of those cognitive stimuli through which the child defines his own boundaries and his relationship to the world (14, 15).

Without hearing, spontaneous mimicry and spontaneous learning of verbal language are impossible. According to Spitz, the normal appearance of speech is one of the primary "organizers" of the psyche. It marks a turning point which heralds and initiates a new expansion of the person-ality by its impact on both the maturing organism and the surrounding world. In fact, he calls it prerequisite for "the development of object rela-tionships in the human pattern" (16) which stimulates affectionate inter-change between child and parent. In adaptational terms, it may be said that without speech the development of such welfare emotions as mutuality, empathic feelings, and tender regard is hindered.

With hearing and verbal language shown by Piaget (17) to constitute one of the foundations of intelligence, their absence is bound to impose various limitations on development. The lack of an important sensory avenue through which to acquire and associate symbols reduces the ability to pry into the feelings of one's self and others. Interfering with the codification and expression of changing age-specific interests, it has been shown to impede those aspects of abstraction which involve symbolic recall, recognition of similarities, and deduction of consequences required for thinking, feeling for others, and exercising effective self-control (9, 10, 14, 18–20).

It seems that the cumulative effect of these limitations amounts to a kind of deprivation which heightens the child's coercive need for attachment to his mother. Our clinic patients present similar histories of prolonged temper tantrums in childhood. This behavior may be a response to the intense mutual frustration which is experienced by parent and child when they seek to convey and gratify their needs without verbal tools for free expression. Unconscious guilt and hostility over having a defective child tends to increase the parents' distance still further. Under such circumstances, the institution of social requirements such as toilet training and the like, even if delayed, is likely to engender an extraordinary degree of anxiety and rage. The records of clinic patients reveal that it is usually the parents who capitulate in the ensuing power struggle.

In summary, it may be stated that developmental experiences of separation, isolation, and confused awareness of the self in relation to others are typical of the deaf. Limitations in both emotional exchange and the ability to abstract essentials from a situation tend to interfere with the establishment of firm object relations beyond the level of primordial or delegated omnipotence (21, 22). These impoverished object relations as well as uncertainty as to the consequences of one's behavior, and prolonged power struggles, with the child often victorious, may in turn result in a weakening of internalized constraints and inhibitions. Unimpeded by ties of loving concern for the welfare of other objects, coercive rage overflows into action when it exceeds the force of the fear which restrains it.

What has been said for persons with congenital deafness applies to those with early acquired deafness as well. In this group, however, one has to consider the additional stresses that may arise from the loss of an established perceptual modality, from prolonged illness and hospitalization, and from residual physical defects other than deafness.

## The Psychotic Deaf

Observations of this kind make it advisable to re-evaluate our large group of psychotic deaf persons, in whom one may look for further consequences of early hearing deprivation and its associated developmental deviations. With this purpose in mind, deaf inpatients will be compared with hearing patients hospitalized at a given time, as well as with 56 psychotic deaf patients seen in the outpatient clinic.

The table summarizes the diagnostic categories of hospitalized hearing and deaf patients. The majority of deaf patients in all categories enter because of behavioral disturbances, which are usually described as impulsive and aggressive. The proportions of schizophrenia cases are about the same for the two hospitalized groups. This finding is in line with the results of previous studies which failed to demonstrate a significant increase of schizophrenia among the deaf (23). It may also be noted that the paranoid form of the disease does not seem to be increased in this special group (24).

The rate of patients classified as mentally defective shows a definite increase in the deaf, even after removal of incorrectly diagnosed cases in which this classification was applied conveniently to disturbed persons with poor communication skills. Apparently, this excess stems from the frequent combination of residual deafness and mental deficiency in central nervous system disease.

## TABLE I

**Distribution of Mental Disorders in Deaf and Hearing New York State Hospital Patients**

| Type of disorder | Number of deaf patients | Number of hearing patients* | Percent of hospital population | |
|---|---|---|---|---|
| | | | deaf | hearing |
| Schizophrenia | 120 | 52,225 | 52.2 | 56.5 |
| Psychosis with mental deficiency | 42 | 3,401 | 18.2 | 3.7 |
| Senile and arteriosclerotic psychoses | 17 | 14,975 | 7.4 | 16.2 |
| Cycloid and involutional psychoses | 12 | 7,401 | 5.2 | 8.0 |
| Organic psychoses | | | | |
|   Retinitis pigmentosa (11) | | | | |
|   Other (16) | 27 | 11,047 | 11.8 | 12.0 |
| Other behavior disorders | 10 | 3,170 | 4.3 | 3.4 |
| Undiagnosed | 2 | 190 | 0.9 | 0.2 |
| Total | 230 | 92.409 | 100 0 | 100 0 |

* New York State Mental Hygiene Annual Report 1957.

The similarities in some other categories are more apparent than real. In the group of organic psychoses, for example, deaf and hearing patients are proportionally represented, although they clearly differ in the types of illness involved. About one third of hearing patients with this diagnosis are classified as psychoses with alcoholism. In the deaf, one third of the cases are affected by a special form of genetically mediated disease, retinitis pigmentosa with congenital deafness (25), while there are no cases of alcoholic psychosis. Indeed, the combined clinic and hospital populations have yielded only two deaf patients diagnosed as psychosis with chronic alcoholism during the seven-year period of investigation.

Along the same lines, the percentages referring to cycloid and involutional cases are approximately the same for deaf and hearing hospital patients. They correspond even more closely when allowance is made for the disproportionately large number of deaf mental defectives. When it comes to symptomatology, however, a difference becomes apparent. In the hearing there are 2969 manic-depressives and 4432 cases of involutional psychosis; approximately 50% in both groups may be expected to have predominantly depressive signs (26–28). In contrast, there have been no manic-depressive depressed cases in the deaf group, and only one real depression which belonged in the involutional category. Another deaf patient may have been depressed upon admission in 1934, but appeared paranoid at several recent interviews.

The infrequency of psychotic depressions among the deaf is confirmed by data from the outpatient clinic. It is true that brooding resentment and feelings of helplessness may be present in the face of financial or family problems, or as the result of the inability of the deaf to resolve unconscious conflicts. However, no reactive depressions of psychotic proportions have been seen, and there has been only one case of manic-depressive psychosis, with a truly depressive episode followed by a manic phase. Of nine cases with an involutional psychosis, only two showed any depressive features at all. The majority of cases were distinguished by either a predominantly paranoid form of the disease or by an anxious, agitated state without depression, as may be illustrated by the following case:

Case 6. L.P. was a 55-year-old white, congenitally deaf female who came to the clinic soon after moving across the country to New York. She had been dysmenorrheic with frequent flushes for approximately 18 months. The move to New York had been under consideration for slightly less than a year, and the emotional symptoms of the patient were said to have been of nearly the same duration. She had become increasingly anxious, refused to leave her house, and was fearful of eating meat or drinking milk. There was an all-pervasive dread, without further paranoid elaboration or guilty self-incriminations. The main complaints were anxiety and insomnia, and the patient had lost almost 20 pounds. When first seen, she was somewhat suspicious, trembled uncontrollably, and appeared too frightened to make real communication. The thoughts divulged in subsequent interviews were mostly dominated by barely contained anxious resentment over her husband, accumulated over 20 years and brought to a head by his unilateral decision to move to New York, although earlier decisions of a similar nature, such as to move from New York to South America and later to return, had called forth no such symptoms. On a regime combining drugs and supportive psychotherapy she gained 20 pounds within 3 months and gradually learned to adjust to her new environment. After a while, her symptoms subsided completely.

In the agitated form of involutional psychosis, retardation as a symptom may be replaced by repetitious expressions of guilt, sin, self-derogation, or self-loathing. However, these features are absent in most of the deaf clinic cases and in the majority of hospitalized deaf patients with involutional psychosis. On the whole, the usual retarded symptomatology of psychotic depression appears to be rare among the deaf, while in the observed cases of involutional psychosis, delusions of worthlessness and guilt tend to be missing as well.

## Discussion

The combined clinic and hospitalized deaf populations yield two cases of manic-depressive psychosis. Statistical inference from this finding is hazardous for a number of reasons, not the least of which is the difficulty of ascertainment. If there were many deaf people with sustained bouts of depression and its severe subjective distress, the clinic roll call should be larger. Less uncomfortable self-limited manic episodes, which could be rendered grossly indistinguishable from other forms of excited behavior because of the communication barrier, might more frequently escape detection. Such episodic excitement conceivably could be reflected in police records under the heading of "disturbance of the peace." However, a search of such records in a concomitant study of deaf offenders found them inadequate for the present purpose, perhaps in part because of unusual leniency on the part of law enforcement agencies in dealing with minor infractions among the deaf. As for ascertainment of severe cycloid disorders during interim asymptomatic phases, this task is as difficult with the deaf as with the hearing (29, 30).

Another factor making statistical comparison difficult is the increasing stringency required in the diagnosis of manic-depressive psychosis (31, 32), which makes this diagnosis suspect in many hearing cases with long records of hospitalization, and leaves no generally acceptable current base from which to compute a comparative rate for this disease in the general population.

When it comes to involutional psychosis, the total New York State deaf population is 10,355* (33), of whom 4570 are in the vulnerable age range (45 years or more). If the 20 hospital and clinic cases of involutional psychosis are related to this segment of the deaf population, an estimated morbidity rate of 0.4% is obtained. Of course, the census of one moderately publicized clinic cannot possibly include all the extra-mural cases of a given disorder throughout the state. While representing a minimum rate, this figure is nevertheless within the range of 0.3–0.8% reported by other investigators for this disorder in the general population (34).

In view of these considerations, there is no reason to assume that either an increase or decrease exists in the prevalence of manic-depressive or involutional psychoses in the total deaf population. Nor is there any

* Literate deaf over 10 years of age.

evidence for the assumption that early total deafness limits, or is linked to, the somatic propensities for the development of these forms of dys-regulation, the genetic nature of which has been demonstrated by various studies (34). If anything, a common molecular basis for these illnesses in deaf and hearing cases is indicated by the achievement of similar successful results by means of chemical therapeutic agents (35).

What is of interest is that when these disturbances occur in the deaf, the pattern of disorder differs in some respects from that generally ob-served in persons without impaired hearing. These modifications may also be reflected in the pattern of response to situations where normal grief would be expected. Experienced workers with the deaf report a curiously limited reaction with shallowness of affect in such circumstances rather than a true mourning* (36). While genetic vulnerabilities may be un-altered, the variations with regard to psychotic depression observed among the deaf have a bearing on psychodynamic theories which aim at describing these disorders at another level.

According to classical psychoanalytic theory, the description of events leading to depression has been that of a real or unconscious loss of a love object provoking deflation of mood and self-esteem. Subsequently, an introjection of the love object and regressive splitting of the ego occur, so that one part, the super-ego, sadistically berates the other, the ego, which has incorporated the object (37). Early developmental trau-mata are generally assigned a central role in setting the stage for this progression (38–41).

After a tacit reconsideration of the process of identification was initiated by Abraham (42), Rado abandoned the language of topography and recast the dynamics of depression in terms of motivated emotions and their course (43). He called attention to a premelancholic phase of coer-cive resentment toward the love object and the environment, and related the depressive spell to the fate of this rage. According to this view, when the rage fails to regain the magical services of the object, or when it is held in check by guilty fear of inescapable punishment, the adaptive maneuver of repentance is invoked. With the idea that self-punishment will bring forgiveness and restoration of love, the rage is impounded, internalized, and turned upon the self. While the self-reproaches are intensified by self-loathing for the initial failure to coerce the love object, the whole process of guilty expiation ironically continues to serve this primary goal. The clinical picture depends on the balance established by guilt, rage, and fear. If guilt predominates, self-recriminatory expres-sions of repentance will be in the foreground. With more restrictive internalization and recoil of rage, the clinical picture is one of retardation. If guilt is minimal and strong rage is projected or held back by fear

---

* With observations in the clinic limited to pathological (disturbing) reactions, I have not had the opportunity to corroborate these reports personally.

alone, the presenting form should be paranoid or anxious and agitated (44).

The various psychodynamic descriptions of depression were derived from clinical material, and it has been difficult to validate them by predictive methods. It may be hypothesized, however, that there are certain conditions under which retarded or guilt-ridden depression would not be expected. For instance, such depressions should not occur when control machinery (super-ego) is limited and impulsivity predominates, so that tensions are discharged in forceful action rather than contained through intrapsychic maneuvers. Nor would they be anticipated when coercive rage is the preferred or successful adaptive tool, failure of which is either not accepted because of earlier successes, or not recognized due to limitations in ability to abstract causal relationships. These depressive symptoms would also not be expected when, by virtue of such limitations, guilty self-derogation and the pattern of true repentance tend to be late developments, superficially appended to an already formed personality, rather than solidly entrenched in its evolving organization. Moreover, if object relations are distorted and distant, symbolic conceptual abilities delayed, and patterns of guilt and expiation imperfectly formed, then impulse and anger should be restrained by fear alone rather than guilt. In such a case, dangerous rage boiling close to awareness would give rise to anxiety or be dealt with by projection, rather than be internalized and directed against the self. The resulting clinical manifestations would be either paranoid delusions or agitated reflections of anxiety.

Actually, these are the clinical forms seen to predominate in the deaf, and the developmental conditions usually prevailing during their formative years. In other words, the relative lack of retardation, guilt, and depression in persons with early total deafness serves to corroborate some aspects of the psychoanalytic theory of melancholia. This modified symptom complex is also consistent with the character traits noted in this special group, and with theories regarding the place of speech in personality development.

## Summary

The essential thesis of this report is that internalization of rage is deficient in the deaf person, so that guilt and retardation are less likely to appear. The deficit has been related to the distortions in object relationship imposed by the communication barrier of deafness and by the limitations in abstract conceptual ability which accompany this handicap. Contributing factors are failure to recognize the consequences of behavior, lack of conviction that punishment is inevitable, deficient control of impulses, and lack of empathic concern and regard for the love object.

The infrequency of retarded or guilty depressions under these unusual circumstances serves to emphasize certain normal features of growth that provide the framework in which genetic predisposition and early traumata interplay. Such normal growth includes development in early years of a conceptual level sufficient to conceive of giving up immediate gratification for the greater reward of pleasing or controlling a loved object, and a closeness of relationship where the wish to please is fostered. The usual development of these qualities seems to require the freedom of communication which accompanies the early use of verbal language as a tool for defining feelings and nurturing empathic concern. When object relations and conceptual abilities are limited, the establishment of a system of self-restraint and self-punishment based on guilty concern rather than fear alone is also impeded. In mental disorders which appear later, the clinical and dynamic manifestations that depend on this system are then modified.

## References

1. Barker, R. C., Wright, A. W., Myerson, E., and Gonick, M.: Adjustment to Physical Handicap and Illness: A Survey of the Social Psychology of Physique and Disability, New York, Social Science Research Council, 1953.
2. Berlinsky, S.: Measurement of intelligence and personality of the deaf: A review of the literature, *J. Speech Hear. Disord.* 17:39, 1952.
3. Levine, E. S.: *Youth in a Soundless World,* New York University Press, 1956.
4. Heiner, M. H.: *Hearing is Believing,* World Publishing, Cleveland, 1949.
5. Sifton, M.: Fulfillment, in Ewing, I. R., and Ewing, A. W. G. (eds.): *Opportunity and the Deaf Child,* University of London Press, 1947.
6. Kallmann, F. J.: Proceedings, 37th Convention of American Instructors of the Deaf, U. S. Government Printing Office, Washington, D. C., 1956.
7. Baroff, G.: Rorschach study of deaf clinic patients, in Rainer, J. D., Altshuler, K. Z., and Kallmann, F. J. (eds.): *Family and Mental Health Problems in a Deaf Population,* New York State Psychiatric Institute, 1963.
8. Rado, S.: Developments in the psychoanalytic conception and treatment of the neuroses, *Psychoanal. Quart.* 8:427, 1939.
9. Altshuler, K. Z.: Psychiatric considerations in the school age deaf, *Am. Ann. Deaf* 107:553, 1962.
10. Myklebust, H. R.: *The Psychology of Deafness: Sensory Deprivation, Learning and Adjustment,* Grune & Stratton, New York, 1960.
11. Bowlby, J.: The nature of the child's tie to his mother, *Int. J. Psychoanal.* 39:350, 1958.
12. Shirley, M. M.: *The First Two Years,* University of Minnesota Press, Minneapolis, 1933.
13. Buhler, C.: The social behavior of children, in *A Handbook of Child Psychology,* Clark University Press, Cambridge, Mass., 1933.
14. Levine, E. S.: *The Psychology of Deafness,* Columbia University Press, New York, 1960.

15. Bruner, J. S.: Cognitive consequences of early sensory deprivation, in Solomon, P., *et al.* (eds.): *Sensory Deprivation,* Harvard University Press, Cambridge, Mass., 1961.

16. Spitz, R. A.: *A Genetic Field Theory of Ego Formation,* International Universities Press, New York, 1959.

17. Piaget, J.: *The Origins of Intelligence in Children,* International Universities Press, New York, 1952.

18. Knapp, P. H.: The ear, listening and hearing, *J. Am. Psychoanal. Assoc. 1:*672, 1953.

19. Levy, E. Z., Ruff, G. E., and Thaler, V. H.: Studies in human isolation, *J.A.M.A. 169:*236, 1959.

20. Deutsch, F.: Analytic synesthesiology, *Int. J. Psychoanal. 35:*293, 1954.

21. Rado, S.: Hedonic control, action-self, and the depressive spell, in Hoch, P. H., and Zubin, J. (eds.): *Depression,* Grune & Stratton, New York, 1954.

22. Ferenzci, S.: Stages in the development of the sense of reality, in *Selected Papers of Sandor Ferenzci,* Basic Books, New York, 1950, Vol. I.

23. Altshuler, K. Z., and Sarlin, M. B.: Deafness and schizophrenia: Interrelation of communication stress, maturation lag, and schizophrenic risk, in Kallmann, F. J. (ed.): *Expanding Goals of Genetics in Psychiatry,* Grune & Stratton, New York, 1962.

24. Altshuler, K. Z., and Rainer, J. D.: Patterns and course of schizophrenia in the deaf, *J. Nerv. Ment. Dis. 127:*77, 1958.

25. Hallgren, B.: Retinitis Pigmentosa Combined with Congenital Deafness: with Vestibulo-Cerebellar Ataxia and Mental Abnormality in a Proportion of Cases, E. Munksgaard, Copenhagen, 1959.

26. Patton, R. E.: Personal communication, 1962.

27. Hamilton, D. M., and Mann, W. W.: The hospital treatment of involutional psychoses, in Hoch, P. H., and Zubin, J. (eds.): *Depression,* Grune & Stratton, New York, 1954.

28. Mayer-Gross, W., Slater, E., and Roth, M.: *Clinical Psychiatry,* Cassell London, 1954.

29. Kallmann, F. J.: Genetics of psychoses: analysis of 1232 twin index families, in *Congres International de Psychiatrie,* Herman & Cie, Paris, 1950.

30. Slater, E.: The inheritance of manic-depressive insanity and its relation to mental defect, *J. Ment. Sci. 82:*626, 1936.

31. Hoch, P. H., and Rachlin, H. L.: An evaluation of manic-depressive psychosis in the light of follow-up studies, *Am. J. Psychiat. 97:*831, 1941.

32. Hoch, P. H.: Manic-depressive psychosis, *Med. Clin. N. Am. 32:*641, 1948.

33. Rainer, J. D., Altshuler, K. Z., and Kallmann, F. J. (eds.): *Family and Mental Health Problems in a Deaf Population,* New York State Psychiatric Institute, 1963.

34. Kallmann, F. J.: Genetic principles in manic-depressive psychosis, in Hoch, P. H., and Zubin, J. (eds.): *Depression,* Grune & Stratton, New York, 1954.

35. Rainer, J. D., Altshuler, K. Z., and Kallmann, F. J.: Psychotherapy for the deaf, in *Advances in Psychosomatic Medicine,* S. Karger, Basel-New York, 1962, Vol. III.

36. Nash, T.: Personal communication, 1962.
37. Freud, S.: Mourning and melancholia, in *Collected Papers,* Hogarth Press, London, 1925, Vol. IV.
38. Klein, M.: A contribution to the psychogenesis of manic-depressive states, in *Contributions to Psychoanalysis,* 1921–1945, Hogarth Press, London, 1948.
39. Abraham, K.: Notes on the psychoanalytical investigation and treatment of manic-depressive insanity and allied conditions, in *Selected Papers on Psychoanalysis,* Basic Books, New York, 1927.
40. Benedek, T.: Toward the biology of the depressive constellation, *J. Am. Psychoanal. Assoc. 4:*389, 1956.
41. Jacobson, E.: Depression: the Oedipus conflict in the development of the depressive mechanisms, *Psychoanal. Quart. 12:*541, 1943.
42. Abraham, K.: Manic-depressive states and the pregenital levels of the libido, in *Selected Papers on Psychoanalysis,* Hogarth Press, London, 1927.
43. Rado, S.: Psychodynamics of depression from the etiologic point of view, *Psychosom. Med. 13:*51, 1951.
44. Ovesey, L.: Unpublished lectures, Psychoanalytic Clinic for Training and Research, Columbia University, New York, 1956.

# Appendix II

## INTERPRETATION, COMMUNICATION AND UNDERSTANDING*

### John D. Rainer

Ladies and Gentlemen, participants in the Workshop:

When I was asked, as a psychiatrist and Director of the New York State Psychiatric Program for the Deaf, to deliver the keynote address to this Workshop on Activating Interpreting Services, I wondered for a moment what I would be able to say about this field. I paused especially because in our own mental health program we felt from the outset that *psychiatric* interviews could *not* be carried on by means of an interpreter. The late Dr. Kallmann, in one of his early visits to Gallaudet College back in 1955 before the project began, decided to interview some co-eds about some fairly intimate and personal matters. At first he used an interpreter and the replies that he got were conventional and unrevealing. Then he decided to ask the interpreter to leave, and to resort to pencil and paper. The students soon became more frank in their discussion and he got answers of quite a different sort. From that moment he insisted that everyone connected with the project become familiar with all methods of talking with the deaf and be able at least to carry on an interview in manual language. One of the first persons to be recruited by the new project was a sign language instructor. Thus, there are indeed realms of discourse between the deaf and the hearing where the presence of a third party is undesirable, where the confidentiality, the subtlety and the personal nature of the material, as well as the need to develop a special kind of one-to one relationship with the doctor precludes the use of an interpreter.

Moreover, in such a situation, an interpreter without knowledge of the signs and symptoms of psychiatric disorder might do very poorly in communicating to the psychiatrist what really was taking place. I am reminded of the time in working with hearing patients that I had to do a psychiatric examination of a disturbed young Chinese man, newly admitted to the hospital, who knew no English at all. Luckily, I was able to find an older Chinese patient in the hospital who spoke the same dialect and who had been there for some time and seemed quite stable, and I asked him to interpret. At my request, he asked the newcomer a question and received a flood of language in reply. The interpreter translated none of this to me but again questioned the young man. The same thing happened. Becoming both curious and impatient, I asked my interpreter what the new arrival had said. "Oh," he assured me, "he's not saying anything important. Just a lot of crazy talk."

* Reprinted from *The Deaf American*, Vol. 19, pp. 43–45, September 1966.

For such reasons, in my psychiatric experience with the deaf, I have rarely used interpreters. In a few cases, a deaf patient who had no manual *or* oral language except a few private family signs had to be approached through a family member. But, of course, a family member is probably the worst person to interpret in a psychiatric situation, since he is apt to color and distort what he hears because of his own emotional involvement.

In psychiatry, then, my colleagues and I have felt that direct communication with the deaf patient is most desirable. Of course this is the ideal situation, and I realize that very few psychiatrists are now trained to communicate with the deaf. For the present, then, interpreters may enable deaf persons to consult in the hospital or office with psychiatrists who have no special knowledge of the deaf, which is better than none at all. Perhaps in this way some of these psychiatrists may be stimulated to get some specialized training and experience. Next year we plan to have a workshop in New York to interest and educate psychiatrists who have contact with the deaf.

For a moment, I felt then that I might not do at all as a keynote speaker this morning. It only took a moment, however, before my thoughts moved beyond the special difficulties in psychiatric interviews to the really paramount problems of the deaf which those interviews revealed. Then I realized that almost all, I might even say every one, of the emotional difficulties of the deaf, and the deaf have as many emotional difficulties as the hearing do, are compounded, if not caused, by barriers in communication. So many deaf persons are frustrated in communicating as infants and children. Later, as adolescents and adults, they are misunderstood and are considered as relative outsiders in the increasingly complex world of science, the arts, law, business, government and social welfare. I realized that, indeed, one of the most basic things we need is interpretation, a two-way avenue of communication and understanding between the hearing and the deaf. In the broadest sense, of course, interpretation means not only translating to hearing persons unfamiliar with the deaf the sentences which a deaf person is saying at the moment, but it also means explaining the background of the deaf, the education of the deaf, the social organization of the deaf and the achievements of the deaf so as to help lift the veil of ignorance and unfamiliarity. Of course, this process goes both ways. Interpretation of spoken material to a deaf person or a deaf group requires more than a knowledge of the sign language on the part of the interpreter. It requires a real understanding of the needs and the concerns, the interests and the enthusiasms, of his deaf audience. *Interpretation, communication* and *understanding;* these make up the inseparable framework of mental health and social well-being.

You will not be surprised if a psychiatrist and a psychoanalyst, in discussing this keynote statement more thoroughly, turns first to consider the earliest years of life.

A good deal of attention has been given in current psychiatric thinking to the development of what we know as the ego: the executive part of the mind, the part of the mind that perceives, that selects, that regulates and that communicates.

In the development of this aspect of the personality, to use the words of Dr. Anna Freud, the infant progresses normally from the newborn's utter dependence on maternal care to the young adult's emotional and material self-reliance. At first the infant and the mother are as one. Gradually the child makes his needs known, and begins to see the mother as separate from himself, able to grant satisfactions or withhold them. He learns how to relate to his parents by trial and error, reward and admonition; as he grows up he can use what he has learned with his parents in his dealings with other people. But if the pathway of communication is lacking in the earliest years, a number of things can go wrong in this pattern. First of all, the very young child can feel rejected, left out, abandoned. Bowlby, Spitz and others have described well the anxiety and depression which such early maternal deprivation can cause. Secondly, without communication, the growing child has no outlet for his impulsive needs and restlessness, and he may behave destructively, have temper tantrums, and further alienate the parents. Finally, the important process of learning how to relate to parents, with all its trials and tribulations, is necessary in order to develop a social sense, a feeling for others, and, if this process is shut out by isolation at home, the child may grow up with severe deficiencies in this area.

People are giving a great deal of thought today to the question of the relationship between thinking and language. Professor Furth who first learned about the deaf by working in our Mental Health Project has just written a book called *Thinking Without Language* in which he shows on the basis of many experiments that thinking processes, logical thought, adaptation, may take place in the young deaf child without the kind of language experience that the hearing child obtains. Nevertheless, his full intellectual potential is not developed if there is communication isolation during the early crucial years, and the emotional effect described before may be even more far-reaching. We are concerned with the fact that the young deaf child does not, under any present methods of early education, develop the ability to communicate with his parents as the hearing child does. We are concerned with the parents who find out that their child is deaf, and the effect of this discovery upon the patterns of communication and understanding and acceptance and love in the home. If there is one thing that we know about early development, it is the retardation in thinking, in feeling that comes about when there is rejection or deprivation of closeness in early years.

There are other undesirable effects of poor emotional communication between children and their parents. The development of conscience, the ability to handle power and strength, as well as the formation of proper self-identification, is a direct consequence of the relationship to the family,

to the father, to the mother. This relationship depends to a large extent
on communication, on some form of communication, and is defeated when
the parents feel defeated.

I do not plan here to delve into the often heated conflict between the
proponents of oral and manual instruction, except to say that, like so
many either-or propositions, the conflict may be more apparent than real.
For our purpose I will leave to the language specialists the question of
*how* to develop communication, but I will insist that communication must
be developed and done so early. Children cannot grow emotionally without
a proper relationship to their parents and communication is so much the
essence of that relationship; communication and understanding, anticipation and allowance and love. It is the *emotional* climate that results from
non-communication that I am particularly concerned with at the moment,
even more than the intellectual deficit that may result. I recall one family
with a deaf son who gathered at the dinner table each night and con-
versed noisily among themselves, all but the deaf son. Literally all he
ever heard or uttered was a variation of one phrase—"Please pass the
potatoes." One of the most poignant descriptions of the feelings of a deaf
boy in a family who never really bothered to include him was conveyed
to me by way of a dream reported by another 14-year-old deaf patient.
This boy told me that he dreamt he was in a large baseball stadium,
standing behind home plate, wearing a catcher's mitt. The stadium was
dark. He could not see the people in the stands nor the opposing team,
but toward him there came at intervals not hard, round baseballs, but
swirling masses of white smoke. They came toward his mitt but each
time he tried to catch them, they dropped down to the ground and he
missed them. I know the boy who told me this dream was very much
interested in baseball and being thought of as a good baseball player.
I also knew that there was very little communication between him and
his family at home. I asked him to tell me more about his dream and he
described again the dark stadium, the ghostly balls coming toward him
and how each time he missed them. I continued to ask him more about
the dream until finally he signed to me, "Doctor, you don't understand,
I told you all I can. I'm deaf. We deaf people are stupid. We are not
smart as other people are. We can't understand as much. I can't tell you
any more about this dream." And I looked at him and told him, "Son,
I think you have just told me what your dream is about. The dream
describes, in a picture, in a baseball stadium picture, the feeling you have
when you're sitting among hearing persons at home and you see words on
their lips but they are ghostly, they are fuzzy. You cannot make them out.
You try to catch them but you miss them and all around you is darkness
and you are alone. You feel stupid and like a failure. You are not stupid,
but your experience makes you feel that way."

How different from this boy's experience is the description by Mrs.
Freddy Bloom in her excellent book, *Our Deaf Children,* of the early

days in the upbringing of her deaf daughter, Virginia. She describes with humor and intelligence the patience, the sympathy, the understanding, the determination to include this child into the communicating circle of the family.

As stated so well by Mrs. Bloom, in the development of any personality the question of acceptance is of primary importance. She goes on to say, "If a man in the street had more understanding, he would not be so completely shattered if he should become a father of a deaf child. He would also be able to help his neighbor more if the neighbor were the father of a deaf child." "Sometimes," she says, "the man in the street is a doctor or a teacher, or an administrator." I might add he might also be an interpreter. "In any official capacity," she said, "he would see to it that the parents who have just been told that their child cannot hear, be given immediate and complete attention."

There are many reasons, of course, why parents neglect communication with their deaf children. I refer particularly to hearing parents. I suspect that deaf parents who have deaf children are more aware of this problem and that the particular communication lack we are discussing is not as great. The deaf parents may indeed have less language, but they may have more understanding. Among the causes of the parents' rejection of deaf children are some of their own serious psychological problems, the feelings of guilt and frustration and anger aroused by the discovery that their child is deaf, which often, paradoxically enough, result in more rejection rather than in more acceptance. However, aside from these emotional problems for which parents should have help and advice, there is still the widespread ignorance about deafness, the widespread ignorance about the problems and the potentials of the deaf. These are things which have never been interpreted often enough or well enough to the man on the street so that if he or one of his friends has a deaf child, he knows very little of what the whole story is about. The father may be a business-man who has never had contact with deaf persons; he may be a profes-sional man who has never had deaf patients or clients; the mother may have never bothered to communicate with her deaf neighbor down the block.

Turning from the important early days at home, the deaf child goes to school where, of course, he is in the hands of skilled persons who are trained to use and to develop his communication abilities. However, the feeling of not belonging, of futile striving or of giving up the battle to be understood, once formed in early childhood, is not so easily overcome. When the deaf boy or girl comes into adulthood, as a citizen and a member of society, he should for his sake and that of the community participate fully in that complex world of the arts and the sciences, the law and government which I referred to earlier. The rough edges may still be there; the lack of understanding, the misconceptions, the lack of opportunities. But, if early damage has been done, perhaps some of it may be undone through greater understanding, through *interpretation* of the deaf to the hearing, and the hearing to the deaf, so that the strangeness disappears.

Many areas in which this work needs to be done come to my mind and they will, I am sure, be covered during the course of this workshop: the law, particularly, where persons need to be equal and need to understand each other in order to obtain their rights and benefits; the business world where fair dealing and fair exchange require meaningful communication; the world of employment; the world of religion; and then the leisure time world, opening up the treasures of our museums and our schools through lectures and discussions. There is the prerogative of the citizen to listen and participate in political debate, and his right to benefit when needed from the healing professions, the world of medicine, of dentistry, of hospitals, of doctors, of clinics.

How can we recruit and train persons who will have the skills, the knowledge and the understanding to act as the interpreters, as the go-betweens, as the conveyors of understanding in all these fields? This is the task of your workshop. The interpreter can bring all of these services and benefits to the deaf person and obtain for the hearing world the benefit of full participation by the deaf in the community. He must do more than translate, however; he must provide interpretation in the fullest meaning of the word, explanation, involvement, arousal of interest, understanding. How often do we learn that a certain hearing person has always had a special interest in the deaf because he knew a deaf family when he was a child, or was associated with a deaf friend. Only last month President Johnson at his gracious surprise address to the graduating class of Gallaudet College revealed that he was deeply interested in the deaf because of the inspiration, friendship, and help offered to him as a boy by his deaf neighbor, the mother of Judge Thornberry. The true interpreter can be the joiner of minds and perhaps multiply, many-fold, these chance associations which have almost alone led to fruitful understanding in isolated cases. Perhaps he can, in some way, help to undo the trauma of early isolation and, by removing the last stigma attached to the deaf in the minds of the unknowing hearing world, remove at the same time the even more destructive image which too many deaf persons consciously or unconsciously harbor of themselves. Perhaps by helping to foster increased interchange and familiarity with the deaf throughout the nation, he can influence parents themselves and prevent the fear, the guilt and the resulting rejection and ostracism of the deaf child which is so central to the problems we face in our field. As you discuss the progress in activating interpreting services and how to fill the gaps that still remain, I want you to realize how basically important your work is in establishing the climate of communication and of understanding, so vital for further progress in the welfare of the deaf throughout the country.

# INDEX